FOLLOW THE RED THREAD

Sandra Fabian

Heart-Vision Press
2021

In the deserts of the human heart

let the healing fountain start

W.H. Auden

Contents:

Dedication:

to Dad,
for who he was and who
he might have been

PROLOGUE
THE MAN IN THE WHITE HAT

I had the same dream on many nights when I was small.

I'm at the seashore. The air is warm and hazy, the way it is when the wind blows in from the southwest. The waves roll in bigger than usual because of the wind. They break onto the shore carrying sand and seaweed, bits of shell and stone.

I've been swimming and I sit on the shore. My bathing suit is filled with sand and tiny pebbles. I watch a little girl walk into the water. She steps in deeper. I watch the waves breaking over her. She laughs and shrieks, it's so much fun.

Then suddenly she disappears under the water.

There's a man wearing a white military hat. He runs into the waves lifting his legs high and diving under the water so that his feet and his white hat fly up into the air. He disappears too.

The water swirls with crashing waves. The girl is thrown underneath the foam, tumbling over and over. The water churns with seaweed and sand. With no up or down, she flails and can't find her way to the surface.

And then suddenly the man flies up from the water with the little girl in his arms. His hat is gone. She's limp and silent. He carries her like a baby out of the water, up onto the sandy beach, and lays her face down on a towel. He sits beside her tapping on her back until she spits out salty water and coughs. I see his hat taken by the waves, floating out from the shore.

He puts her in his lap and cradles her. He covers her with a towel as he watches his hat drift further and further out to sea.

LESSON ONE:

ANYTHING IS POSSIBLE

1

DESTINY

The bus coughed and careened along winding jungle roads on its way to Acapulco.

I stumbled down the aisle grabbing at the backs of every seat to steady myself. But still, the bus's unpredictable movements tossed me into other passengers, all women on their way to or from markets. They carried wicker baskets on their heads brimming with vegetables and hysterical chickens dangling by their ugly, bound feet. The odor of chicken dung floated in the hot, dusty air. The hens must have known their fate.

I threw myself down in an empty seat and sobbed.

The driver left one careless hand on the wheel while turning his head to chat with the woman behind him. I muttered, *watch where you're going* under my breath. Mexico was famous in the 1970s for terrifying bus rides. It was not uncommon for reckless drivers to miss one turn or another sending the bus off into the valley below where it would come to rest belly up in a dying bug pose. I may have been despondent, but I didn't want to die.

When a lady moved to sit next to me, I straightened out the tight pleats of my purple Navajo skirt and pulled it closer. She wore a traditional white blusa with bright embroidered flowers and her long black hair was braided with colored ribbons intertwined. Her eyes searched for mine as she laid her thick, work-worn hand on my knee and cooed, "Pobrecita."

Poor little thing, she'd said, as if she was caring for a child. But I was stuffed too full with the shame of being cast aside to receive her kindness. When I was upset and Dad was sober, he would call me *Goopie*, a name from a Victorian children's book. But I'd never cried this hard with my Father. I continued to weep for the eight-hour journey, unable to express how my love had been spurned, and my known world shattered.

I was lost in Mexico with no idea who I was, where I needed to go, or what I needed to do to find myself.

Four Months Earlier

I set up house in a dilapidated casa de huespuedes, paying ten pesos a night for a large near-empty room one block from the Pacific Ocean. I sat on my bed for most of each day, like a nesting bird, assuming as a mother bird might that eventually something would hatch. One thousand miles down the coast from the border with California the heat in Mazatlán was extreme even in September; in fact, the sand at the beach was too hot to walk on. In a semi-stupor, I taught myself Spanish from a paperback dictionary or binged on Mexico's ubiquitous lard filled cookies while reading Kazantzakis' *Last Temptation of Christ*. I dreamed about earthy dark disciples who followed Jesus with no idea where they were going.

I could have just as easily been back in my childhood home with my parents. Dreaming was one of the things I did best, usually about handsome dark men who would rescue me and take me away. That and sulking. As a child I spent hours in my room with hurt feelings wondering why no one came to save me from myself. But unlike home, my Mexican room was bare. I liked it that way. I was accustomed to being alone. It wasn't that I had no friends; I kept a lot of thoughts to myself.

My dreams and fantasies were real to me, which helps explain why I was able to hitchhike across the U.S. alone, eventually ending up in Mexico. I didn't spend much time questioning my fantasies. I was too busy living within them.

On a normal day in Mazatlán, I'd put on my bikini and walk the block to the beach in the late afternoon. The air was dead, the streets silent until I passed by. Men lurked everywhere: standing in the shade of a doorway, eating beans and rice at a small table on the sidewalk, or perched on a stone wall running along the Malecon, the walkway that bordered the ocean.

"Sst sst, senorita," they'd all say. My blonde braid and long legs justifying their leering (a popular Mexican beer ad said, *La Rubia es Mejor*; blonde is better). If I could've blushed, I would have, but I was already flushing crimson from the heat.

It was a relief to step onto the still burning sand, put my towel down, and turn my back to the street. I would sit, recover from the walk down, stare at the ocean, breathe in its briny warmth and then run tiptoes into the surf. I missed having someone watching, like Dad or a potential boyfriend who would admire my skill at body surfing, the way I knew when to throw myself in front of a wave at the precise moment to catch the longest ride into shore. It was all about timing.

One afternoon, four red headed freckle faced kids, from five- to sixteen-years-old, materialized out of thin air. Before I knew it, the three older kids waded out next to me to wait for the right wave. We stood in waist level water, our feet bouncing on the ocean bottom, conversing idly, lifting ourselves high over any wave that wasn't perfect. We agreed that we'd all experienced a periodic rogue wave that would crash heavy and slam you down under the foam.

The older girl, Becky said they were so bored and asked why not join them for dinner. I'd restricted myself to tiny makeshift eateries run by families who opened the front rooms of their houses to the street and set up two or three tables. My money supply was low. I ate once a day in the evening, subsisting on sopa de pollo and bolillos tostados con mantequilla, chicken soup and toasted rolls with butter. I was hungry and could smell the cumin and cilantro of Mexican dishes I wasn't eating.

The red and freckly kids led me to their red and freckly five-year-old sister Katy and their mother Ruthie who sat on the sand drinking a Negro Modelo. She was deeply tanned and sat with no towel, knees up, her tough looking feet bared to the hot sand. She wore an oversized pink oxford shirt and cutoff jeans. It looked like she had no intention of swimming. With her red hair in two braids and a red bandana around her forehead, she was a perfect hippie mom.

Conversation with the family was the first English I'd heard in three weeks. Ruthie said, sure I should come along and offered me a beer. I couldn't think about beer in the hot sun, but of course I'd have supper with them. They were going to eat at the Shrimp Bucket, a tourist destination, and the fanciest restaurant in town.

A long deep breath moved through my body.

***

We sat on a terrace overlooking the ocean as waiters in white jackets delivered tortilla chips and salsa, Coke, and another beer for Ruthie. She looked as young as her sixteen-year-old daughter. I could tell that Becky was the real mother of the family.

"Order whatever you'd like," Becky said.

Becky, Kim, and Billy all had frogs' legs, the most expensive item on the menu. "Like fried chicken," Kim the fourteen-year-old said.

Ruthie took a long swig of beer. "Their Dad died six months ago," she said.

"Oh, I'm really sorry." The waiter was standing over me. "I'll have the chicken enchiladas por favor."

It was the cheapest item on the menu. I always looked at the price column before choosing my meal. I didn't want to take advantage.

"That's okay. Mom cashed in an insurance policy and that's how we're here," Becky said.

"Yeah, sixty thousand dollars at twelve percent in a Mexican bank," Billy, the twelve-year old said as he took some firecrackers out of his pocket. "That's a heap of money." Billy left the table and went down to the beach in front of the restaurant. Ruthie shook her head and sent Kim to bring him back asap. "I told him not to set those things off."

Billy plodded back to the table head down. "Mom and Grandad are sending me to military school."

"Right. Asap," Kim said. "That's because you're a juvenile delinquent."

I walked back to my room after dinner rocking my head back and forth singing, *Our house is a very, very, very fine house…* I could see myself as a big sister to the kids, although I admitted that teenaged Becky at sixteen was more grown up than me at twenty-three. And I admired Ruthie taking her kids on a big adventure to get over the death of their Dad. They also seemed happy to have me. Maybe it made them all feel less sad. For me, it felt like being in a family, not so alone. On top of that, I ate a real meal for the first time in months.

***

I'd come out of the water late one afternoon and was busy drying myself off, trying to get clumps of sand out of my crotch. I squeezed the water from my braid and plopped down on my towel near the kids. We were usually alone on the beach. Mexican families only came on Sundays and never swam.

A guy walking toward us on the sand caught my attention. He was swarthy and dark with wild dark curls and a thick black beard. Other than my mental picture of Jesus' disciples in the book I was reading I'd never seen anyone like him. He squatted on the sand in front of Ruthie and I noticed his big knees and strong legs. I also noticed his lederhosen leather shorts, which would've seemed weird, but they were well-worn and minus the suspenders. I thought they were unique. He talked to Ruthie but had one eye on me. I pretended I wasn't interested. I tried to breathe. But I saw stars, real tiny lights twinkling in front of my eyes.

His eyes on me made me aware of my bikini with its old faded lime green polka dots. I moved my towel up and down drying my legs, noticing how long and brown they were. I dried my feet and wiped the sand off in between my toes. As he and Ruthie continued their conversation, I moved the towel up and down my arms slowly, reaching each arm out as far as it would go. I toweled my chest in a languid kind of way and then moved the towel slowly down to my belly. Time stretched out.

"Oh, this is Alicia," Ruthie said, "and this is Luke."

I was instantly shy, self-conscious, overwhelmed. His eyes were golden in the blinding sunshine, *like an exotic cat*, I thought.

He nodded and smiled, "Why don't you come to supper too, Alicia,"

"Okay." I was dizzy.

"Eight o'clock," Luke said, "when it cools down a bit."

I cleared my throat twice as he walked back up to the Malecon. "Ruthie, who was that?"

"What? Oh, just two guys on a sailboat. He and Marshall got blown in after a storm at sea. They've been around for weeks, docked outside of town in the harbor with the freighters."

I shook my head trying to clear my vision. Wasn't it amazing the way one thing led to another? A question had been answered that I hadn't realized I was asking. I'd discovered the reason I was here. And here he was. My egg had cracked wide open and this was no baby bird.

***

Ruthie picked me up after sunset. She was alone, no kids invited. I wore my daily uniform, a tightly pleated, purple knee length Navajo skirt, knee high fringed brown moccasins, a black scoop neck jersey and a black velvet vest. We drove down the two-lane road in her orange VW station wagon, following the ocean toward the harbor.

We parked in the town lot and walked along the pier between freighters from Russia and Sweden. They loomed like tall buildings and sailors waved enthusiastically down at us from their decks. The harbor water was slick with oil, fumes rose up swirling in the thick air.

"There she is," Ruthie said. She pointed to a yawl at the end of the pier that was dwarfed by freighters on either side. Luke was on deck ready to help us aboard.

"Hey, welcome to Destiny." Luke took my hand and helped me step down onto the deck.

"Destiny?"

He smiled. "That's her name, all thirty feet of her." He pointed out how beamy—wide—she was and how that made for a more spacious and comfortable lower cabin and a stable stance at sea. I envisioned myself sailing on her.

I whistled out air through my lips. "I can see that. My Dad always has a wooden boat, no matter how small."

"Good man," Luke said. "Please, come below."

The cabin was warm, holding onto the heat of the day, and the smell of sandalwood incense had worked its way into the boat's damp salt encrusted wood. I wanted to move in.

The settees, which opened into beds at night, were covered in Indian bedspreads and lined with pillows in ocher, vermilion, and azure. Shells and starfish, feathers and smooth stones, baskets of paint brushes and quill pens, were randomly placed in the salon. I picked up a purple stone and felt the smooth round warmth in my hand. I ran my fingers over the soft bristles of the brushes. My hands tingled.

I felt right at home in Destiny's cabin. When I looked at Luke's sailing partner, Marshall, as he poured me a glass of chianti, I thought I'd be very lonely with him. He seemed indifferent to our presence, and when he sat down, he grew quiet and flat, as if he didn't care about anything. Obviously, the beauty and comfort on the boat was Luke's doing.

Ruthie and I sat down with our wine across from Marshall and Luke. I arranged my skirt around my knees which almost touched Luke's. I felt heat coming from his body traveling up into mine.

"How'd you end up in Mazatlán?" Luke asked.

All in one breath said, "I was hitchhiking all over the states, north to Lake Louise, south to Tucson, up and down the Pacific coast. Everywhere! I couldn't stay in San Francisco forever and I wasn't ready to go home. I had to go somewhere and the rock band staying at my friend Linda's all said, go to Mexico!" I took a deep breath and shrugged.

I had the brief feeling of being a strong, courageous woman who knew what she was doing.

"Alone? Wow, that's really brave."

He didn't know the half of it, how brave I really was because he didn't know how scared I'd been. "I didn't know anything about Mexico, except for the jumping beans I had when I was little."

Luke's serious face broke into a small smile. "And Zorro maybe?"

There was a second of silence. I was caught in my mind and couldn't think of how to respond. I had trouble keeping conversations going with men and often had sex as soon as possible to break the ice.

Ruthie on the other hand had no trouble with chit chat. Her words fell onto the table in random piles. I wasn't sure who she was talking to or what she was even saying. It gave me the chance to watch Luke when he wasn't looking at me. My eyes moved all over his body caressing him. I couldn't help it. Something big was happening, something I'd been waiting for. The air was thick and hard to breathe.

I noticed two paintings on the cabin walls, fiery abstracts in reds and yellows.

"My artwork," Luke said, following my eyes to the paintings.

My eyes fell from the paintings to gaze at his legs, the strength of his dark calves and the muscles of his thighs. "How'd you end up here?"

His eyes were golden, startling, and I forgot my question. I seemed to be dissolving in front of him, melting so that the edges of myself flowed into his. He was the image of all my fantasies, dark and interior, mysterious to me.

"I was on my way around the world and when we got a thousand miles down the coast from Marina del Rey, I didn't realize it was hurricane season."

He described the storms, the walls of black water rushing at them, towering over the boat, Destiny climbing up to the top and then plummeting down into the trough between each wave. He said the roar of the wind was deafening and the four-hour shifts alone on deck all through the night were lonely. I shivered. I was afraid of the smallest swells in the ocean. They feel like they come from a deep place that could overwhelm me at any moment.

But even *I* knew that hurricane season began in September and they'd left California at the end of August.

As Luke and I talked with Ruthie's voice in the background, conversation began to flow, though I had no idea what I was saying. I just wanted to look at him. He got up to bring us a supper he'd cooked on the propane stove in the galley. Sautéed strips of chicken with onions and peppers on a bed of rice and sliced avocado. Salsa on the side.

"This tastes as good as the food at the Shrimp Bucket," I said.

Ruthie agreed and started in about her dislike of cooking. I scraped my plate to make sure I got every piece of chicken and grain of rice then sat back against the pillows.

Luke lit a joint then handed it to me. "A little dessert?"

His fingers lingered on mine. I began to feel stirred deep in my belly. The smoke hung in the air.

"Sssthufrin thucotash," I began in my best Daffy Duck voice. "Thith ith sswell stthuff."

Luke laughed and then I laughed and then we laughed together. I sensed he didn't laugh easily. I'd pleased him. I looked straight at him with a smirk.

"You're a funny girl." Luke's head tilted down as his eyes looked up.

I was something more than funny. We stopped talking. He gave a small but audible groan.

I want to stay. I want more of you, Luke. You can have me.

Ruthie yawned a *Hey I'm ready to go* kind of yawn.

I guessed she'd hoped for something with Marshall, or Luke, but what was she thinking? She's twenty years older than them. Maybe she didn't want to share the guys.

I wasn't ready to leave, but she had the car and it was miles back to town.

The tide went out while we had supper so that when we climbed the ladder from the galley onto the deck, the dock was a good eight feet above us. Luke put his hands on my butt, and I felt the heat of his hands. He took a long time lifting me up so that I could crawl onto the dock on my belly and roll over.

I lay gulping with laughter for a few seconds before I rolled back over, got up, and turned to look at Luke. I smoothed my skirt pretending to put myself back together.

"Nighty night," I said.

Luke grinned, nodded, laughed. "I'll be in touch."

I saw the boat's stern and the way *Destiny* was carved with graceful golden letters. This is what I was waiting for, why I was here in Mexico. It was worth my months of solitary travel across the states. It was worth my furious Father who appeared to cut me out of his heart when I announced I was heading to San Francisco.

I had the answer to all my doubts and fears. And yes, the vision I'd had back in Cambridge months before, the vision that told me I'd find my soulmate if I took to the road. That vision was real. Yet now that he was here, a thought flashed through my mind, too quickly to catch, that there was something more, something still missing.

I had no idea what that was.

2

THE YOYO OF LOVE

That night I was too excited to think clearly.

I tossed in my bed for hours as young men laughed and flirted at the pizza stand below my window. The bed sheet stuck to my sweaty body. I lay with arms and legs spread wide, listened to the endless breaking waves rolling onto the shore, and smelled the sharp saltiness that hung like a fog in the air.

Time crawled by.

In the morning I sat up rubbing my eyes hoping some small breeze would come in through the French doors. The curtains were so old the white had turned to pale gray. They hung limp, emphasizing the fact that nothing was moving.

Once a safe space from men whose attention I didn't want, my room now felt like a trap.

Luke's sharp featured craggy face was imprinted in my mind. I felt sick in my belly and I needed to be healed. A voice—not identifiable as my own—said it was risky to count on anything. But why else had I come all this way? Each moment felt like forever.

A gentle knock on the door startled me. Maybe it was Becky wanting to hang out, or the landlord wanting my rent? A second knock, a little harder.

I opened the door—*Luke*— My eyes opened wide and yet I wasn't surprised. Ever since adolescence I'd dreamed about Luke, although I didn't know his name, or where in the world I would find him. I'd been counting days and years, as if I'd been asleep only needing to be stirred.

He walked in slow, polite, his eyes softening as he took in the large high-ceilinged room, its pale green walls, the one straight backed chair, the single bed, the French doors opened to the sea with their frayed curtains only now beginning to wave slowly in the hot ocean breeze.

I stared at him, my teeth biting into my bottom lip, waiting.

"I said I would come."

I was nauseous, my body vibrating.

He took my hand and looked at it. He held it gently as we sat down on my bed shoulder to shoulder, thigh to thigh. My bed was narrow and thin in the empty room. I lay back into the bed, waiting. He watched me, looked down at me, through me, into me.

He brought his body down to mine. He nuzzled my face with a low sigh, as if he couldn't help himself. His gaze lingered on mine like I was something sweet to be tasted.

I woke up with the first kiss, his hand on my belly, moving down ever so slowly, that first wetness as he pulled down my underpants and I let his hand lead him, caressing, circling before he lay down on me. He pulled me up gently as he entered into me long and slow. I inhaled yeasty pungent breaking waves. I heard the ocean rolling bigger and bigger, crashing onto shore. I writhed like a fish in the sand, begging, crying…

***

We lay together on our backs and stared at the cracked, stained ceiling. A stupefied lizard rested on the wall over our heads. Luke smoked a Mexican cigarette and exhaled deeply. His skin glistened sweat and pleasure, his spicey scent circle up with the harsh smoke. The sun was rushing in, already hot. He turned and looked at me, his dark head a jumble of curls against the pillow.

"I need to tell you something."

"Me too." I wanted to tell him about my vision, how I knew the second I saw him that he was the one, the prize at the end of my journey. But I let him speak first. I knew he'd say this is it, you're the one, this is our destiny.

He said, "My girlfriend from California is flying in from Europe. Today."

***

This was so familiar I could have written the story myself. I meet a boy. He likes me. We have sex. He leaves me. It never gets old, it always thrills, then stuns, and then hurts, leaving me with wider cracks after each break.

But I'd never been this wrong and it had never mattered so much.

Luke went back to the boat. He left with no plan, no explanation. Father would have scrutinized him and demanded, *What could you be thinking, Alicia?* I was speechless. I tried to hold my heart together as I worked on the subjunctive with my Spanish dictionary, *espero que me quiera, or tengo miedo que no me ame*. Spanish offers a special conjugation for desire and doubt, the perfect language for romance: *If only he wants me, I'm afraid that he doesn't love me*.

That afternoon I hung out with the red freckled family on the beach. Later, Ruthie treated me to dinner at the Shrimp Bucket. I thought I might have detected a tiny resentment on her part, but she didn't say anything.

I was empty and food was the only antidote. I gave up on the cheaper items and ordered the frogs' legs.

***

As days went by, I thought I should be strong and leave, go somewhere else in Mexico, but where?

I only knew Mazatlán. I couldn't go home. I put too much effort into my escape. It would have been humiliating to crawl back in a broken state with Dad so angry at me for leaving. I brooded, bumping up against one dead-ended thought after another.

Someone knocked on my door. "Si?"

I wished it was my landlord, the sinewy handsome young guy who walked the dark halls like a tom. I had a feeling he'd take me if I let him. That would be so easy.

Maybe I'd just go ahead and do that.

***

Instead, I opened the door to see Becky standing in the hall with her red braids and freckled face, her brown eyes smiling. "Luke says he's trying to work things out with Cyndie. He really likes you and he's going to come over as soon as he can."

What does that mean? Come over for sex? Would he cheat on his girlfriend? Was he breaking up with her? Was he desperate and I was the only other gringa around?

Becky had no idea. I didn't know what to feel. He'd looked at me so sweetly and spoken to me gently, pierced my desire. And then with only a few words, he dropped me as if I were something to throw away.

My body tightened around my heart. I went on high alert.

The following day Luke came as Becky said he would.

"I told you I'd come back." He was breathless, talking fast, his eyes bright in the dark hall.

"What happened to Cyndie?"

"She's on the boat. I told her about you. She's too upset. I can't stay there."

Of course, she's upset, you idiot. You dropped a bomb on her.

For a moment I recognized something in Luke. He was eager to escape his boat. It had been his home for five years, but now he was afraid. A runner always recognizes another runner.

I had to get away from my home. I'd spent one year after college in the Teacher Corps in Detroit. Dad had accused me of going there deliberately to, "Marry a black man."

"I had nothing to say about where I was sent. They assign you a city."

After the Teacher Corps I lived in an apartment in Cambridge only an hour from my parents' home, working as a waitress in Harvard Square. It was too close. I felt as if they could see everything I was doing and were endlessly disappointed.

Mum looked so pretty the day I came out from Cambridge to Groton to tell them I was leaving for California. She was her perfectly tailored self, gray flannel skirt, Faire Isle sweater, feet firmly on the ground, her brown hair in gentle waves, classic, but not dowdy. But those eyes when she looked at me, shards of blue that could cut.

I spent the night in my old bedroom. My mother came in the following morning to wake me up.

"California?" Mum had been dumbstruck. "You just came home from that program, for god's sakes. How would you even get to California?"

She'd never been out west.

"My friend Bobby has a motorcycle."

"Who is Bobby?!" The tone of her voice rose several notes.

"He works with me at Barney's. He's the busboy."

That did it. She collapsed onto my bed. I'd knocked her right off her feet.

"You're killing us, Alicia," she said.

Sometimes I wished that were true. I'd harbored an elaborate fantasy for years. Mum and Dad would fly to Europe. They'd have a wonderful trip together. Tragically, on their return flight, their plane would disappear into the Atlantic, their bodies never to be found. I would be an instant orphan, but free.

That seemed preferable to our relentless conflict. They made things so hard. But it did please me a little bit to see the impact I had.

"And what in heaven's name is in California?"

"Mum, everything's in California."

After all, it was 1970.

***

As it turned out, everything was *not* in California and I'd had to extend my quest into a country I'd never even thought about, thousands of miles from home.

And now, when I was so certain I'd found him, I was having doubts.

I stared at Luke as he stood in the hall radiating his innate appeal. He was like mercury. I used to break thermometers to watch the poisonous liquid move and change shape. If I touched it, I might die. Luke felt risky, and I wasn't experienced in making big decisions.

In a few fast-moving seconds, I tried to think it through. I couldn't be sure if he *wanted* me or if I was a way station, like a rescue at sea. I'd come so far, but should I say no?

I played it over in my mind. *You had your chance and you blew it. Too bad, buddy, I'm not interested.*

Dad would have warned me, *Who is this guy and how can you trust him?* And Mother didn't trust anything or anyone from west of Worcester; an expression shared by her peers that was useful for protection from the riffraff of the outside world. Luke, in her mind, would be from far, far west of Worcester.

But I was weary, tired of traveling alone, tired of being afraid, tired of sleeping with guys along the way who I didn't know or truly care about. I had my own inner place hidden from Mum and Dad, a place of visions and dreams. My vision of a soulmate at a journey's end came was more powerful than the risk of touching mercury.

Luke looked like my fantasy man, like George Maharis on the show *Route 66* or Ray Ciocci, a Groton School boy who led the town's Memorial Day parades. Luke could be my destiny.

As these thoughts raced through me, my head began to spin. I looked at his golden smiling eyes, threw up my arms, opened my palms, and said, "Come in."

It was simple.

Luke squeezed me tight and walked right into my room.

3
GETTING TO KNOW YOU

When he opened his eyes, the next morning, mine were two inches away, staring at him.

My bed was narrow for two people and I wasn't sleeping well. That was partly due to the hot nights, but more because I couldn't believe Luke was *here* with *me*.

"Hello," I said.

"Morning Al, how's my sweet thing?"

Using my nickname already and we'd barely met. His eyes were warm and held me. It felt homey, in a good way. I was amazed his breath was sweet, only a little smoky. I apologized for my breath, which I was sure was sour. Luke said no problem.

I pushed one leg in between his and my other leg on top. He took me in his arms and kissed my breasts. He took his time and didn't rush like most other guys who didn't seem to know or care they were leaving me behind in their hurry. It always embarrassed me that I took so long to respond. I thought I should be ready for sex in an instant.

Luke lingered. I knew that was a good thing, but still it left space for me to feel uncomfortable. Gradually sensations came, currents flowed, then I was ready.

It was late morning when we made it to the café where the kids and I all gathered for breakfast every day. A few small tables sat outside facing the ocean on a terrace across the street from the Shrimp Bucket.

"Dos cafes con leche, por favor," Luke said to the waiter, using most of his Spanish vocabulary. His other phrase was *huevos revueltos*—scrambled eggs—apparently the way he liked his eggs.

Faces of the staff would fall when we arrived at the Mariposa Café. As the days passed, the waiters had learned that we bought too little and stayed too long. Their politeness did not allow them to ask us to leave. Sometimes we sipped on a second coffee and on the few occasions we ordered a pastry, we shared it. The café preferred the cruise ship passengers who came into Mazatlán on a regular basis. But we made fun of the oversized American men in their flowered shirts and equally overfed women, their straw purses with shells glued onto them. Their bodies spilled over the chairs, but they had money and spent it quickly, then went back to their boat.

"I'm ready for a swim," I said to no one in particular.

"What's the hurry? We have all day," Luke said. He sat back and lit a cigarette. Obviously unaware of my routine.

The water was the only antidote to the heat and yet it seemed like the last place Luke wanted to go. We went back to my room. I changed into my bikini.

"You go ahead," Luke said. "I'll join you in a bit."

But he didn't.

***

Every morning after breakfast I'd run across the burning sand and throw myself into the warm waves as if I was going home : the rolling sound, the briny air, the surf shining in the sun, and that first ride of the day. Becky and Kim were already in the water, and Billy was further out with early breaking waves. Ruthie was on the beach in her cutoffs, her skin browner and more like leather by the day. She never swam and always kept a beer close, like a life jacket.

"Watch Katy with those big waves," she called out. Becky and Kim came closer to shore. "Billy, get in here right now. You're too far out!"

Poor Billy. He came closer to me in the water. "I guess I need military school."

Luke appeared later and sat chatting with Ruthie as they both stared out at the sea. We constantly prodded him to come in the water, but he wouldn't budge.

Riding the waves took the place of sunning, eating lunch, reading. For the kids and me it was the center of our day. It was our job. After a few hours, I'd had enough. Luke usually came up later Was he avoiding me? Did I irritate him? I never liked to make people angry. I worried they'd cut me off.

Afternoons held several empty hours. Too hot to be outside, too early for supper, too thick with humidity to think, even too sticky for sex. I'd lie on the bed pretending to read but gazing at the ceiling while Luke sat in the straight-backed chair reading Gunter Grass' *The Tin Drum.* Luke was always quiet. *What is he thinking about?* I couldn't figure out what was going on with him. *Is Cyndie on his mind?*

I'd doze off until I could mention it was time to meet everyone at the Shrimp Bucket. Meanwhile, Luke read some of Gunter Grass to me, saying he was such a fine writer. I listened and agreed.

Luke yawned then closed his book. The one time I suggested Ruthie might not be too happy about paying for us, Luke reminded me that we didn't have the money to pay for ourselves. We agreed to order the cheapest item on the menu.

I felt uneasy, but I didn't know about what exactly. Maybe it was hunger pains.

***

After dinner, in the last small light of day, Luke and I had a standing appointment with the kids on the stone wall along the Malecon. We'd smoke a joint and watch the sun slide into the ocean. It never got old; we were never bored.

Later in the evenings the Malecon grew crowded with Mexican families. Luke and I would go off on our own to stroll along with them. It was as if the pavement was moving and we were flowing with it. We walked side by side so that our conversation projected forward, not at each other. It made it easier for me to say what I really felt. We talked about everything in our lives and all our hopes. Luke had as many dreams as I did, maybe even more. After all, my entire life plan had already succeeded; I'd found my soulmate. Now that I'd found him, I didn't know what else to do.

Back then, walking with Luke in a Mazatlán evening, my notion of a soulmate was thin, someone who would love me and support me, and someone who physically matched my idea of a beautiful man. With time, that definition would change.

"It's all about community," Luke said, one evening "Everything good comes from being shared."

"Right," I lied. I didn't like sharing and wasn't good at it. "But I like to know what's mine, too."

"Sure thing, but living off the land together with friends, growing our own food…" his voice grew dreamy and drifted off. Luke often let his sentences hang unfinished as if he had more to say but… but what?

He was usually the last of all of us to arrive at the café in the mornings. After a sweet stroll and a good talk one evening, the next morning he appeared at our table almost unrecognizable. I was lingering over my second cup with the kids, talking about the ocean, what to do if a sudden rogue wave rose. "Dive under," we agreed, "as deep as possible, avoid the turbulent froth as the wave crashes on shore." Luke looked like a stranger. His leather shorts were replaced by shiny peg leg slacks, a t-shirt by a long-sleeved business shirt, his huaraches coffee by colored Italian shoes that came to a sharp point, and his unruly hair was pulled back in a ponytail.

Kim laughed outright and Becky's jaw dropped. "Whoa," she said.

"Luke. What are you doing? Where did you get those clothes?"

"I had them. From my former life." He seemed surprised that we were upset.

I was embarrassed for him. I wrinkled my nose. I never would have known him if he looked like that.

He looked at me as if I'd heaped scorn on his head. "I'll see you all later."

The whole thing made me upset, the way he could change so suddenly, the way the kids made fun of him, and my own meanness.

The evenings held us, gradually erasing my earlier confusion. The air was warm, soft, and pungent, moist with the spray from breaking surf. We noticed all the Mexican sweethearts were threesomes. Every young couple had a watchful chaperone following along. I was glad Luke and I were so free to be ourselves.

"My parents are disgusted with me," I said.

"How do you know?"

"It's all they ever say to me."

Dad used to yell into the library where I had my record player, "Joan Baez sounds like a sick cow. Kill her or I will." Or, "You look ridiculous in that skirt and moccasins." Or, "Why are you always trying to be someone else?"

I deepened my voice and squished my lips into my chin to mimic my Father to Luke. "Your ideas about life are sadly misguided."

"Ha! When I left for the Air Force my Father said, 'Never forget you're a Jew.' It was like a curse."

"My Dad is furious with me for leaving. He won't even speak to me."

"What's his problem?"

"He's a Marine. Wounded in World War II, drinks and gets crazy, threatens my mother, throws things, and stalks us all as if we're his enemy and he might kill us if he wasn't so blind drunk."

My stomach turned. It wasn't right to say bad things about Dad.

"Wow Al. Hey, my father used to chase me around the house with a broom, he burned my hand with a cigarette once to teach me about fire. But he hardly drinks at all."

"That's strange, everyone in my town drinks. All my friends had a parent who was a drunk. I used to try to help them."

"Maybe you should be a counselor, Al." He poked me in the side. "You're such a good listener."

He took my hand and we swung our arms in the air up and down as if we were about to skip.

Luke saw something in me that I'd never thought of. I'd been so focused on how awkward I was that it never occurred to me that simply listening had its own special value.

***

A friend of mine came from Madison, Wisconsin, to visit in Mazatlán. Linda was an heiress ensconced in Madison, occasionally and vaguely a student. We'd met at the University's dining room where I was hanging out on crutches, recovering from a motorcycle crash that had happened with Bobby the busboy as we headed out west. Bobby had dropped me like a hot potato when my leg swelled to the size of an elephant after the bike went down hard on a dirt road in Ontario. Linda and I hit it off instantly. She had a smart sharp sense of humor, and she had epilepsy—like me—and was the first person I'd met who shared the illness, something I had yet to confess to Luke.

Linda shared the room with Luke and me for a few nights.

She had frequent Jacksonian seizures—transient, ephemeral, localized seizures—that affected one of her legs. This caused her to drag the weak leg when she walked.

My seizures were different, *grand mal* convulsions that were like an earthquake affecting my entire body. They were a dark and secret companion.

One evening as we walked along the Malecon with Linda limping a bit behind us, Luke said, "Linda's brave to travel alone with epilepsy."

"I have seizures too. Not like Linda's. Mine are big ones where I go unconscious."

It was easier to say hard things when we were both looking ahead instead of at each other and I didn't have to see his face.

"Wow. You'd never know, Al."

"They stopped when I left home. At least I haven't had one for a long time."

I described the disorder. It was like introducing him to a mysterious friend, one I disliked who followed me wherever I went. The seizures began at age nine as *petit mal*, small lapses with my eyes rolling back in my head. "What are you doing, stop that," my fourteen-year-old brother Johnny scolded me. We were with three of our cousins at our dining room table in Lancaster, Pennsylvania. We'd moved near to Dad's relatives after being told to leave my grandmother's house in Groton, Massachusetts.

Dad's drinking had made life impossible for my grandmother. She was loved and respected in our small town, heir to one of the town's original and wealthiest landowners, widowed early, raising Mum and her two brothers alone. When Dad returned from the War, the parties took over the house until the celebration turned chaotic and ugly, and the police came to the house one too many times. We were a humiliated family, limping with our wounds open and raw to live near Dad's brother and family in Lancaster.

My brother saw me stop talking in mid-sentence and my eyes roll back. All four kids thought I must be pretending.

Within a year the seizures morphed into grand mal. They were a repetitive nightmare that came just at the edge of sleep. Most frightening was the aura that occurred at the onset. A menacing force appeared as a heavy, leaden gate steadily lowering upon me. I was helpless to stop it. The gate caused my jaw to lock so that I couldn't scream for help. As I fell into a jerking unconsciousness, I'd roll out of bed thudding onto the floor. I'd wake up lolling and drooling, my parents looking down on me, holding my head, my muscles flaccid as a limp doll. The aftermath was a dull, sick headache and a complete listlessness.

The seizures continued, several a month for eleven years. While I had routine EEG's, spinal taps, and glucose monitoring, the tests did not show a lesion in my brain that's ordinarily present in epilepsy. It was a mystery to the doctors. A mystery to me as well, a stranger in my body that I kept as my secret.

"Wow. Poor baby. So, you may be over them," Luke said.

"Maybe I am," I said.

I could feel his sympathy, a tender acceptance of something I hadn't faced. Just telling him lifted a weight from me, a scar that I'd harbored.

***

I liked being with Luke when he slept.

I didn't have to wonder who I was with him or what I should be. His sleep was deep. My tossing and turning all night didn't faze him. In the early morning I'd turn my head on the pillow and stare at him for as long as I wanted. Could I ever be that free with him when he was awake?

I admired his high cheek bones, his arm bent like a baby with his fists by his face, his hair erratic and unruly on the pillow. My family taught me to appreciate beauty, but only when it was orderly and distant, a perfect day (the weather was so unpredictable), a lovely piece of Chinese porcelain, or my lovely Mother. Certainly not the beauty of Luke.

When Luke woke up and saw me looking at him, he'd kiss me tenderly, his lips so soft. He'd turn on his back, light a cigarette, and one morning, said he was selling his boat.

"What about the sail you promised me? For a sailor you don't seem to like the water very much."

"It's not that, it's that Destiny's engine isn't strong enough to go uphill to California. I'd have to sail out to Hawaii first and then east."

"But I thought you loved Destiny. Are you thinking of going back home to California?"

"I do love Destiny, jeez Ali, but it's not going to work to keep her. Anyway, California isn't my home."

"I thought you were from California."

"No, Hartford."

Hartford?! That's disappointing.

I looked at him and he didn't appear as exotic as I'd first thought.

"No one's really from California," Luke added. "They all come from somewhere else."

I thought Luke was the real thing. How had I come this far to escape everything familiar and common and end up with someone from Connecticut?

"Well, I don't get it." There had to be another reason he'd sell Destiny.

"Let's just stop talking about it."

So, it wasn't any of *my* business.

***

Marshall and Cyndie were a problem. I guessed Cyndie didn't have anywhere else to go or she couldn't let go of Luke. But she certainly wanted the boat.

She and Marshall thought it belonged to the three of them, following the unspoken hippie code that said there should be no personal possessions. They came one at a time to my room and whined to Luke. "Jeez man, if you don't want her, let us take Destiny and keep sailing," or "What's happened to you, Luke?"

"It's my boat." It seems, sometimes Luke liked to share and sometimes he didn't.

After he told them he'd found a buyer, Marshall stormed into my room early one morning showing more expression than I'd ever seen in him.

"Two thousand dollars?! That's crazy! I can't believe you didn't even ask us."

"You guys don't have that kind of money," Luke replied.

"How the hell do you know?!"

I didn't know what to believe. Maybe Luke didn't want them to have Destiny if he couldn't have her. When Marshall left, I asked Luke and he got pissed. But he didn't answer me.

"Come with me to pass papers." He was all business.

The buyer was a dissipated looking American expat named Jim who'd come to Mazatlán to deep sea fish years before. He told Luke he was planning to live there until he rotted.

As we stood in Jim's apartment Luke said, "I'm basically giving her away."

Jim just smiled as he signed the sale papers. He knew he'd gotten a deal.

His pet spider monkey flew over our heads and sprayed urine. The room was rank with it.

"Jesus!" I ducked and put my hands on my head.

"Sorry about that. He's a little bastard."

It was done.

We walked out into the hot sun. I still had no idea why Luke sold the boat. Then he told me he'd had a VW bug for several years before he got his boat. He stopped making payments on it and played a cat and mouse game with detectives hired by the car dealer to repossess the car. He thought it was funny.

Me, not so much.

There was a lot of him that I couldn't understand.

***

The next day we went down to the harbor.

"I have to empty her out," he said.

He was pensive as he stood on the dock looking down at Destiny. He thanked her for the five years he'd lived aboard her. "She was a wonderful lady."

I felt like crying, like he was abandoning her.

"She gave me some good years," he added, "but it's time."

A group of young children appeared, wharf rats who hung around the docks looking to earn a few pesos. The word got out that the gringo was emptying his boat. Some of the Mexican mamas swarmed around Destiny as Luke went below and brought up pillows, sheets, kitchen utensils, dishes, pots and pans, clothes, and his beloved objects of beauty. He handed everything out, piece by piece in a managed chaos. While the kids grabbed, the mothers were restrained and accepted whatever objects were handed to them.

Luke kept a few treasures. A pouch he'd made from rabbit fur, the beak from a Frigate bird that he wore around his neck, a Norwegian foul-weather sweater that smelled of the sea, a book of Bukowski's short stories. He only hesitated when it came to the sextant in a large wooden box. He said he hadn't been able to figure out how to do the necessary math when he needed to find his location at sea.

"I'm still lost. Maybe it'll help me on land."

I made a face.

"That was a joke," but he kept it and shipped it back east.

I could never give everything away as easily as Luke did—including his girlfriend Cyndie—and all of it so soon after he met me. It made me nervous.

I had shadow worries about everyone's motivations. Maybe Luke was using me because he was too scared to go back out to sea and I was using him to avoid being alone. And we were both using Ruthie to feed us while she used us to divert the kids from their grief.

Those thoughts took me nowhere good. I pushed them back into a dark corner of my mind where I stored whatever I wasn't ready to see.

***

The November winds took us all by surprise.

They blew into Mazatlán and ushered in a chilling front. Dried leaves from trees I'd never noticed flew up into the air along the empty Malecon. One day we were hot and happy riding the Pacific waves and the next it was too cold to be on the beach. One day summer blossomed and the next it was gone. I didn't like that about life, that things could change with no warning.

Linda had developed a crush on an American racecar driver and left for Mexico City to follow a world racing circuit. Her leg seized that morning, but it didn't stop her.

Although I would see her in the years to come, she grew increasingly disabled and died in her early sixties from her epilepsy.

Ruthie and her kids took off, all five of them packed inside their VW station wagon with their German Shepherd, Shadow, squeezed in the back. They waved and yelled that they'd meet us in the zocalo, the central square of San Miguel, five hundred pothole filled miles away.

We'll all have so much fun, we claimed. *We'll celebrate Christmas together.*

Without any words between Luke and me, it was assumed that we were a couple. And in the same way, without any words from Ruthie, we assumed we'd follow them. After all the weather had changed. I posted my first letter home, to my cousin.

Dear Rozzie,

Here I am in Mexico; can you believe it? It's a long story how I ended up here. But I think I know why now. I found my soul mate! I can't believe it, Rozzie. He is so handsome and kind and definitely not an alcoholic. Anyway, it's going great. We're leaving Mazatlán soon and going to the mountains for Christmas with this American family who are renting a villa. I can't wait. Write back right away! Send to general delivery, San Miguel de Allende.

Love,

Ali

4

HOME FOR THE HOLIDAYS

Luke and I walked up the hill from the bus station to the jardin, San Miguel's central zocalo, a plaza surrounded by ancient stone buildings in patinas of ocher, apricot, salmon, apple green; the colors all made more vibrant in the mountain light.

"Our first Christmas in Mexico!" I said.

Every Mexican town had its own zocalo. There were beginning to be more colonial towns preserved and protected by the government and San Miguel was our first, radically different from Pacific villages.

Exhausted from a sleepless night with bedbugs in Guadalajara, we grabbed a seat on a bench alongside Mexicans and tourists chatting or reading newspapers in Spanish or English. We sat facing an over-the top rococo cathedral or Parroquia in various shades of pink and salmon. It was the most cheerful town I'd ever been in. My eyes circled the jardin with geometrically trimmed fig trees, their bases painted white, the manicured plantings of bright flowers, and the gazebo with kids playing tag in the center. A perfect place to celebrate Christmas.

A ruffian child offered to sell me little packages of Chiclets.

"I'm in love," I said to Luke. "I can't stop smiling. And we're going to be living in a real Mexican hacienda."

Becky had promised to check the zocalo every morning until she found us. We waited a short time and then we saw her from the other side of the jardin, her red hair shining in the sunlight.

She warned us to be prepared. "We have a hacienda, but it's not quite what you'd expect."

She led us up a long steep hill on a narrow cobblestoned street into a wealthy neighborhood or *colonia* called Atascadero. We breathed heavily. We were 7000 feet up, Becky said. We passed one elegant old house after another until Becky stopped and looked at us mischievously, "Ta-da."

It was like the other old houses, perhaps once a magnificent hacienda, but now a ruin. My dilapidated rooming house in Mazatlán looked luxurious by contrast.

As we followed Becky in through the high walled entrance into the courtyard, we passed a neglected garden with a fountain in the center that was dry and full of weeds. The peeling exterior of ocher stain on stucco and stone became a cold, visceral interior. The first room we entered—the Mexican version of a sitting room—was cavernous, devoid of furnishing, with floors of traditional, bare red Saltillo tile.

I began to shiver as we progressed through one empty room after another. Five-year-old Katy ran out from some mysterious hiding space and hugged us.

"It's like a castle," she said.

"Yeah, castles get really cold at night," Becky said.

Ruthie came out from the kitchen. “The real-estate woman promised me a ‘lovely spacious eighteenth-century hacienda.’ Try that one on.”

Luke and I put our backpacks in a room at the rear of the house. Except for a bed, it was empty and dark. One of the windows had no glass. But I had to admit it was spacious, though I did grumble that no one mentioned how cold it would be.

I tore through my clothes looking for something warm to put on. All I had was a faded black sweatshirt with a hood that some guy had left at a campground in Alberta. It wasn’t enough. Luke said to make the best of it.

Becky told us they waited every day for the viejo to come down from the mountain with his burro. The tiny wizened man carried saddlebags filled with twigs and branches, the only wood native Mexicans were permitted to scavenge from the protected mesquite trees.

Kim told me the viejo tried to keep a fire going in the one fireplace, but the room was too large, the ceilings too high, and the stone walls and tile floor held the cold.

The warmth of Mazatlán was long gone, the joy of riding the waves, the easy days and evenings all disappeared. It was as if the perfect days had never happened, the way it can feel when a good time is overtaken by some unexpected change.

We were all still together. But nothing was the same.

***

"Chrithmeth ith coming!" Katy was the town crier running through the rooms with her second baby tooth missing.

She showed us the peso the tooth fairy had left in the night. I tried to be on Katy's page and summon up excitement for the holiday.

"You're always very positive," Luke said as he took my face in both hands.

I could see it was going to be a tough job. He was counting on me. He said his memory of Christmas was driving around with his parents looking at all the sparkling decorated houses filled with people who celebrated a tradition that was forbidden to them.

We adults were running low on pot. Luke and I made it our mission to find the dealer in town. It wasn't difficult. We asked some likely looking young Americans in the jardin and they gave us explicit directions.

Then said, "Just stay cool when you're in their house. They're touchy."

The two dealers lived near the very top of San Miguel's hilly landscape. Their contemporary house was unusual for Mexico, all steel and cement, and fronted by a wide expanse of glass. I wondered why they risked living in a house that stood out, almost announcing its presence. Luke suggested that was because they didn't have to worry.

He knocked on the door.

I pondered what he meant when the door opened. Inside, we saw a group of people seated in a circle on the floor. The dealer who met us at the door was obviously a gringo, neat and trim with no facial hair, oddly un-tan, and no expression. He pointed to the floor and we joined the group.

I whispered to Luke, "He looks like a Republican."

The product was being sampled; a joint passed from person to person in a silent ritual.

Maybe no one spoke because the stuff was so strong that everyone was already stoned, but it felt more like an enforced silence. A second guy stood watching the group with a flat expression, his body tight and still, ready to spring into action if necessary. I was nostalgic for the dealers back in Cambridge who were cool, but always mellow as if they had no worries. I wondered if these guys had weapons, even though guns were illegal in Mexico. Whose side were they on anyway?

The sample came my way and I took a long draw. A young blonde woman with her hair in tight dreads looked at me from the other side of the circle and made a funny face, like *who are these guys?* I began to think they weren't so much frightening as they were ridiculous. Paranoid, I began to giggle. She did too. The second dealer scowled at me. His jaw vibrated. I snorted trying not to laugh out loud. He was sooo stern. That got the young woman laughing more.

Luke elbowed me hard, shaking his head. I couldn't stop laughing.

The first dealer looked at me, pointed to the door and said, "Out. Ahorita. Right now."

He held the door open and as we left, I looked back at the woman with my arms and palms up in the air and mouthed, "No sense of humor."

I stood outside waiting for Luke, gazing at the stars which appeared incredibly bright and twinkly. A Policia cruiser crawled slowly past the house. The two cops stopped and asked what I was doing in the neighborhood. I said I was out "caminando", making my fingers pretend to walk, "no me molesta por favor."

They hesitated for a minute and then drove on. Luke watched as they left.

"I can't believe you did that Al. They probably wanted a mordida," he said rubbing his thumb and two forefingers together.

"Huh?"

"They've got a deal with the dealers. This is how they make their money. And you almost got us in trouble inside. Get hold of yourself."

"Ohhh… I didn't get that." I wobbled my head. "Next time I will certainly take it seriously."

"I can't take you anywhere. Something dangerous crops up and you think it's a big joke."

I thought we'd been successful. What was the problem? Luke got what we came for.

***

We went home with our catch and all of us but Katy, shared a joint.

We decided to go down to the zocalo. The Mexicans celebrated holidays in a big way and we agreed we all needed cheering up.

And warming up. We could see our breath as we walked.

A raucous brass band played Christmas music in a gazebo, slightly off tune. A mix of tourists and Mexican families milled around the jardin.

"Everyone looks Texan," Becky said.

We laughed at all the tanned Americans with their big turquoise jewelry. Gross, we agreed. Tourists were so fake, buying up everything the culture had to offer. I never thought of myself as a tourist and yet I had very little awareness of the Mexican people. I was too busy with myself.

The day before Christmas local families opened their houses to display their Nativity scenes. The kids made fun of that as well.

We stopped by the Post Office. A letter from Hartford had come for Luke which he quickly put away in his rabbit pouch. I looked for something from my parents. It was my first Christmas away from home. Maybe they'd miss me and send some money, but there was nothing. I thought of the roaring Christmas fire back home, too many presents, too much effort to be happy. Dad and Aunt Rhody getting pickled. Or soused. Or shitfaced. Still I felt homesick.

I was hoping for fireworks in San Miguel, but it turned out that Christmas day itself was a family occasion, not celebrated publicly. We were on our own.

We attempted to set up a facsimile of a tree in the living room, a few mesquite branches in a bucket with painted tin decorations of skeletons, burros and palm trees that we'd found in the market hanging from it. If we'd been happier, maybe not in a foreign country, or maybe back in happy homes, it might have looked charming. But none of us was used to happy homes and somehow being away left us each with nothing but our own discontent. Back then I only was aware of my own sad interior.

On Christmas morning Luke used all the wood we had to make a big fire. The heat warmed the front of our bodies as we sat as close as we could to the flames. But a frigid wind at our backs and a tile floor beneath, left us shivering.

Becky suggested we make a carrot cake. There were no decent sweets in Mexico, so we'd made up our own recipe in Mazatlán using Mexican oil, flour, and sugar. The only ingredient that bore any resemblance to what we knew in the states was the carrots.

I passed by Ruthie as I went out into the kitchen to help mix the batter. She sat on the cold tile in the hall with her long red hair in braids, her legs bent, feet bare, and her arms hanging limply over her knees. Her feet looked worn and were wide, like they wouldn't fit into shoes if she ever tried to put them on. She was dressed in her cutoffs and big cotton shirt as if we were still at the beach. She held a Negra Modelo in her hands, her head wobbled, and her eyes strained to focus.

"Why don't you sit in a chair Ruthie," I said. "It might be a little warmer."

"What chair? There are no chairs. Do you see any chairs?"

I looked at her in disgust. She was just like my father, a drunk. I hadn't wanted to see it because I had my ideal about Ruthie. A cool hippie mom. It took me all this time to see that Ruthie was in trouble, like Dad. It made me mad that she appeared to be so different from what I knew and then turned out to be the same.

Becky and I beat the carrot cake batter and put it in the oven at an approximate temperature. We didn't know the Centigrade equivalent to Fahrenheit. We returned to the fire, squeezed in close to each other, and passed around a joint. I knew it might get me more depressed, but I took it anyway and passed it to Luke. If he'd asked me, I would have suggested he not smoke at all. He never seemed to enjoy it like the rest of us did. He never laughed with us. It did nothing for him except magnify the spaces between his thoughts and his words. But he didn't ask.

Not even little Katy was able to cheer us up. Christmas has a way of uncovering truths that can be hidden by daily life. I realized life for the kids with Ruthie was not so great. And I wondered what it had really been like between Ruthie and her husband. Being married to an alcoholic was tough. I understood that from watching Mother who always seemed resentful and unhappy.

I could picture Dad with a Chesterfield in one hand, tall tumbler of whiskey—milk mixed with it to sooth his ulcer—in the other, sometimes passing out before Christmas dinner. Men. Fathers. All gone missing. The kids never mentioned that it was the first Christmas without their Dad.

We listened to some of Kim's Led Zeppelin, but it felt discordant with the day.

We ate the heavy cake right from the oven. The more we smoked, the more we ate, and it landed heavy in my belly. I felt my body slide down on the icy floor and pushed myself back up against Luke's chest. I pulled his arms around me because they had no will of their own, as if he needed all his strength to keep himself propped up.

We all sang along with Leonard Cohen, our heads back, our eyes up to the ceiling, "Jesus… spent a long time watching from his lonely wooden tower…"

Ruthie's head bobbed as her body began its own slide down the wall.

"Go to bed Mom," Becky said.

The characters were different from my far off home, but the scene felt familiar.

***

I was sick of moody people. And I was sick of feeling *I* had to do all the work to make everyone happy.

I went looking for Becky and Kim. We'd gotten hold of some LSD and on that same afternoon, I suggested the three of us trip. I would never have considered tripping at 16, much less 14. But Becky and Kim were seasoned pot users. Kim said, "Sure, we've dropped acid back at home." I didn't tell were Ruthie whose drug of choice was alcohol, and Luke who I knew would not be able to handle it.

When I approached an acid trip, I marshaled my forces like a soldier preparing for battle. I readied my brain for a journey into an alternate world. I had many friends who were afraid to trip, and I knew of two who had lost their minds and fallen into psychosis. I had no fear about my drug use. It was one more risk—like hitchhiking alone—that I chanced because it made me feel free and brave.

I prepared myself for the beginning stage when the LSD would come on in waves that could initially feel scary. I knew doors would be forced open in my brain onto a landscape I couldn't control. But I loved that landscape and I was confident that I knew how to ride the waves, move through the hallucinations, and learn from what I experienced.

As the LSD entered my system, I went my own way, leaving Becky and Kim to have their own experience. While they were laughing and staying close to the villa, I wandered up into the hills behind the house so that I could be alone.

I climbed up what felt like a steep stretch of loose scree and dirt until I came to the very topmost part of San Miguel. The town lay below me, already seven thousand feet high and now I was on top of the world. I saw a dome of sky opening inside me, pulsing as a giant flower. The land around me looked as if a tornado had torn through leaving remnants of old houses, steps that went nowhere, and walls without roofs. What was inside me and what was outside of me became one. That seemed only right, that I was part of the world and the world lived within me. I realized I was only passing through this world and time was made up; now and tomorrow and forever all within me. I didn't need to be with other people, we were already one. I was never alone.

I was startled when I came upon a large black dog. He sat on the stone step of a building that was nothing more than a façade. The dog bared his teeth and snarled low and mean. The hair on his back stood straight up. He was about to charge. I knew he was a force of evil. I summoned all my psychic strength to meet his dark power to slowly and steadily walk by him. I felt the intensity of my own energy and my ability to channel it as a force. When I turned around and came back, I don't know how much later, the dog had disappeared, and a young boy was sitting on the step in his place. As I came down the hill toward our casa I thought, *I am one with everything, even with that dog, that boy, and yet I am myself and I'll be ok...deep inside, I am strong.*

Later that day, I found Luke in our room again. I tried to tell him about my experience, that I had seen something deep and true about myself, that I was someone Luke might admire, even if he wasn't showing me love right now.

"Sounds more like a hallucination to me," Luke said.

He tossed me off like I was an interruption. He was absorbed in writing something, ripping up his words and rewriting. I saw crumpled wads of paper in the wastebasket. His head was down, turned away from me, and I felt the coldness of his back.

My spiritual opening, my illumination, my vision fell to pieces.

"Fuck you, Luke." I left the room and slammed the door.

5

TOGETHER, THROUGH THICK AND THIN

An American couple we knew from Mazatlán resurfaced in San Miguel.

Luke and I had saved them when they were arrested and thrown into Mazatlán's city jail for possession of pot. The irony was Scott and Vicky were prim and proper and didn't touch pot. The police planted it in their car looking for a bribe. The couple were indignant and refused to pay, and so were taken to the state penitentiary where there were other unfortunate expats languishing with no way to get out.

The buyer of Luke's boat knew the state magistrate and he intervened. The couple gave in, paid the mordida (which had grown from fifty to seventy-five dollars), and were released. After Christmas, Luke ran into them in the zocalo. They offered him a ride across Mexico to the coast.

One frigid January morning over Mexican style cornflakes in our freezing kitchen, Luke said, "It's time to go."

My eyes widened, but I agreed. Ruthie was hardly ever pleasant to us; the family seemed downright miserable. I didn't ask where we were going. All I cared about was going with him. I trusted that when we got away by ourselves things would be better and we could talk things out, get back the good feeling we had in Mazatlán. He was barely speaking to anyone. We'd only been together three months, but it felt like forever. I planned on keeping it that way.

The morning we left the kids looked sad. We didn't know when or if we'd see each other again. Becky held me tight, but Ruthie seemed relieved to see us go.

Luke and I climbed into the backseat of Scott and Vicky's wagon. All morning and for that entire long day, I clung to Luke in my mind, my heart in my throat. He was so quiet, almost silent for the seven hundred-mile ride to the coast. I blamed myself, but I didn't know what I had done or failed to do.

Scott and Vicky said we'd spend a night along the way. The roads were rough, and it was hard driving having to keep constant watch for potholes. Near the end of the afternoon we found a casa de huespuedes somewhere in the middle of Mexico that overlooked a waterfall falling into a fresh pool. The four of us swam in the cool waters, the sun making rainbows in the falls. Another time I would have loved feeling the spray on my face, but now I only felt cold.

Lying in bed that night I longed for the warmth of his body, but he gave me a small kiss goodnight then turned away from me. The next morning at a little restaurant on a deck above the falls, the woman gave us fried turtle's eggs for breakfast. I took one bite and put my fork down. They were too rich, and I couldn't swallow them.

The couple dropped us off in Puerto Escondido the next afternoon, wished us well, and headed south.

The town was a surfing mecca, one of the last Pacific villages frequented by buses before the border with Guatemala. Luke asked a couple surfers carrying their boards for the way to the solitary bus stop. Random street dogs, dusty and hapless, trotted aimlessly down the dirt road hoping a scrap of something might come their way. I saw a young boy kick one and throw a stone at him. My stomach turned. The world was cruel.

Luke and I came to the end of the road and in the dead hours of a torpid January afternoon, we waited.

"Where do you think we should go?" I asked.

Luke was taciturn, taking a long time to answer, but he was efficient with his words. "We can either go north or east, Ali. I've heard good things about Zihuatanejo, north of Acapulco. But you choose. North or east to Veracruz. *I'll go in the other direction.*"

"What?"

"I said, you go in one direction and I'll go the other way." He stuttered over his words, as if something was happening over which he had no control.

There was a long silence. I couldn't get any words out. And when I did, I stammered, "I thought we were going together. I don't want to go anywhere by myself." I pawed the dusty ground beneath me with one foot.

"Al, you have to choose," he said. He blew out a long breath from ballooned cheeks, like he was trying to move through excruciating pain. As if he were the one who'd been stabbed. As if something was being done to him.

I shook my head. *No. I don't have to choose. I refuse to help you send me away.* We stood in silence. I thought my legs wouldn't hold and I'd fall down.

With perfect timing, a bus arrived from the south with Acapulco in ugly yellow letters barely visible on its front. It appeared that my decision was made for me.

"You go ahead, Ali, you go north," as if he was extending his palm politely, holding a door for me.

I felt the warmth of his hand when he pressed a wad of pesos into mine and held it for a long time.

"I don't need money," I said, which wasn't true because I only had about $25 American dollars and a few pesos.

"I want to give it to you." He pressed the small wad into to my hand.

Then he took my backpack and handed it carefully to me as I followed dumbly after some Indian women and climbed aboard the bus. I looked back at him. My eyes burned. Luke was crying. He had a look of bottomless remorse, like Dad the morning after a drunken rampage, when it was too late for an apology.

The bus crawled out of town; its windows covered with the parched heat of January dust so that I couldn't see if Luke was waving. Either way, I wouldn't have waved back. Luke had to pull me off him, like a piece of sticky fly paper and I was not about to let him humiliate me further.

Why is he abandoning me? What have I done?

***

I sat bumping up and down on the bus, sobbing, trying to sort out what just happened.

I misread him so badly. I didn't see that he'd been planning to leave me before we left San Miguel. He probably hadn't expected me to jump in Scott and Vicky's car with him. I'd had to rush, stuff everything in my backpack in minutes. But I thought that was because Luke wasn't communicating. Of course, he wanted me to go with him.

This was even more humiliating than I thought. *I'm an idiot. What signals did I miss?*

I did have some warning. I just didn't want to see it. I'd been worried after Christmas that Luke was spending more time alone in our room than he was with me or any of the family. His absence was loud, like a hole in my belly. When I went looking for him one day, I found him in our room fiddling with something in his pack.

I put my hand on his shoulder. "Is something wrong, Luke?"

"No, I'm all right."

"You could fool me. You're not even talking."

He looked at me, his forehead furled, his eyes sad. "I'm sorry. I'm just feeling quiet."

When he left for town later that same day holding an envelope, I began to feel suspicious. Was he writing to Cyndie, did he feel he'd made a mistake by choosing me over her? I worked myself into a panic.

I went into our room, rifled through his backpack. Then thought what the hell and dumped the entire sum of his possessions onto the floor. A letter in the pile of clothes jumped out at me. We rarely got any mail. I felt like I was committing a crime when I opened it.

Dear Son,

I have no idea what you are doing or when you are thinking of coming home. I hope to god you were not on your boat during that terrible hurricane off of Mexico. Your mother says to tell you Morrie Schwartz is about to be married to Arthur's daughter, Elaine. I remember you dated her yourself.

Uncle Morris and Aunt Ruth were shocked when they saw you in California. I'm glad your mother wasn't there to see you. You gave up a promising sales position at Bright Star. Opportunities like that don't come around every day. Remember, life is what you make of it.

It's still possible you could get in with Sy and have a real sales job. It sickens me to think of you down there wandering aimlessly. The early bird catches the worm and it's getting late for you.

I love you son,

Dad

The letter was nothing more than a few clichés.

I remembered Luke saying it didn't matter what his parents thought; that they would get used to it. It was my parents who we thought would be the big problem, not his. It didn't make any sense that his father could affect him so badly with one letter. So why had he shut down and closed off to me? I'd tried to stay cheerful and affectionate. I'd done everything I knew how to do to make him love me.

The bus lurched suddenly. The women standing in the aisles were thrown back, scrambling to keep from falling on top of each other. Hens squawked and the smell of chicken offal filled my nostrils. I didn't trust the stupid driver. He was so careless with sharp turns.

My pack hit the lady sitting beside me. "Perdoname."

I pulled it back in front of my legs. I stared out the bus window, my thinking as cloudy as the scenery outside. I couldn't stop crying. Then everything came into focus for a quick moment. There was something so wrong that Luke had to leave, something he couldn't even speak out loud. And deep down, I concluded that it was me.

I was the one who was damaged and broken. And unfixable.

6
THE BEACH

No one in their right mind would stay in Acapulco any longer than necessary. Other than its perfect halfmoon bay, it was tacky and drug cartels were already killing tourists in 1970.

My bus arrived late, so I had to spend the night. I continued to weep, my nose dripping. The hotel staff gave me Kleenex at the desk and spoke kindly to me. After a few spoonfuls of sopa de pollo and a toasted bolillo in the hotel dining room, I went up to my room and threw myself across the bed where I gave in completely to my heartbreak.

I wrote a letter to my parents:

I met a guy. I liked him so much. He left me. I'm leaving Acapulco tomorrow, but don't worry about me.

The ink ran and blurred on the airmail rice paper as I sobbed and gulped with every sentence.

I headed north for Zihuatanejo the following morning, the obvious next stop of any consequence. I stared out the bus window at the ocean, its deep blue flatness a companion for my vacant interior. Four hours later I arrived in Zihuatanejo.

I moved on automatic pilot from the bus stop toward the water, my head down, my feet dragging in my huaraches, scuffing the fine dust up into my nose. The place swarmed with hippies.

Their sweet and sour odor hung in the air from patchouli and unwashed armpits. This was the place to be, although the first I'd heard of it was from Luke.

At that time there was barely any town. Zihuat, as it was called by hippies, was a cluster of tin shacks with a few fishing dories in faded pastels pulled up onto a small beach. Two family restaurants shared a dock overlooking a bay as pristine and glistening as the one Acapulco was famous for. I sat down at an empty table and ordered a Coke. I was thirsty, but there was no potable water at that time.

A group of travelers sat talking at the next table. I looked at them but didn't feel like talking to anybody. A guy with curly blond hair and wire rimmed glasses came over and asked if he could sit at my table. I nodded. He asked if I'd come in on the last bus. He spoke fluent formal English with a clipped accent, from Amsterdam, he said. I said I was looking for a place to camp by myself.

There were palapas on the surfing beach for ten pesos a night, he told me.

No, I replied, I meant alone.

He'd heard about Playa de Las Palmas on the other side of the mountain. He said he'd go there himself, but he was on a shoot for National Geographic and it was too hot and too far to carry his equipment. I thanked him and excused myself.

Sounds perfect, I thought.

It was easy for me to find a random teenaged boy eager to guide me there by foot the next day for a few pesos. When I really wanted something, I made it happen.

After a sleepless night in a stuffy room with no window, I met up with the boy shortly after dawn. Miguel and I left behind the dusty roads of the village, the cozy harbor, and all the barefoot happy hippies. After a few minutes walking we turned, walked behind one of the shacks that lined the road, and magically entered another climate zone. Only locals would have known there was a path.

We trudged uphill, step by step, through a steamy jungle with flashes of scarlet and emerald shooting out of the trees, the squawks and shrieks of parrots and spider monkeys above us. Suddenly Miguel raised his walking stick in the air. A Tarantula the size of my fist was in the path. He slammed the stick down on the creature, smashing it.

"Did you have to kill it?" I asked.

"I was protecting you, senorita."

I wasn't scared until that moment. I wondered what else was in that jungle and what made me think I could survive alone on a beach? I began having second thoughts. My parents scolded me for following any old idea that popped into my head with no thought about consequences (The same impulse had led me to hitchhike alone across the U.S.). But it was Dad who taught me that a little danger is what made life interesting.

And in truth, I was too ashamed of my sorrow to be seen by other people.

***

An hour later, when Miguel and I stepped out of the jungle as suddenly as we'd entered. I stood on the sands of a crescent cove that lay naked in stillness and silence, nothing except for the thin rhythmic shhoo… of tiny wavelets gliding onto the shore. The sunlight was blinding.

He grew serious when he realized I wasn't returning with him to town. "A woman alone," he said, "perhaps I should stay with you."

He left me reluctantly, saying he would return to check on me.

"Please don't. Gracias and adios."

Maybe he was the only one I should be worried about.

I stood alone and heard the sea lapping on the beach, my heart thumping, and the flapping of three pelicans skimming the water. The beach curved the length of a football field with green hills at either end that rose up and then fell into the horizon. I chose the left end of the cove because it had a piece of shade cast by a boulder on the sand. I set my pack down in the shadow and made a small space for the oranges, bananas, and semi-sweet biscuits that I'd bought the day before in the town's one poorly stocked tienda. Due to the lack of potable water in Mexico, foreigners drank soda without ice or beer. Even fresh fruit juice often resulted in dysentery because it was diluted with unpurified water.

The small patch of shade was soon swallowed up by the scorching January sun as it rose higher in the sky. There was no relief unless I was to go back into the shadows of the palm grove, to the world of tarantulas. The air was like wet putty, almost too thick to breathe. I was exhausted from sleeplessness and crying. I stood frozen. Time and I had come together, both screeching to a halt. Now what?

Go for a swim.

I took my skirt off and waded into the ocean. Even the shallows were hot. An exposed rock in the knee-deep water was covered with a blanket of sea grass. With a few tries I was able to pull myself up and balance on its slippery top. The thought of swimming out over my head to find cooler water was too risky. There would be no one to save me if I needed it.

A drumming in my head reminded me that Luke was gone and had left a hole inside me. It wasn't only the ache from the breakup. Luke was going to balance me. He was the someone to sit at the other end of my seesaw so I wouldn't fly off. Without Luke, I fell flat and hard.

I waded back to shore and sat cross legged beneath the blank blueness of the sky. I was as alone as I'd felt in those last days with Luke. I pictured the expats back in town, cozied up together, telling stories of idyllic nights in the ruins of Palenque and horror tales of hippies caught with drugs and abandoned in Sinaloa jails.

Maybe it was all my fault. I'd kept myself distant from Luke. I thought back to my nine-year-old self, walking down our driveway kicking up pebbles in my blue Keds. A thought rumbled in my child's brain like a thunderbolt: *I was separate from the universe, I was one little person in a big world, and I was alone.* Making friends became more difficult as I got older. Perhaps I didn't know how to be close to anyone.

On the beach that day, I took out my pocket-sized mirror and studied my reflection. My hair was in a long blond braid, bleached by the sun, my skin was golden brown, my eyes were navy blue, my features unremarkable. Strangers often mistook me for someone they thought they knew. I didn't know what that meant. I was a girl who was always worried. Was I pretty enough? Was I too heavy? Did my face betray some hidden sadness? Was I even presentable to face the world? Sitting on the beach with no one to see me, the most basic question followed: was I still there?

Throughout that day I continued looking at myself in the mirror. *Don't panic.* I was trapped inside listening to a mind that was frenzied and frantic. I tried to get outside of myself, but I couldn't see anything other than a vacant glassine sea with all its color disappearing into sunlight.

As the first day surrendered, I saw the three pelicans again flying low across the water. I watched in relief as a grudging sun descended below the horizon. I stood up and stretched my arms high into the sky, breathing some small relief. But then night darted in like a swift and swallowed the space around me. The darkness filled my body until I wanted to scream, *Somebody, come get me.* I imagined the ocean rising in one giant wall of water and pouring over me. I would drown in the night. Or something would come out of the jungle, a wild creature, a man. I stood on the sand immobilized and blind.

And then, gradually I began to see in the darkness. I could make out the water and the white tips of the wavelets, and I could even differentiate where the line of high tide stopped, and the dark wet sand became light and dry. It was silly to think the tiny waves would pour over me. I looked in the other direction and saw only a gentle swaying movement of the palms at the edge of the jungle.

I measured the distance between the high tide line and the jungle and unrolled my sleeping bag in the middle. I sat down in the moist darkness and tried to breathe. I wasn't ready to bed down so early, but there was nothing else to do. I lay on my back, the hard sand beneath my bag, arms straight and stiff at my sides as I looked up at the dense thick jumble of stars. Not the same twinkling stars that filled my eyes when I first met Luke and not the wide benevolent night that blessed Destiny when he was sailing in the moonlight. The stars I saw were indifferent, thoughtlessly crowded into a cold cobalt sky. I realized only Miguel and the Dutchman knew I was there in the silent night. I was nothing to an endless universe and the stars kept looking down at me and I kept staring back at them until I passed out.

***

I woke up at first light, lost for a moment before I realized where I was. Everything looked the same as the day before. There were the three pelicans flying low and graceful over the water, diving for their morning catch. There was the sun climbing fast in the flat blue sky. I had made it through a night alone. My first victory.

The following night I decided to choose a tiny constellation of three stars and attach my gaze to them. Heck with all those other billions of stars. I refused to look at them. Although I didn't recognize the little threesome from my sky at home, they seemed friendlier and they helped me fall off to sleep. Fears in the dark moved around in my mind, but they lessened with each quiet passing night.

Four or five days later, when I woke up one morning, I noticed two boys at the other end of the cove diving for oysters. It was a relief that they showed no interest in me, but also a fact that I was nothing to them.

On the beach in an un-peopled world, I could gnaw undisturbed on a bone of rejection. Luke had found me wanting. I wasn't right, I wasn't enough. Each evening at dusk I cried for Mother as if she was another lost day. It wasn't really that I missed *her*. I missed the mother I never had. Now there was no one to say, "Stop your crying Alicia, stop being so dramatic."

I wouldn't always take everything as a personal rejection. Over time I'd learn that people had their own motivations and ways that often had nothing to do with me.

But I was very young on the beach and much of life remained a mystery.

***

The days that followed were marked only by light and darkness. I'd sit behind the boulder for as long as there was shade. Then I'd surrender to the sun. As the salt and heat entered my pores, my skin grew sticky with sea and sweat. I set aside times for eating, parceling out my meager food supply: a quarter of an orange, a biscuit, a small piece of banana. My stomach shrank, and my hunger diminished.

Years later I became preoccupied with Bobby Sands, the IRA fighter, as he starved himself to death in an Irish prison, a martyr for the Northern cause. I admired his journal, filled with poetry and love until he became too weak to write.

I flirted with fasting on the beach. After a few short days I already felt clearer, my perceptions heightened, and body lithe as if my bones had become dry open channels for the air to move through. But something told me to make myself eat. There was no one else to take care of me and I needed to remain conscious and strong.

Time crawled in the light and darkness came fast leaving me alone with the stars and a sliver of moon.

Thoughts faded.

My feeling for Luke lessened day by day.

A peace came over me.

***

One evening about a week into my stay, I was sitting looking out at the sea in what remained of the daylight, when a small dog staggered out of the jungle and approached me. His little ribs jutted out, his mouth hung open, and a skinny tail curved back between his legs as if he had given up on himself. He was familiar to me, but I didn't know why. It was important that I try to help him. I named him Cangrejo after the tiny crabs that scritched in the sand all around me. He didn't stay long before he wandered back into the trees.

Unlike me, Cangrejo was smart enough to stay out of the sun and only appeared at dusk. The next evening, I waited and sure enough, he came out of the same spot of the jungle. We sat together by an imaginary campfire I made with a circle of shells. *Come here, little Cangrejo, let me feed you.* I reached out my hand and offer him pieces of ripe banana to come closer.

One night he took a small piece, but he couldn't eat it. He could barely remain standing. *Don't give up on yourself Cangrejo*, I heard myself say. I grew nauseous watching him weaken over the next few days, as if something about him might be contagious, until I wanted him to go away.

And then one evening he didn't come. I was beyond crying, but I couldn't get his emaciated body out of my mind.

***

I fell back onto the rhythmic flight of the pelicans with their great wings of morning and evening, air and water. They knew something I didn't yet grasp about the order of all things.

What I did take from Cangrejo was that I was very thirsty, and I had to do something about it. Oranges were my only source of liquid and my throat was parched. I realized that there were coconuts fallen from palms at the edge of the jungle and that they had milk. *Oh!* I picked one up, very green, and smashed it on the shade boulder. I broke it into too many pieces, but I got some sweet milk out of it and with a few more tries, was able to break one carefully so that I got more milk. The discovery of those coconuts made me feel like Robinson Crusoe.

Despite my crafty cleverness, I decided to go back to the village to restock my fruits and biscuits. I left my pack on the beach so that I wouldn't be tempted to stay in town. I walked quickly over the mountain, accustomed now to the heavy air. I returned even faster. I couldn't wait to get back to the beach. Luckily, I didn't have to speak to anyone; they might have thrown off my precarious solitary balance. Upon return, I sank back in with the ease of a long deep breath into solitude, entering some inchoate place too dark for any self-reflection. I looked in the mirror occasionally. Coconut oil and sun-sweat covered my nose with tiny white pimples that bothered me. I scrubbed my face with wet sand.

Gradually I even let the mirror go, another small victory.

***

One morning, I opened my eyes at dawn, as usual. Something was different about this morning. I lay awake on my bag, listening to the water, breathing in the pungent air, fragrant with salt, saying a silent hello to the light, when I noticed wide tracks inches from my feet. It looked like a bulldozer had rolled by. The tracks led out of the sea, went by the end of my bag, and continued all the way up to the edge of the palm grove. I studied them for a moment not understanding what they were. I stood up and tried to span the width of the tracks with my long legs. I couldn't do it.

Up close to the jungle I saw two boys digging furiously in the sand. I walked up to them, and in my first human communication in three weeks, I asked what they were looking for. They told me the great sea turtle had come, as she did every year at this time. Her eggs were a delicacy and they would sell them.

How could they have known when she would arrive? They only shrugged and smiled at my questions. I realized these were the boys I saw diving for oysters two weeks earlier. They must have been on the lookout for her, even checking out my end of the beach when I was sleeping and thought I was alone. One of them was Miguel. Maybe he'd been checking up on me to see if I was okay.

They explained that at the next full moon when the tides rose to their highest point, her eggs would hatch, and the babies would be swept out to sea. I saw that the boys were proud, filled with their understanding of the moon and the tides and the turtle's journey. They went back to their digging.

Please don't let them find the eggs. I felt part of her journey as well. There were mysteries unfolding within me that connected to what was happening around me. A giant primeval creature, finding her way from the ocean's depth to the smallest shore had somehow entered my unconscious in the night with her lumbering passage, as if I were one of her babies.

***

The boys finally had to admit defeat and gave up their digging. I returned to my routine. A few days later three young travelers walked out of the jungle and set up camp at the other end of the cove. Startled by their presence, I pretended to ignore them. I watched them out of the side of my vision as they gathered palm fronds and built a small fire. I smelled meat grilling. I could hear my stomach grumbling.

I felt afraid when one of them walked down the beach in my direction. What did he want from me? But when I saw him up close, his face was open and friendly. He invited me to share their food. I relaxed and said sure. They were from Minnesota.

We sat around their fire and chatted, and they gave me some carne asada, rice, and beans. I told them how long I'd been there and about the coming of the turtle, leaving Luke and my heartbreak out of it. They seemed as awed by nature as I was. We laughed into the evening and I returned to my spot at the other end of the beach. I sat comfortably inside my own skin, as if I had a place, on the beach, with the guys.

Maybe it's time to go. Their food and their warmth awakened me, and I was hungry for more. The thought of going back into the world meant I would leave the beach behind. No one except me would know the fullness of what I'd experienced, my fears or my small victories. But the Minnesota travelers had seen me, had seen the beach, and heard some of my story. I didn't want to lose what I'd experienced on the beach, yet I knew it was time to leave.

On my last night under the stars, I lay with my arms folded behind my head, looking up with no fear, with no loneliness, breathing deep and easy. I thought about Luke, about the way he'd rejected me, and I felt my heart mended, or at least sealed over so that it was no longer open and raw.

And then I thought of Dad and the way he rejected me as his daughter. I could even remember the moment it happened because it followed the arrival of my first period. He was coming into the study as I was coming out, *hey Dad,* I reached up to hug him. He pulled back in a way that said, I don't know you anymore. Newly sober he'd fallen into a well of depression. But the message I received was, if he couldn't love me, what man would? As a teenager I began changing my clothes several times a day and picking at my face. I concluded something must be very wrong with me.

On my last night on the beach, I looked up and out and then within me. I could only see dimly into myself but what had always been impenetrable darkness felt a bit less frightening. I knew Dad was there in the darkness and I knew I'd have to face him in his person and the way he lived within myself. He was large in my mind, a shadow that lay over me, one that made me afraid to … to what? I didn't know. Some years passed before I learned about the red thread that led from my surface to a deeper sense of self.

The next morning before the sun had a chance to slow me down, I readied myself to leave. I looked out one more time at the three pelicans. I gathered my few possessions and walked to the other end of the cove to say goodbye to the guys.

I walked back over the mountain to the village and rented a stuffy cement room with a hole for a window looking out at the road. At night, the animals raised the dust in the streets. A joyful cacophony of cows, pigs, chickens, and goats tearing up and down the road together. I laughed. I missed my stars, but then I didn't miss my stars. Every dawn I swam across Zihuatanejo Bay and back. I was strong and spare, filled with energy.

In pure serendipity, a few days later I ran into the red-haired family in town. Ruthie asked me to drive the kids across Mexico to Veracruz for Mardi Gras while she took a brief trip back to the states. I grabbed the chance. I'd had enough of being alone.

For two more months I traveled with them, stuffed into their station wagon.

But I held on secretly to the great sea turtle, to her mindless triumphant faith in creation, as if she was my immortal mother.

A seed of her faith rooted itself within me.

LESSON TWO:

IT'S NOT WHAT YOU THOUGHT

7

HOME SWEET HOME

A chilly determined rain fell onto baby green leaves as Mother and I drove west toward Groton. Mum always said spring was cruel. Promising and spiteful, all at once. She took the weather personally.

It was April when she picked me up at the bus station on Stuart Street in Boston, almost a year after I'd left Cambridge on the back of a motorcycle wearing a sparkling blue helmet covered with stars and the name *Stella* on its front. We hugged carefully in the terminal, as if we didn't know each other well. I felt her soft cheek and inhaled her sweet perfume.

She pulled away and looked at me with her probing blue eyes. Quickly, after scrutinizing me, she withdrew into herself. She wasn't curious about where I'd been or what I'd done in my year of travel. It was as if it hadn't happened, as if hers was the only known world and I had temporarily removed myself from it.

Mum gunned the engine as we entered Storrow Drive, leaving Boston in a cloud of dust. Dad referred to my mother as Barney Olfield after the famous car racer. Driving was Mum's freedom, her expression of independence.

"Whew! I'd forgotten how fast you drive! Everything in Mexico was so slow."

"What's that scent you're wearing?"

"Patchouli, Mum."

"Well, you stink."

I stopped talking and turned to the blur of green out my window.

***

As we sped into Groton, I was reminded how pretty it was, how innocent it appeared with its brave maple trees lining Main Street, the chartreuse buds bursting like newborn babies. Too bad I was born too late for the dignified giant Elms that canopied the street when Mum was young. Maples are pretty, but common, she'd said.

White clapboard houses with black shutters sat high along a hill, one after the other as we entered town, our house among them. They were stately and graceful, holding onto a small world where there was no threat of foreign intrusion. We were old money, so old in fact that there wasn't much money left. Luckily, my grandmother died in time to leave enough for Dad's necessary and lengthy leave of absence from work. He'd developed cirrhosis of the liver when I was fourteen, lingered near death for weeks, and was only now emerging from a seven-year period of depression.

We drove up the long driveway and came to a stop by the kitchen door. Our house was called *Scottowe*, which means *house on a hill.* Mother lived there for most of her life and my brother and I were born there. My grandmother Nanny shared her house with us for my first seven years until we moved to Lancaster—

Amish country—where Dad attempted to manage his drinking and establish a new life. Seven years in Groton, seven years in Lancaster and now with my grandmother gone, we were back in the big house.

I took my pack out of the back of the car.

"You look like you've been living in those clothes for the past year," Mum said.

She was right. I couldn't remember if I'd ever washed them. It wasn't as if we'd had much access to bathrooms or showers and none to laundries, but I couldn't tell her that. As I headed for my bedroom, I peeked in at the print room where Nanny planted herself for her later years in a large armchair with a gray Persian cat named Fluffy resting on the shelf created by Nanny's large, soft breasts. Nanny loved food. Mother brought her a tray in for lunch each day, a little Amari dish of this, a small rose medallion plate of that and something sweet and custardy at the end. My grandmother stayed close to a small lavatory, but often dribbled along the way and the tiny hall between print room and bath smelled of urine and *4711 Eau de Cologne*. A decade had passed, and the chair became Dad's.

I still missed her.

The house felt like a museum, filled with beautiful relics from the past, but all so far from where I'd traveled. Who lived like this anymore? Many objects had small pieces of paper glued to their undersides with tiny writing: *belonged to Isaiah Davis, 1863, given to Maria for her wedding, 1890.* There was a story behind every piece of furniture, much of it tending toward the tragic or premature death. There was the young son of our 18th century Scottish ancestor who'd been fatally struck by falling rock while lifting huge slabs of granite, or Nanny's 19th century cousin who'd taken her life in the guest room. I thought my hands could feel the spirit of one ancestor or another whose hands had also touched that porcelain pitcher, sat at that same desk, or died on that same sofa.

Everywhere I looked I heard, *Never, forget us.*

***

I took my pack upstairs and leaned it against the small upholstered chair in my room. My bed was neatly made, and the room smelled like lavender. The house had a familiar combination of smells, Old wood, clean crisp air, and the wool of oriental rugs.

I went down to the kitchen by the back stairs the help would use when there was help, which there hadn't been for some time. Mum was standing over the sink draining tuna fish for lunch. She looked up at me and I could see she wasn't pleased. She didn't like the way I looked when I left and obviously, I'd done nothing to improve myself in my time away.

I thought to tell her about my travels, something that might capture her attention, skipping my time on the beach which was precious to me and would have horrified her.

Maybe she'd be interested in the weeks I spent on the Montana ranch? "Ellen Emerson is a real rancher Mum." Ellen escaped from her Ralph Waldo east coast family in the 1940's, married a cowboy, and was now a widow running their cattle ranch in the northwest corner of Montana. Mother went to grammar school with Ellen.

"We were dismantling Buffalo Bill Cody's cabin, to take it back to the ranch. She's going to rebuild it on her property."

"Really?" She waved a dismissive hand toward the cutting board. "Chop this celery, please."

"Yeah. She took in kids for three weeks at a time and gave us room and board in exchange for work."

I didn't mention that Ellen was hostile toward me when I first arrived. Perhaps she remembered Mother. She'd assumed I was a privileged rich New England brat who didn't know how to hold a hammer. It took me a lot of hard work to win her respect, but by the end I could look her in the eye and stand my ground. She took my hand in both of hers when I left and said I was a good worker and come back.

"You should see Montana in the summer, Mum. It's filled with wildflowers and the sky goes on forever."

"Mm hm. Get the mayonnaise, please."

"We'd ride in the back of a pickup truck for miles every morning to get to the cabin."

"Mm hm. Put those plates on the table for lunch, please."

"I had sex with the foreman in the bunkhouse."

"Mm hm…"

I knew it.

"Did you know that Buffalo Bill once killed two thousand buffalo in one hunt? No wonder they were almost killed off." I'd decided that Buffalo Bill was a macho pig, not a hero.

Mum never responded to memories or stories. She wasn't sentimental. She never said, "You were so cute in your lavender seersucker dress" or "Remember that day at Brookside when you first learned the elementary backstroke?"

If pressed about the past she'd say, "You were impossible to dress" or simply "I don't remember."

"Well, Alicia, now what are you going to do? When are you going to get a job?" She called back up the stairs, "George? Lunch is ready."

Most of my friends weren't any further along in life than I was. No one I knew felt any pressure to move along. That didn't count with my parents.

"I'm thinking," I said.

"Well, it feels like you've done nothing but think for the past year, and a year of menial jobs before that. Time to do something with yourself instead of wasting your college education."

An education she never had.

***

Dad barely spoke to me. Seven years sober but still angry a year later after I'd left. I didn't know how to approach him, much less start up a conversation.

I never used to know what to say after Dad's alcohol fueled rampages, often lasting late into the night. They always began the same way. The first drink I'd notice him taking was in the late morning. A tall tumbler of whiskey topped off with milk. After one small sip I'd hear his voice change. His face would become oily, like he'd been lubricated, his skin sweaty and greasy.

Lunchtime would pass unnoticed because Mum would take stock of the situation and disappear, an amazing feat since at that time we were in Pennsylvania and our house was so tiny only one person at a time could fit into the one bathroom. Dad built the house with the intention of using it as the garage of a larger house, but that never happened. My brother was gone, sent to boarding school at twelve.

The one downstairs room would begin to rumble and the walls to shake as Dad's voice dived lower and lower. We were on the precipice of something dangerous, life threatening, and I wasn't sure who was in danger.

My father wasn't my father. I remember choosing to believe that another being had taken his place. His rampages included multiple showers through the day with him emerging from the bathroom dripping and only a bath towel around his waist. His chest was broad, and his body bloated. He'd begin swearing, ugly streams seeping through the space like molten lava. The words like weapons stabbing or shooting in their attack on me. I couldn't escape.

The storm continued as day moved into night gaining strength from alcohol like warm water feeds a hurricane. Mum would appear from their bedroom to heat up a TV dinner which I ate while watching *The Life of Riley*. Dad would storm up and down the stairs threatening to throw the TV through the window. Mother would send me upstairs to bed. I'd sit on the top stair listening to him prowling down below. He was after someone. Mum or people I didn't know, or he might turn on me. She said nothing except a hopeless, "George, stop it."

I'd hear some piece of furniture hit a wall, a glass shatter, books and ashtrays falling off a table. I'd lean my head against the upstairs wall waiting for it to stop. *Am I his enemy?*

Late into the night the raging would drop off, I'd go to bed, hear his sodden snoring, then fall into a heavy sleep.

My head would wake me early in the morning with a dull pounding I didn't understand and a nausea I couldn't throw up. I'd read another *Bobbsey Twins (their life seemed like a fairy tale)* in my room until I heard sound downstairs. If it was Sunday, I couldn't stay in my pajamas because I had an important job driving with Dad to get the newspapers. I'd dress quickly in my khaki shorts, a navy blue and white striped t-shirt, tie my blue Keds and go downstairs. Dad wouldn't look at me, but I knew the routine.

I'd climb into the driver's seat of our '49 Olds sedan. The car smelled of warm, old upholstery, and its gearshift had a big round ivory colored knob. I was ten, but Dad had already taught me to drive. I knew he trusted me. Tall for my age and long legged, I could easily reach the pedals and see over the steering wheel. I'd put it into first and we'd motor slowly down the drive, passing my Dad's brother's house where my cousins were probably still asleep with no idea what was happening in our home. I'd put the left blinker on even though we were still on a private lane. Dad was a stickler for the rules of the road. We'd continue past the neighbors' pasture, their palominos grazing in the early morning sun, and then turn left onto the Millersville Pike. The Pike had two lanes, but traffic was sparse on a Sunday morning when most everything was closed. I'd shift into second and third and then double clutched as I downshifted.

"Good shifting, Goopie," Dad would say. His first words of the day.

I knew he was low, very low. I felt sorry for him.

I'd park the Olds facing front into the curb and go into King's drugstore to buy the *Philadelphia Inquirer.* We'd drive home through the poor section of Lancaster where African American families lived in ramshackle shacks and young children sat on front stoops watching us go by. I felt sorry for them. I had a lot and they had so little.

Dad would tend his station in the kitchen making up a batch of pancake batter. He'd get the pan heated so that the silver dollar pancakes cooked into perfectly browned wafers. I'd eat batch after batch floating in Vermont Maid's fake syrup. I'd read the funnies and eat too many because it would make him feel better and he needed forgiveness.

Sunday mornings were always predictable.

But now newly returned from Mexico and after a lengthy, silent breakfast with Mum, I went into the dining room where Dad sat at the table hunting and pecking on a typewriter. I sat down next to him.

"What are you typing, Dad?"

"A resume."

"Oh. So, you're feeling well enough to go back to work."

"Yes. Something you should be doing," he said without looking at me.

Wasn't he going to ask me anything about the last year?

"Thanks for selling my car for me," I said.

"What a waste of money."

"What kind of job are you going to do?" I asked.

"We spent twelve thousand dollars on your college education and what have you done with it? Nothing."

I wanted to remind Dad that he only got through college because his Mother came up from Philadelphia and rented an apartment in Cambridge to make sure he went to class. He started pounding the poor typewriter and ripped a sheet of paper out. I saw Luke in my mind scribbling in our room in Mexico, ripping up sheet after sheet of paper when he was likely writing to his Father. It occurred to me that Dad was as lost as Luke. I felt a little sorry for him.

I thought of the saddest story I ever heard about Dad from a family friend. It was 1944, I wouldn't arrive for two more years. A large party, one of many, was underway celebrating the steady return of Groton's men from the War. The Marines had already shipped Dad home, his promising military career aborted when he was wounded in Guadalcanal during the Marine invasion of the Solomon Islands. He was devastated by being taken out of the War, and worse, by being the only survivor of his Platoon in the bombing of Henderson field.

Partygoers hung around the kitchen that night, bone dry martinis with an olive at the bottom for the men and old fashions on the rocks with a slice of orange and a Maraschino cherry for the women. It was a raucous hysterical group. Dad went out to the laundry and got a hand drill. He drilled a hole in the kitchen floor all the way through to the cellar below. Everyone was laughing uproariously.

"What the hell are you doing, George?" He was a wild man, they said, one of those crazy fearless Marines. He went back to the laundry room and got a bucket and a mop. He filled the bucket with water and began to pour it into the hole, flooding the kitchen. He took the mop and began to swab the decks of the Navy Destroyer.

Everyone at the party stood and stared. What happened to the young, handsome Marine Colonel? They stopped laughing.

It hurt to think of him back then, humiliated, his illness exposed.

I realized he didn't really want me home even though he was furious that I went away.

I looked at him typing and looked again at his Roman nose and his green eyes, even his skin coloring looked like he could be related to Luke.

I'd never thought of that before.

8

MY OWN SAHARAN DESERT

I tried to remain polite and avoid all controversy with my parents.

Key to my strategy was staying up late after they went to bed, which also allowed me to accomplish my second goal: I had a lot of eating to do, mostly bags of cookies and bowls of ice cream. I also watched Johnny Carson; sorted through my old college papers thinking some of my critical writing was pretty good, but it all seemed long ago when I was a different person; waited for lightening to strike with a plan of where to go and what to do when I got there (my future looked dry and empty); and wondered why I bothered to come home when they didn't want me there (this wasn't home anymore).

One afternoon Mother called upstairs for me to come down.

She handed me the phone. "He's called several times while you were away."

She could have mentioned this before.

It was Luke.

"Ali, oh, I'm so glad to reach you," the words rushed out of him. "Whew. I've been looking for you everywhere. I sent you money. Did you get it?"

He told me he sent money to Oaxaca, Guadalajara and even to Zihuatenejo. What a waste. But then I thought about how different my journey would have been had I known he tried to take care of me: *Left Mexico sooner, missed my time on the beach and arrived home broken and vulnerable.*

It was good I didn't get the money. I owed Luke nothing.

"No, I never got any of it. How'd you find me anyway?" My heart wanted to belch into the phone.

"Your Uncle John. I remembered he worked at Kent School."

He sounded like he'd been running around out of breath for the past four months looking for me. *I wasn't looking for you. I was going on with my life.*

"Well, hey, I'm in Brookline with my friend Eddy," Luke added. "He's got a commune in Maine and I want you to come with me."

Unbelievable!

"I just got home. I don't know what I'm going to do. Why'd you send me money?"

I wanted to hear something that I could hold onto, like *I loved you so much* or *How could I have been such an idiot to abandon you the way I did.* But Luke skated right over what he did to me.

"I was worried that you might run out of cash. I didn't want you to be alone with no money."

"Well, I had Dad sell my Mustang and he sent me money."

"At least come into town. I'll make you supper and we'll talk."

I wondered if my pulling away made him more dogged about coming toward me, as if it shifted him from neutral into drive.

"I don't know Luke." A door was cracking open that I thought I'd slammed and locked. It hurt my stomach to hear his voice again.

"Just think about it for a couple days. I'll call you back, don't even answer now."

I hung up the phone. *I hate you and your ever-changing self.*

All I could remember was the inscrutable way he shut me out and became unreachable. And the way I groveled in Mexico, how pathetic. My mouth was dry and sour. My jaw clenched. I tasted the bitter possibility of revenge.

Nothing had changed with my parents and Luke didn't seem to get it. He didn't realize what he'd done to me and I didn't feel like laying it out for him.

I blew my breath out hard. It would be simpler if he just gave up, like I had.

***

But he didn't give up. He called two days later.

"Why are you calling, *again*?"

"Because I told you I'd call, Al. I want to see you."

"Oh. like you're someone I can always count on."

"Al. Please," Luke sounded desperate. "Let's talk. Together."

I was stuffed so full of Pecan Sandies and coffee ice cream that I already hated myself. Being snarky and sour with Luke made me feel even worse. I was also hot with fury for my parents and felt trapped between them.

I told him I'd meet him for supper—*ugh!*—anything to get out of the house.

I borrowed Dad's car and drove into Brookline. Luke hugged me at the door of Eddy's house while I held my body like a tall, steel rod. He was cheerful and uncharacteristically chatty—his hair still long, his beard neatly trimmed—as he took my hand and led me into his room.

"This is just what we were talking about in Mazatlán, Ali! My old friend Hank is up there in Parsonsfield, Maine, with his girlfriend and they want people to share the Farm and the beginning of a real commune with them."

I studied him with my mouth hanging open, then shook my head. I laughed a measly little *huh* that caught in my throat.

I sat down on his bed. I could barely swallow as I looked up at a ceiling filled with little stars, the bedroom of Eddy's young boy. Luke sat beside me.

He turned toward me but let his eyes drift from mine. "I never meant to leave you forever, Ali."

"Well how was I to know that? You never said anything to me. You never explained. You just stopped talking. I don't even understand why we broke up in the first place."

"I needed some time, I guess. I didn't know what I was doing."

"That explains nothing."

He asked me what I did after we separated. I told him about driving the kids across Mexico when Ruthie went back to Friday Harbor, that we arrived in Veracruz in time for Mardi Gras, that Becky and I were mauled by drunken sailors coming at us from all directions.

"I wish I'd been there to protect you," Luke said.

"Well, you weren't."

I only mentioned my time on the beach in passing.

"I think going to the Farm will be good for us Ali, help us to come back together."

"Well, blah blah blah. You're acting like this was the plan all along and you just happened to leave for a while."

"I think it was like a hiccup, Al. It's only been a few months you know." He looked sorry. Why couldn't he say it?

"While you hiccupped, I threw up." *And healed myself in nature, alone, without you.* "What's this Farm place anyway? How can you have a commune with two people?"

Luke told me about Eddy who married at nineteen, made some money in sales and bought a rundown farm in Maine. He rarely went there. He was a vicarious hippie, but his friends were trying to create a communal life with people who wanted to work the farm.

"It's only Hank and Marcella now, but more are coming. If we go soon, we can grab a room before anyone else comes."

Luke's dream was about to come true. I could say no and kill it and take my revenge.

"Don't count on me."

***

Mum, Dad, and I were eating dinner in the little dining room off the kitchen where we had our meals unless there were guests. Mum had cooked Calves' Liver with Bacon, a favorite of

Dad's, a dry dish that stuck to the roof of my mouth. She was a reluctant cook. The TV was on, Vietnam always present at the table. Huntley and Brinkley were delivering the nightly news. We watched a squad of young American soldiers moving through a small village in Vietnam.

"That is so disgusting," I said. "We have to get out of there."

"Here we go again." Father put his fork down. He didn't look at me. "What do you know, Alicia? What do you know about war, huh?"

"It's not what I know, Dad." I didn't look at him. I cleared my throat carefully. A piece of liver was lingering on the roof of my mouth. "It's obviouth we don't belong there."

"You kids today blow goddamn opinions right out of your butts." I could hear the low rumbling of thunder in his voice, an ominous sign.

"For heaven sakes, George, we're eating."

"Be quiet Eleanor. You know even less than she does."

I winced. In Dad's opinion, I was smart, but wrong. Mum was just plain ignorant. I didn't like winning that battle. It never paid off.

"You have to admit, Dad," and I pointed a finger at the TV, "Michael Calley deserves to be Court Martialed. All those women and children…" I was shaking. I only had to throw a small match. My father flared.

"You little no-nothing. You never saw the Japs hiding behind the palms, jumping out at my men, stabbing us in the back. You know nothing."

He loomed when he was angry, as if he might do something more than words. His voice grew deeper, like a smoking fury. I got up and slammed my chair against the table. I wanted to show him how brave I'd been on my travels, hitchhiking alone, defending myself, sleeping alone anywhere I could find, bearing my loneliness and still going on even though I was so afraid. I didn't want to let him make me cry.

"I know something about surviving too, Dad," my voice cracking like I was splitting in two.

"Oh, so you can dish it out, but you can't take anything, just what I thought, you're all cowards." He shook his head, growling, ready to attack again.

"Excuse yourself," Mum said.

"Goodnight Chet," Brinkley said.

"Goodnight David," Huntley said."

I ran through the kitchen, the pantry, and the large dining room and hall, upstairs to my parents' bedroom and threw myself onto their bed. I needed their phone. I screamed my snotty rage into their spanking white popcorn bedspread. I blew my nose and swallowed. I called my cousin Rozzie and sobbed into the phone like a young kid having a tantrum. She knew how tough Dad could be. We talked about Luke. Rozzie said the chance to be on a commune was so cool. Even if I wasn't sure about him, it still might be a really fine thing. Get out of town she said.

I called Luke.

"I guess I could give it a try." Anything to keep Father from winning. *It'll be your fault Dad if I end up with Luke.*

"Great Ali! This will be so good for us. I'll get a car and come out to Groton in a few days to pick you up."

***

"I cannot believe you're going off again half-cocked," Dad said, his first words to me since our supper three nights before.

"We have absolutely no idea who this man is," Mum said, shaking her head as she spread Chivers Bitter Marmalade on her English muffin, "or who his family is."

"He comes from a perfectly nice family." I sighed and shook my head back at her.

Dad drummed into me that I needed to marry a man, "Who will keep you in the style to which you've become accustomed." What was I supposed to do with that? What style was I accustomed to? Did Dad mean a man like himself who was crazed with alcohol fueled rages?

After breakfast and minutes before Luke was to arrive, Dad developed a bad headache and disappeared upstairs. Headaches were one ailment I'd never known him to have.

I cringed when the doorbell rang. When I opened the heavy front door—a formal entrance that we rarely used—Luke stood on the wide granite step dressed in khaki from head to toe. Like a soldier. He wore oversized, tinted, gold rimmed glasses. Like the Mexican businessmen wore. Luke didn't need glasses. He'd pulled his hair into a long ponytail and his black beard was trimmed, but still covered a good part of his face, like a hippie. I shivered at the thought of Mum laying eyes on him. I might have been mixed up, but his outfit and grooming made Luke look like he had no idea who he was.

"Come into the print room, Luke. Mum's in there."

The room was a small cozy study where my parents spent a lot of their time. A welcoming fire crackled, but Mum cut us off at the doorway before we could enter. She wore a white blouse buttoned up tight to a starched ruffle at her neck and a floor length plaid wool skirt, the plaid of our family's clan. It seemed like everyone was in costume. The Mexican-businessman-soldier-hippie, Queen Elizabeth, and whoever I was in my Navajo skirt and knee-high moccasins. It was a *Through the Looking Glass* experience watching her right arm extend toward Luke as if it was on a long swivel with an extra extension to cover the great icy distance.

Luke was courteous, Mum forbidding.

She stood blocking the entrance to the study, so we were stranded in the middle of the hall, a high-ceilinged big room with thick Turkish rugs. Hard to believe that once it was used by my grandparents for ballroom dancing in the 1920's. Now the three of us stood stiff and straight, precariously attached in an equilateral triangle. If any of us stumbled, we might all fall on top of each other. There was a screaming silence before she spoke.

"Did you come from Hartford this morning?" Mum asked.

Her soft Yankee r's were especially round today. She smelled of Arpege, delicious but untouchable.

"No, actually, I was staying with a buddy in town."

I knew my mother. I knew her measly attempt to be polite was a thin sheet of ice covering a scathing assessment. Suddenly it occurred to me that she somehow knew Luke was Jewish. That would be the final blow.

We stood at the bottom of the front staircase. I glanced at the grandfather clock on the landing half-way up. The only thing worse than Dad's disappearing act was the possibility that he might make an unexpected appearance. I hoped his headache was severe.

My mother offered nothing to drink or eat. I felt sick.

"We should get going, Mum."

"Yes. Well…" She turned a cool powdery cheek toward me for me to make an air kiss goodbye.

"Very nice to meet you, Mrs. Thorne."

We walked down the hall stairs. The door closed behind us. Luke's recently purchased drab green 1950 Desoto sedan waited in the circle beneath the maple tree in the center of the circular driveway.

Sixteen years before, Mum, Dad, my brother Johnny, and I stood in that same place about to get in to our 1950 Ford sedan. My uncle was there, Mum's brother, and my grandmother Nanny, Mum's Mother. We lingered back then beneath the leafy greenness of the maple tree, one suitcase apiece, all of us crying, unable to believe that my grandmother had expelled us. She was terribly sorry, she said, but Dad's drinking was bringing the police to the house and my uncle had to protect her. I was seven, holding on tight to a doll under each arm. Johnny was twelve and carried his own suitcase. He had to leave behind his pet rabbits. We were saying goodbye and I didn't know why.

Dad carried a large suitcase in each hand. He put them down and shook my uncle's hand.

"Sorry Bronx (Dad nicknamed my uncle because his last name was Park) about the other night."

My uncle's lips were set, stretched tight. He nodded.

Dad kissed Nanny on the cheek. "It's all my fault."

Nanny was crying. "I hate that it's come to this, George." Her voice shook.

Mum hugged Nanny and cried. I cried too.

The bags barely fit in the trunk of our Ford sedan. We drove slowly down the long winding driveway between the giant hemlocks that seemed to be crying as they waved in a morning breeze. We headed east on Main Street for the turnpike that would take us to Dad's brother in Pennsylvania. It was my first taste of shame.

I'd asked if we'd ever see Nanny again.

"Of course," Dad had replied, looking over at Mum, but I didn't believe him.

"How do you like her?" Luke asked as he opened the car door for me.

"My Mum?"

"No Ali, the car."

I sat down on a large soft cushioned seat, warm with the smell of old car, the familiar cream-colored knob on the gear shift, broad dash, the feel of sitting in a comfy living room. We made our way down the long curving driveway as giant hemlocks on either side waved goodbye.

"You could have told me, Ali. I had no idea you lived in a house like that. I don't think your mother liked me."

"I don't think she likes me either."

"Where was your father?"

"He said he had a headache …, but why would you dress like a soldier when you knew Dad was a Marine? Why would you do that?"

"I don't know. I was just trying to spruce up I guess, look presentable. I'm sorry."

We drove down Main Street and headed north to Maine. Luke had failed the test.

And I had the familiar feeling of recoiling into myself, as if I'd been banished instead of making the choice to go.

9

THE FARM

In his left hand he held a Pall Mall with the smoke drifting out the half open window. His right palm sat like an afterthought on top of the wheel, and his eyes wandered so that we drove on the left side as much as on the right.

Corners were terrifying.

Luke was so cautious on his boat, respectful of the sea. But when he was driving, the landscape captured most of his attention.

"Luke, can you look straight ahead and keep your eyes on the road? You're making me nervous."

"Sorry Al, it's so lush and green up here."

Luke was manifesting his dream of community. His dream, not mine. Yet I had to admit I was excited and curious. Not about Luke, but about living on a commune. Of course, it wouldn't be like Charles Manson's California commune, turned cult, turned crazy, turned vicious murderers. It would be more like Woodstock's 'back to the garden', love and harmony.

I put my head back and said a silent prayer as the Desoto rolled, heavy and calm through forest and meadow until we came to Parsonsfield. I looked out on both sides of the road at a bleak gritty landscape—trailers and small ranch homes in disrepair, TV satellites as big as the houses, junked cars and trucks, piles of tires all littering the grassless yards. I wanted to speed up in order to get through as quickly as possible.

A gas station, a 50's diner, and a two-story warehouse with a sad sign that said *Foodmart* sat in shades of brown and gray along the town's main street.

"Who lives here?"

The town ended before Luke could answer my question.

We took a sharp left turn just past the end of town and Luke said, "Whoa baby," as if the Desoto was a horse going back to the stable. "She knows the way," he said as we rumbled onto a poorly graded dirt road.

People here depended on logging, truck farming, and a lot of government assistance.

The car's shocks strained as we bumped up and down through a series of water filled holes.

What happened to the lush green countryside? Where are the pastoral scenes of old red barns with cows grazing in green pastures by still waters?

We passed a few better maintained ranch houses with whirly-gigs on the front lawns, a small statue of a black footman holding a lantern, a wooden girl in petticoats bending over with her bum in the air. Luke assured me it would get better.

We continued through a monotonous stretch of scrub and briar patch ending six miles later at a ramshackle farmhouse. The road looked like it had gone on behind the house at one time but was now overgrown and impassable.

He pulled onto a grassy area next to a rusty rototiller and leaned forward looking out through the windshield thick with dust. I wondered how I'd ever get out of here if I had to. I remembered being dropped off at camp at age eleven, making a futile run after Mother's car as she sped away.

A center chimney, cape style house peered at us through dark windows. Paint peeling and a roof that badly needed shingling said no one had paid attention for a long time. This was why Luke's friend Eddie was able to buy the place, Luke said.

Hens bobbed up and down, pecking at the dirt by the kitchen door. Luke knocked and called for Hank. I waved away a cluster of black flies swarming around my nose and eyes. But then Luke remembered Hank and visitors from a nearby commune were working for the town removing big rocks off the main road so they could pay the property taxes. Luke had helped them the week before. Back breaking work, he said.

Had I come up here to pick up rocks?

I shook my skirt to get the dust off.

And it was black fly season.

Luke opened the front door and we walked through a mud room, a pair of mud crusted boots on the floor and a heavy canvas jacket with red flannel lining hanging on a hook. Wood was neatly stacked on either wall in rows with the warm dry smell of sawdust on the floor. They burned fifteen cords a year, the only source of heat.

The mudroom opened into a spacious kitchen that smelled of wood smoke. The sun filtered in through cloudy windows and particles of ash and dust floated in the pale light. heat radiated from the pot belly stove softening the April chill. There was a big, decades old black oven. Two loaves of fresh baked bread sat on the counter, still fragrant with warm molasses. I gave one a sniff and a squeeze. Anadama, I determined.

A cracked porcelain kitchen sink was empty and clean. Luke said all the water had to be drawn by hand from the well by a rope and carried in bucket by bucket. Washing dishes would take forever.

The kitchen connected to a living area. We walked across wide, unfinished, and uneven pine flooring, the cracks between the boards filled with hard packed dirt.

"This place has a lot of potential," Luke said. "Good bones. Imagine what we could do with it."

"Maybe," I said. *Maybe not.* Whenever Luke was enthusiastic, I wanted to stamp it out. I was still angry with him.

On the far side of the room was a rectangular, rough-hewn picnic table with some daisies in a mason jar and long narrow benches on either side. Two rocking chairs sat close to the wood stove on a tattered Turkish rug. Scott Nearing's book *Living the good Life: How to Live Sanely in a Troubled World* lay bookmarked on a primitive, hand-crafted table between the rocking chairs. A lamp that looked like someone's grandmother made me think of reading by the warm stove at night, but Luke said the generator was small and we couldn't expect much light after dark.

Luke had already spent a couple weeks here. Why didn't he prepare me?

He took me by the hand into the back of the house to claim our bedroom. Two more cloudy windows with broken sashes offered a vague view into scrubby woods thick with bracken. Luke propped one open with a long stick wedged against the sill.

"I know you like a lot of fresh air, Ali."

I sat down hard on a thin foam mattress held by a plywood base. Other than the bed, the room was empty.

"Where's the bathroom?"

"Outside. A two-seater. We can sit together."

"Very funny."

I walked back into the kitchen and outside the front door to check the outhouse. It smelled like cedar. I was used to primitive toilets in Mexico or even better, a hole in the ground where you had to squat, or just plain squatting in an open field. I saw a plastic scoop sitting in a pail of ashes and a Sears catalogue for toilet paper.

Two seats?

Sharing one 'bathroom'?

I tried to remember if Luke had told me there was no plumbing and no electricity.

"I can't find a mirror anywhere." That was worse than the thought of sharing toilets. I depended on checking my image frequently, so that I would know exactly what others saw when they looked at me.

"It'll get better, Al."

I wondered if he meant the Farm or the distance that sat unspoken between us.

***

Hank and Marcella arrived at the end of the day.

"Welcome friends!" Hank said, his face lighting up as he gave us both a hug, "Glad you're with us. New blood."

That made me wonder if others had come and gone and been destroyed in the process. But I couldn't help smiling when I met Hank. He looked like a friendly clown, brown skinned and bald except for curly locks sticking out on either side of his head. A faded red flannel shirt and denim overalls completed the picture of a country guy. He couldn't threaten anyone. He'd come a long way from suburban Connecticut where he used to drive his British green Jaguar roadster to school. Luke told me he admired Hank for what he'd learned about living off the land.

Marcella, by contrast, was chilly and gaunt. She was tiny with long dark hair that fell onto a sharp angular face. "Bonjour, ca va?" She gave us each a kiss on either cheek. Luke told me she was estranged from her *bourgeois family* in Avignon. We had that in common. Marcella wore tight jeans, a black t-shirt and a burning Gauloise hanging out of her mouth. She surveyed me with a probing eye, and I felt too big, fleshy, and materialistic. I hoped I could show them both that I could fit in, but she gave me the shivers.

I discovered the only mirror later that day. It hung on the wall outside of our room by the center chimney. It was cracked and cloudy so that my face was distorted, which was not helpful. Even though it was obvious that Hank and Marcella paid attention to how they looked and were deliberate with what they wore, I was embarrassed to be seen looking at myself. I didn't want to appear vain.

***

Over the next few weeks, I tried to adjust to the pulse of springtime life on the Farm, rising at dawn and bedding down shortly after dark. We were all exhausted by the end of the day. I could feel myself being pulled slowly into a group rhythm and the pleasure of being part of something simple and basic.

Everything took longer without running water and electricity. Water had to be drawn bucket by bucket and heated on the wood stove for dishes. Watering the vegetables and flowers required multiple trips to the well and toting heavy buckets out to the garden. Bathing was a luxury. Supposedly there was an old-fashioned copper tub that took hours to fill with hot water, but I never saw it, and no one mentioned taking a bath. The odor of garlic was strong on Hank and Marcella. I smelled too, but no one cared. Hank said we'd swim when the weather got warmer.

We divided the chores. Baking bread, cooking, cleaning up dishes and kitchen, sweeping the floors, collecting eggs, digging and weeding the garden, chopping wood, feeding the fire… The list went on and on, just to keep the place going. Work, work, work, multiple chores apiece because there were only four of us regulars.

I liked passing by Luke several times during the day. Working together made me almost forget that I still had not forgiven him.

***

On our first Friday I met the Charlestown urban commune. They came to the Farm on most weekends, walked in with their bags as if they owned the place, and expected maid service. It reminded me of Luke's sailing partners Marshall and Cyndie who both assumed Destiny belonged to them. Hank made it clear they were important and that in fact we did have to wait on them. That was because they paid him to stay there.

Scientists, lawyers, and other professionals—all members of the Progressive Labor Party—the Farm was their vacation destination. I knew the type. Four years earlier, I'd tried to join the PLP when I was in the Teacher Corps in Detroit just after the riots of '68. The Detroit leaders suggested it wasn't the right group for me. I thought it was because of my mini-skirts and eye makeup. But it could have been because I didn't understand their bible, Mao Tse Tung's Little Red Book made no sense to me. It didn't seem relevant to our society, even if we were messed up Capitalists. And I didn't want to work in a factory in Dearborn, Michigan. All the Detroit members were alike, white, cerebral, non-descript in their appearance, and serious. I was predisposed to dislike them.

They expected to be fed as soon as they arrived. Hank prepped the meal and Luke cooked it. Ten of us sat on benches in two lines facing each other at the long picnic table. Large bowls piled with pasta floating in a garlicky red sauce sat in the middle of the table. Baskets of home baked bread were at either end with slabs of yellow margarine on small plates.

Most of our food was army surplus from the warehouse in town. "It's important that we never have more than the folks in town," Hank informed me. That was why our lunches usually consisted of sandwiches made with Jiffy peanut butter and Welch's grape jelly. And why the pitchers of milk came from powder in boxes. There would be nothing green until the chard and spinach came up in the garden. And there was a humongous block of orange Velveeta cheese that was always available. The food turned my stomach, but I still piled the soupy pasta onto my plate.

I'd baked the bread for the meal, one of my first chores at the Farm. Unfortunately, I'd presented only two loaves when the recipe called for three.

"The bread is great, but what happened to the third loaf?" Hank asked.

He didn't miss a thing. I couldn't admit that I'd nibbled piece by piece so much of one warm loaf that in the end I had to eat it all. I cleared my throat and said I must have made a smaller recipe.

Liz, a visiting chemist, looked at me like she was seeing me for the first time. "Work—hard simple work—is necessary for the Revolution."

"We work really hard here," I said, as I grabbed a big slice of bread before anyone could stick their hand in the basket.

"Emma Goldman says, 'The time of bourgeois decadence has to end,'" Liz said.

Murmurs of agreement traveled around the table.

"Tres bien, right on, Liz," Marcella said.

I elbowed Luke and whispered, "Who's Emma Goldman?"

"A communist Marxist, Socialist whatever," he said under his breath.

I noticed Marcella hadn't changed her clothes for three days. We didn't have any way of doing laundry other than by hand. Her smell of heavy sweat and the harsh perfume of Gauloise tobacco was familiar from riding the Paris Metro. I liked it. French women also showed a lot of black hair in their armpits. I envied them their confidence. At the Farm, being sweaty, and even smelly, was proof of your value.

"We heard you all had quite a massacre here this week," Bea, the lawyer said.

I tried to forget the sight. A few days before we'd come home from town to a bloody mess of feathers and carcasses in front of the house. The hens and the rooster gone. Fox or coyote. Or a Fisher cat from the back woods.

"Quelle dommage, it was terrible, all the blood."

"Can we not talk about that while we're eating?" I said.

"Oh, I forget. Alicia is squeamish," Marcella said.

She knows I have trouble collecting the eggs. She can't stand me. Before the massacre deprived us temporarily of chickens, it was my chore. The coop was clean and didn't smell too badly. The hens were a multicultural group of Little Bantams, Rhode Island Reds, and the Polish ones that looked like ZaZa Gabor with puffy blond heads and blond furry legs. They sat together in the coop, six on the top row and six on the bottom. I was trying. I tiptoed in each morning and slowly and carefully picked the eggs out from under each one. One morning, for no reason at all, one of the Polish hens became hysterical, squawking and crying out with her little babushka head feathers fluttering. She got everyone upset and I was afraid I'd be attacked.

"The scrambled eggs we have every morning, merci, they come from the girls. We let Alicia make the bread instead."

Does she know I ate an entire loaf?

"We got a lot a work this weekend," Hank said, helping himself to a pile of pasta and a big chunk of Velveeta. "Puttin' composted chicken shit onto the garden, cleanin' out the coop for the new chicks, fixin' the well rope. And Luke, you and I'll go in to see Old Man Morrell and partake of his corn liquor in his cellar."

Hank was a suburban rich kid, but he sounded like a bumpkin. He had to show the Charlestown group how hard we worked and how little fun we had.

"Sure thing," Luke said. Luke was always a good team player.

Drinking one-hundred-percent proof with the locals was one more chore, Hank's way to stay connected to the Morrell family who were influential in the town. It was funny that when we showed up at Town Meeting the week before, trying to be one with the people, Mr. and Mrs. Morrell pretended they didn't know us.

The Charlestown group's only man was a stringy pallid biologist who dressed in khaki from head to toe. He looked awkwardly rustic as if traveling to the country was going to a foreign land. He said his plan was to go into the woods behind the house to photograph wild mushrooms. I perked up.

"What sort of mushrooms?"

Liz intoned, "Psychedelic drugs are anathema to the movement."

I rolled my eyes right at her.

Then she quoted Emma Goldman's remarks on the dangers of *naive pleasure seeking*, as if all I wanted was fun. Then she finished off with, "Marriage is nothing but accommodation." She made me want to be as bourgeois as I really was.

She had me pegged as the kid whose favorite subject is recess. She was right. *When are we going to have some fun?* Certainly not with the Charlestown group. They read and pontificated, took walks and ate our food, and never lifted a finger to help.

I waited to say what I really thought until supper was done, cleanup was complete, and Luke and I were alone in our bedroom. I couldn't speak to Hank or Marcella. I didn't want to appear like a complainer.

"I can't stand those people," I said.

"Who? Hank and Marcella?"

"No. The Charlestown group. They're like Bible thumpers. I can't believe we have to cater to those idiots every weekend."

Luke rolled over toward me and kissed me with warm soft lips. "Do you think you might be still mad at your Dad for refusing to meet me?"

"I don't know. Maybe. I'm sick of worrying about people who tell me what to think."

"Do you think your Dad knows I'm Jewish?"

"I don't know. He's never known anyone Jewish. I mean he feels awful about the Holocaust. We used to talk about it together when I was little."

"Almost everybody feels bad about the Holocaust, Al. Feeling sorry for Jews is not the same as accepting one into the family, right?"

I hadn't thought about being with someone Jewish. For me it only meant that Luke was exotic. It hadn't occurred to me that Luke might be Dad's idea of *forbidden fruit*, the kind of man who was dangerous. Father had always been unclear about what the danger was.

"I'm furious I let him stop me from going to Woodstock. I was thinking about it today out in the garden. I'm kicking myself."

"You could have gone if you really wanted to."

"No, absolutely not."

I couldn't explain the way I was unable to go against Father. The only reason I'd left with Luke for the Farm was because I was so angry with Dad and Luke that I was damned in either direction. It was easier to be with Luke than to face how mad I was at Dad.

***

Luke and I snuck out on a Friday afternoon when Hank and Marcella were talking politics with our obnoxious, pompous, entitled weekend visitors. Luke said we needed a vacation, and we were going to Portland.

"I like that idea, but do you think we should?" I asked.

"We should do whatever we want to do, Ali."

“I feel like I’m bailing out, leaving Hank and Marcella with all the work. Do you have money?”

“Let the Charlestown folks step up. And yeah, I’ve got some cash hidden.”

Luke was always surprising me. We drove an hour into Portland. At that time, it wasn’t much more than a big town, but it felt like a metropolis to us. We parked the car and walked up and down the main street looking in the bookstore window, women’s clothing shops, and gazing longingly at menus of restaurants we couldn’t afford. Luke saw an antique shop he wanted to investigate. Tomorrow, we decided.

We found a small hotel in the middle of downtown, a little run down, but one we could afford. He registered us as Luke and Alicia Fine. Fewer questions, he said. I thought of Liz and her cynicism around marriage. I practiced *Mr. and Mrs. Fine* as we rode the elevator.

The hall was dingy, but as the concierge promised, the room was light and clean. I sat down on the bed and ran my hand along the crisp white sheet folded over a soft blue blanket. All the linens at the Farm were gray from age and lack of washing. I bounced on a real mattress with springs.

“I’m going to jump in the shower,” Luke said. “We smell pretty ripe, Al.”

Patchouli could only take us so far.

“Come join me,” he called from the bathroom. “The water pressure is great!”

The shower was a little tight, but it didn't matter. Luke and I squeezed together letting the hot water pour down on our heads and faces. He took a warm washcloth and gently soaped my chest and belly and between my legs. The soapy water ran down my thighs. I did the same for him, washing his chest and back.

"Your bum is so cute and shapely," I said.

"Thanks Al, I wouldn't know."

I gave it a squeeze, like a good loaf of bread. Delicious. I forgot I still needed to punish him.

As we dried each other off we began kissing, forehead and nose, mouth, and throat. Luke led me over to the bed. We pulled down the covers and laid a dry towel across the bottom sheet. We planted kisses lower and lower, and made sweet love, sweet smelling love, like we were new to each other and curious.

"Hmm, you smell so good, hmm. You taste so good. Like sticky pancake batter." I sighed deeply as we lay on our backs. "We need to do this more often. Get away, be together. All this sharing. I don't know if it's good for us," I said.

"I know what you mean, Al. Living off the land is one thing, but maybe the Farm is taking *back to the earth* too seriously. Let's give it time. We'll see."

I meant it was easier having sex when we weren't always together in a group. I was surprised that Luke was having his own doubts. I felt better. Maybe I wasn't a completely spoiled brat, which is the way I felt at the Farm.

We had Lobster Rolls and fries with ketchup for dinner at a seafood place. We slept like babies. The next morning, I bought *A Stranger in a Strange Land* at the bookstore. Luke found some old brass hooks in an antique shop. "For our first home," he said.

When we got back to the Farm on Sunday afternoon, we told them we'd gone camping. Our little secret, like the stash of money we kept to ourselves.

***

One early morning, before we'd all gone onto our own chores, a guy walked into the kitchen carrying a guitar. He was dressed in white from head to toe, his fair hair flowed like those pictures of a blond Jesus and his eyes were a burning blue. Tommy was known to Hank and Marcella, and he and his brothers were famous in the area.

Hank grabbed both of Tommy's arms, "So good to see ya my friend," he said. "When did you get out?"

"Hey man, whew," his eyes rolled, "good to be here. Two days ago. I thought the pigs might let me die in there."

I slowly gathered that Tommy had been in prison.

"Hey. It's not like you killed someone, heh," Hank said.

"No, but that might be coming. It's all about the Revolution. Who knows what we have to do?"

"Okay, man, let's drink to your freedom," Hank said.

He went into his room, brought out his private stash of whiskey, and poured a drink for the two of them. Tommy took a swig. He sat with his guitar and sang a Wobblies' song about the working man.

I wondered what, if anything, Tommy did for work. He made my skin crawl.

***

Luke tried very hard to be a good commune member, but he had some old ways that didn't fit.

One of these ways got Luke into trouble with Leslie, a young woman about our age who wore overalls, her hair in two tight braids, and didn't bother removing the thick hair above her upper lip. It mesmerized me to the point it was all I saw when I looked at her.

And like Tommy, Leslie arrived out of the blue from somewhere. It wasn't as if anyone could tell us they were coming to visit. There were no phones, no mail. We often had no idea where people came from and how they found us. They came, stayed for a few days, and left.

Leslie liked it so much that she stayed for weeks.

"What are you girls up to this morning?" Luke asked. Marcella, Leslie, and I were cleaning the kitchen. Leslie's face looked like she had a bad taste in her mouth.

"Women. We're women, not girls," Leslie said.

"Hey, I'm sorry," Luke said, both palms up.

I cringed. He should have known that this was a big trigger for women. Worse yet was the next day when he tried *ladies*.

"Are you doing this on purpose, Luke? Because it's offensive," Leslie said.

"Oui, c'est vrai. Use your words more carefully, Luke."

"Sorry," Luke said.

Yet the more he tried the worse it got, as if he couldn't stop the wrong word from jumping out of his mouth. It was so bad that Leslie shook her head at Marcella, and they rolled her eyes every time Luke walked into the room. Behind Leslie's eye rolls and head shaking was the implication that perhaps men weren't necessary.

Luke kept forgetting and stepping into it. This was the problem with men. They were impossible to train.

Meanwhile, I had no idea whether I was a girl or a woman or a lady, *and* Leslie and Marcella were mean to me as well. Marcella only paid attention to me when there were no other women there. I didn't trust either of them. But then, I didn't trust most women. Mother never stood up for me. She was so scared herself, I guessed, that she left me to deal with Dad alone. And even my best pal in my middle school years was too scared to speak up. I remembered when we were in a club with three other girls. We tried to earn money by going door to door in new housing developments selling coffee tins covered with wrapping paper or pencils we collected and sharpened. One of the girls, Gail, was the treasurer. She lied about how much money we had. I knew she was lying, but my best friend wouldn't take my side. She didn't want to make Gail angry. Although I still loved my best friend, I stopped trusting her.

Marcella softened some when she and I baked bread. She sang French ditties from her childhood, some of which I knew from school such as *sur le pont d'Avignon* and sang with her. When Mother used to sing in the kitchen, I felt safe and happy. She had a lovely lilt in her voice. Somewhere along the line she stopped singing.

Luke and I never said to each other, "I don't like it here." But we began to look for any chance to go off and be by ourselves where simply being was easier.

10

THE END OF SUMMER

As summer blossomed, life on the Farm flourished.

The flies disappeared, the garden shot up bright and green, suppers brimmed with fresh picked green beans, broccoli, yellow squash, peppers, and big red tomatoes. With longer days, we finished our chores and still had time for play. We had fun when visitors from a commune across the border in New Hampshire came, in the way you put your work aside when you have guests. We swam most days in one of the many swimming holes close by. A spot where fast water ran over slippery rocks offered us thrilling slides down into a deep refreshing pool. We lingered in the evenings, told stories of our growing up, laughed together like a real family where everyone contributed and got along. Luke reminded me that he'd said it would get better, that we'd have a real community. I slowly forgot how angry I'd been with Luke. I felt like I belonged, I was part of the team, and the group cushioned our relationship.

Visitors came and went. We welcomed them, but we four were the core, and we remained when they left. Maybe Luke's dream of a close-knit trusting group and a vibrant communal life was possible.

***

It was an evening in mid-July, full of the warm whirr of cicadas and crickets. We'd finished supper, cleaned up the kitchen, swept the floors. Visitors had left, even Leslie had moved on. Hank and Luke rocked back and forth in the rockers while Marcella and I sat across from each other at the table. Hank lit a joint and we passed it around in the soft glow of candlelight. He praised Luke for fixing the fencing around the chicken coop and me for weeding the garden.

I took a deep draw and blew out the smoke. It was a good feeling to relax at the end of a long workday. At the time I didn't know the Zen expression c*hop wood, carry water* but I was living it. We were all living in the moment. Visitors were envious, remarking on the pleasing rhythm at the Farm, the generous gardens, each of us in our place contributing to a finely tuned daily life that was its own purpose. I was proud of us. It took time to adjust and give in, but now I saw how working as a group made life easier and more fulfilling.

Late in the evening, the kitchen door opened to Tommy Manning. I'd hoped never to see him again. One thing about the Farm: anyone could arrive at any moment and we'd take them in. We'd welcomed one guy and discovered he was in the middle of a psychotic break. We'd had numerous visits from a local logger, Philly, who was gentle, toothless, and dangerously sick with alcoholism. Come one come all.

Tommy still resembled a religious figure in his flowing white robes, but I knew he had nothing good to offer. *He's an ex-con, disguised as a saint.* He'd brought a friend.

He introduced his brother-in-law, Mike Mason, who only recently had married Tommy's sister. Mike stood near the door, a looming hunk of a presence, his black lidded eyes moving from one of us to the other, silent, but loud. Tommy took Hank into the kitchen where they stood head to head in a lengthy discussion the rest of us were unable to hear. Any friendly veneer that might have shrouded Tommy when he first visited us was gone.

I looked at Luke, my eyes questioning. Why all the secrecy? A dark energy had infected the house and I didn't know if it was coming from Tommy or Mike, or from the two of them. The air was low, held the tension of an imminent fight. Calm for the moment, but on the precipice of turning.

Luke stared hard at Mike his forehead furled. If Tommy and Mike could step into our space unannounced anyone could come. I felt an internal growl, my response to something frightening and dangerous. I wanted to run out the door into the night and breathe clean air. I thought about how isolated we were, six miles from town, and all the thick woods behind us.

Soon, Tommy said goodbye, but left Mike behind. Mike stood looking us over, his eyes dark pools. A beard covered most of his face. He was husky and barrel chested with long black hair. He looked like an exhausted wild man who'd experienced a bad acid trip and couldn't find his way back. He shook his head to orient himself.

"Hey, folks," Hank announced, "Mike here is going to stay a time with us."

"How far are we from the road?" Mike asked.

"Let's get him something to eat," Hank said, as if he owned a restaurant and Marcella, Luke, and I were the waitstaff.

"Is there any other entrance to the property?" Mike's eyes darted back and forth.

He sat down at the table while Marcella quickly made up a plate with macaroni and sauce left over from supper and a last thick heel of brown bread.

"Haven't eaten for a while," he said.

Luke and I watched as he bent his head close to the plate and began to shovel the food in.

"Who comes here besides you all? What's back there beyond those woods?"

He continued gobbling up the pasta and bread. He gulped down a glass of goat's milk. Questions poured out fast, peppered with his breath, heavy as if he might explode. He hadn't even said hello.

"No worry friend, we'll take care of you," Hank said.

There went Hank, pandering again as he had with Tommy. I stood with my arms crossed tight around my chest. I didn't move. I couldn't take my eyes off Mike. His presence sucked all the air out of the room. He saw that we were all frozen in place.

"I have four planets in Scorpio," he said. If a normal person had said that I would have been sympathetic. I'm a Scorpio myself and four planets in such an intense sign could be an affliction. But nothing about Mike was normal.

He cleaned his plate, left it on the table, and took Hank aside. Hank went into his room and came out with a shotgun. Mike took the gun outside and I heard multiple shots being fired into the darkness. I looked at Luke as I blew air out of my mouth. Luke's eyebrows came together and deepened the already strong etched lines on his forehead.

"What's that all about, Hank?" he said.

"Making sure it works," Hank said, like we fired a shotgun every day.

Hank could be dismissive if we annoyed him.

Our visitor hadn't said one word to me and already I disliked him. Danger had entered the Farm. That night in bed Luke told me he'd try to talk with Mike and get a better sense of him. Something didn't feel right. I tossed all night wondering what the stranger was doing, if he was sleeping, what would happen tomorrow.

The following day, Luke volunteered to drive Mike into town for supplies. By supplies, Mike meant bullets, Luke told me later. He also told me they'd been stopped by the local cops who knew the Farm. That wasn't unusual. We called it *hippie harassment*, a constant low-grade worry. But Luke said Mike was sweating bullets when they checked his papers. I didn't know what he meant, and Luke didn't explain.

After we spoke, I wandered around the Farm, sat outside by the garden, tried to regain some calm. My jaw tightened as it did when I was angry and when I was afraid. I waited all day, hoping Luke would have more to tell me when we were alone. Every time Mike was nearby, I felt like I'd done something wrong and he was angry with me. I tried to stay away from him.

When we climbed in bed that evening, Luke moved closer to me so that our eyes were nearly crossing as we looked at each on the pillow. He whispered, “Al, you won’t believe this. His name isn’t Mike Mason. It’s Cameron Bishop. He’s on the FBI’s most wanted for blowing up electrical towers in Colorado.”

“What is he doing here? What are we supposed to do with him? I don’t want to go to jail,” I said.

Everyone knew about the towers. There’d been big articles in the papers and some fiery editorials about young people’s protests threatening the fabric of democracy. I guessed Mike was a member of the Weathermen, the offshoot of SDS (Students for a Democratic Society) who believed violence was necessary to further the Revolution. I hadn’t known any Weathermen personally.

Adrenalin shot through my body. I was excited in the wrong way as I often was with Dad when I got excitement and fear all mixed up together. I had to find courage and be brave. It made me feel more alive. I might have been shaking with fear and yet I wanted more.

“The Farm is on an underground railroad for radical fugitives,” Luke said.

“Oh my god. What does that mean?”

I’d never heard of an underground railroad except for slaves. And I’d never met anyone who had an alias and was traveling incognito. Without warning, the Farm became a battlefront. I nestled closer to Luke, my chest against his back, one leg wrapped around him. I wished our bedroom door had a lock on it.

The next morning before Mike, who was really Cameron, came out for breakfast, we asked Hank to explain. The Underground Railroad had begun as a means of hiding young men evading the draft for Vietnam. The Railroad went up through New England all the way to the Canadian border. As radical activism swelled in the late 60's, the Railroad expanded to protect people like Cameron who were fugitives. "We owe it to these guys who are on the front lines," Hank said. "We need to do our share."

"But he's not just a radical, like us. He's more like a criminal, isn't he?" I said.

The danger that excited me in theory, now filled me with dread. I wasn't as brave as I liked to think I was.

"Ali, sometimes we have to fight back," Hank said. "Sometimes violence is necessary to achieve a goal."

"I don't know. Cameron seems kind of crazed. It's scary," I said.

"It's more than scary," Luke said. "It's dangerous. And he's playing with guns. What, is he going to make a last stand here? We could get ourselves shot or arrested for harboring a fugitive, right Hank?"

It didn't look like Hank had thought it through. He was angry, we all were angry. About the War, our parents, Nixon. We were all about the fight, but Cameron made it look ugly.

"I gave my word to Tommy. I can't go back on it," Hank said.

What about the rest of us? Who was Hank loyal to?

We retreated into our own thoughts and went on with our chores, but suddenly we were self-conscious with each other. We spoke only in generalizations. How are the carrots and beets doing in the garden? How many eggs did we get today? I even volunteered to clean out the chicken coop so that I could get out of the house. Thoughts and beliefs we'd never shared threatened our union. Where we'd had newfound peace and harmony, I now only sensed menace.

The Charlestown group came for the weekend as usual. They seemed contemptuous of Cameron. No one in the Progressive Labor Party would ever look as unkempt as he did. Yet they believed in the same Revolution against imperialistic capitalism as Tommy and Cameron—we all said we did—and they refused to rule out the possibility of necessary violence against the establishment. So long as they could speak from the sidelines.

A pall hung over the Farm as if someone said, "This is what you hippies have been yelling about all this time. Here's the real thing. You asked for it."

Even though I believed in protesting the Vietnam War, fighting for Civil Rights, I trembled at the thought of being on the front line and confronting police with their high black boots, shields, and guns. If I couldn't stand up to my own Father, how could I face a bigger enemy? I felt like a coward and a hypocrite.

Cameron caught my arm one afternoon, "Don't open that door without telling me first. I want to know when you're going out and where you're going."

"I'm going to the garden to pick some vegetables," I grumbled and yanked my arm away as I pushed past him with my wicker basket. It was hot and sticky outside and I was logy from the heat. I didn't want to justify myself to a paranoid criminal.

We stopped sitting together in the evenings. it wasn't fun anymore. We all headed to our rooms as quickly as possible to get away from Cameron.

After ten days of creeping around, all of us acting like we were the criminals, Luke spoke up. Luke talked privately with Hank, telling him we wanted no part of this. We hadn't signed on to a radical underground. I breathed more freely when I saw that Luke was true to himself. He was often clear about where he stood while I worried about making someone mad at me. Hank didn't seem clear about what he really thought or believed. I thought he was play acting the part of a revolutionary.

Hank resisted. It was all about the Revolution and our job on the Farm was to support it. But why hadn't he let us know about the underground?

Cameron called a meeting and barraged us with his needs for safety and that his safety would determine all comings and goings. Hank said he understood what Cameron wanted, but there were certain things we had to do to "Keep the farm goin'."

Cameron shut right up. He needed us and we didn't need him. But he brooded, and I could smell the dark mood in his sour sweat. The following week, Luke told me he'd had enough. Someone needed to go. I was certain Luke would take care of it. He spoke to Hank again and Hank reluctantly agreed so long as Luke delivered the bad news. Maybe Hank also had second thoughts but couldn't admit it. Luke told Cameron he had to move on.

***

Cameron looked resigned and strangely meek on the morning he left. We were not the compadres he expected and if we didn't support him, who would? Without the shelter of young radicals, Cameron was nothing more than a criminal on the run. He'd relished the adulation of hippies like me who were too scared to take direct action but admired others for risking their lives. I thought how lonely life must be for someone like Cameron who couldn't trust anyone. In the end we'd do what we needed to do for our own safety. He must have felt betrayed.

Luke told him he'd drive him to the Canadian border. When he left, he was lying down on the floor in the back of the Desoto until they got well outside of Parsonsfield.

Cameron disappeared into an underground for a few years. He became a legend in radical circles because he was the first to commit sabotage in the name of protest. He surfaced again when a cop was murdered in New Jersey. He and Tommy Manning were implicated. Tommy went to prison, Cameron evaded conviction, settled in Maine with Tommy's sister Mary, and raised sheep. Tommy painted half decent portraits of radical heroes and died in prison.

I realized I might have been a hippie, but only in the flower child category. When it came to radical politics, I felt like a coward. Luke and I won the argument with Hank, but at a cost. Our sense of community was marred by the intrusion of potential violence and an unspoken distance threatened to come between the four of us.

Luke and I weren't as radical as we claimed.

***

A positive consequence of Cameron and Tommy was that Luke and I felt freer to pay more attention to our couple rather than to the communal relationship. We decided to take LSD to see what we could learn. We made careful preparations, going to bed early the night before, dressing in comfortable clothes, eating a good meal. We drove the Desoto across the border to New Hampshire and found a secluded area with trees and a meadow where we felt isolated enough that we wouldn't be bothered.

We prepared to spend the hours of the trip there. We placed a blanket under a chestnut tree where it was both grassy and shady. We had water and Luke had some Valium in case one of us struggled. I told Luke I was certain that I could help him if he got into any trouble during our trip. It was a serious moment when we swallowed the tabs, like jumping into an icy pond. I knew we'd warm up when we swam hard, but I dreaded that first splash. We took each other's hand and lay down on the blanket side by side looking up at pieces of blue sky through the greenery. We waited.

I was concerned for Luke because he was never very good with drugs. He described drug experiences as a feeling that the wiring in his brain was a bit loose to begin with, and drugs disconnected the wires completely.

As the LSD set in, we sat up on the blanket and looked in one another's eyes. There was a sense of time passing in an encapsulated form. We saw each other as if we were flowers being photographed with a high-speed camera from bud to full bloom to the moment of falling petals. We were young and then older and then elderly. Luke told me he was seeing me as a beautiful old woman. I saw us growing and aging together, both of us blooming and then fading but gently in beauty. We didn't move, continued to look into one another's eyes deeply, the sense of comfort and pleasure immense. Several hours passed, although the sense of timelessness created by a hallucinogenic experience made it feel like the journey had unfolded in a brief moment.

The images of our aging slowly faded. We lay back on the blanket, held each other's hand and slept. We'd been to the future and received the gift of seeing something positive. The trip did not show us how to get there, only that we would.

When we drove back to the Farm it was with a new confidence that in spite of all our difficulties, all our character flaws, somehow, we'd travel through it together.

***

In late August, the Warner Farm hired Luke, Hank, Marcella, and I. Our farm needed money and the Warners needed workers to harvest their vegetables.

Mr. Warner was a tall spare man with no excess flesh and few words. He was stern and promised swift judgment for any mistake or misbehavior. In the Warner family hierarchy, it was clear that we four were at the low end of the totem. We were below the two older daughters and their two husbands. We would have been below Wanda the teenager, but she'd run off again. In town, they called her *Wandering Wanda*. I imagined she was scared to come home and face her Father. We also ranked below Billy who was mute and of an indeterminable age. He wore a cowboy hat that fell over his eyes, and he carried a fake cowboy gun on his hip. Wherever we were during the day, Billy was nearby with one hand deep and active in his pants pocket.

Potatoes were the most fun. Marcella and I stood on the flat bed of a Rube Goldberg contraption pulled by Mr. Warner on his tractor. A machine dug up the potatoes and threw them onto a conveyor belt. As the potatoes moved along the belt Marcella and I picked out all the stones before the potatoes dropped into big barrels at the end of the conveyor. Luke, Hank, and the sons-in-law ran alongside of us, grabbed the full barrels off the wagon leaving them in the field, and replaced them with empty barrels. This all had to be done in unison as the tractor kept moving and the potatoes kept coming. Keeping the right rhythm was essential. It was dirty dusty work as the August sun beat down on our heads. Later in the afternoon, one of the sons-in-law would come by with a flatbed and our guys would heft the full barrels from the field onto the bed. It was some of our best teamwork.

The rest of the picking was rough. By afternoon, the sun was brutal. We were expected to work from eight to five with only short breaks, bent over most of the time. The cukes scratched my fingers with their tiny nettles. The beans were the worst. It took two hands to pull each bean off the stem which required sustained bending. A Warner daughter might pass by during our lunch break and tell us to get going as soon as possible. We'd grumble beneath our breath, the dogs that everybody kicked. It was a short trip to a passive worker's attitude that said heck with you Mr. Warner. I thought what if this was my life, the only way I had to support myself?

Mrs. Warner went on an alcohol fueled tear whenever Mr. Warner went north to Caribou with a potato delivery. The sons-in-law became the bosses and took over telling us to get working or hurry up if we sat down to rest for a moment. They said the vegetables didn't get picked by themselves, a direct quote from their father-in-law. Everyone had tension they needed to release. Three days later, when Mr. Warner returned, Mrs. Warner hid the bottle, sobered up, everyone else moved down the chain. We remained the crew at the bottom.

As summer waned, the job shifted to apple picking, less arduous work than vegetables because we could stand up on ladders. We were paid by the bushel, so speed was important, but we also needed to avoid pulling off too many leaves with each apple. We wore large baskets in front strapped around our waists in the back. When a basket was full, we walked to the end of the row and dumped the apples into the big crate. One of Mr. Warner's sons-in-law would pass by on the tractor and pick up the crates with a front-end loader. Occasionally, if the sun was strong, Luke and I would extend our break and roll around on the grass. Billy was always somewhere nearby watching us.

On rainy days Marcella and I worked in the barn packing the apples in crates small enough for Mr. Warner to ship. *Ain't going to work on Maggie's farm no more*, we sang loudly with Bob Dylan. We worked well together.

By the beginning of October, we could see our breath inside the barn. The days grew steadily colder. Back at our farm the number of visitors dropped off. The outhouse was freezing, and my body decided it didn't have to go at all. One night as Luke and I lay in bed we heard a terrible high-pitched screeching, like a baby being murdered. Luke held me as the sound circled the house. Maybe it's an omen. Maybe it's time to leave, we said.

For right now, apple picking made sense. Luke and I put some money aside, even though we knew that Hank expected us to pool all our earnings. Luke and I had an unspoken agreement that the time was coming when we'd be on our own and need money. The six-mile-long dirt road back to the Farm stretched longer by the day. The combination of bumping up and down and the endless flat scrub land made for a grueling monotony.

I remembered how much had happened since I first rode down that road and had the panicky thought, *Get me out of here*. As we drove home from the Warners we talked about our day and shared a joint. Marcella and I developed a habit of laughing just looking at Hank. He didn't have to say anything, he was so silly. Luke, on the other hand looked fearful, as he always did when smoking pot. It didn't agree with him.

One afternoon we reported to Mr. Warner by the barn as usual, telling him how many bushels we'd picked. "Today's your last day," he said. We looked at each other stunned and asked why. "Too many apples are coming in bruised."

On the ride home Hank said he'd seen a group of Mexican men at the barn. We were fillers until the migrant workers arrived.

I took a drag on the joint and said, "Maybe it was my fault. I didn't pick fast enough."

"I don't think so," Luke said. "I think he didn't need us anymore."

It was nothing personal, but it was a signal for Luke and me that the time had come.

***

The four of us sat at the breakfast table eating scrambled eggs and toast with Welch's grape jelly. The wood stove threw off good heat. Hank stoked the fire first thing when he got up. The coffee was rich and strong.

"Um, Alicia and I have been talking, and we think it's time for us to go," Luke said.

A few long seconds passed.

"I'm not surprised," Hank said, but I knew he was.

Luke apologized and said he and I weren't as tough as Hank and Marcella. I knew that Marcella thought he was referring only to me. She lit a cigarette, blew out smoke through flared nostrils, and said everyone bailed out the minute the cold came in. I told them how much I'd learned. I couldn't admit to them how difficult the past seven months had been, and that I wasn't used to working so hard and struggling to live with so little. But I'd take some deep satisfaction with me.

Once Luke and I made the decision, we made a quick departure. It didn't take long to pack up our belongings. We had few clothes and most of them stank, so we stuffed them into a laundry bag. I'd bought a Jesse Colin-Young T-shirt in Portland that said *Come on People Now* on the front and *Love One Another* on the back. I wore it with my dirty jeans and sweatshirt. Hank gave us a jar of his home brined pickles and Marcella gave us a loaf of bread.

A couple in Cambridge who knew the Charlestown group had relayed to Hank that we could stay with them until we got our feet on the ground. Marcella looked a little sad when we said goodbye. I was surprised. It had seemed so clear to me that she didn't approve of us.

Hank put his arm around Luke's shoulder and said we'd see each other again. We left for Cambridge early in November. Our dream of the communal life had its special kind of beauty, but it was much harder than we'd thought.

We'd woken up.

11
MOVING ON, BUT WHERE ARE WE GOING?

The Glicks lived on the edge of the projects in east Cambridge to be closer to the *working people.*

"Of course, you can stay with us," Virginia told me. They supported anyone from the Farm. "But please keep us up about your hunt for an apartment."

I didn't know if they were aware that we had no money for an apartment because we had no work. I heard her words as *hurry up.*

We slept on their sofa and occupied their living room. Steve and Virginia were serious people with serious jobs. They kept their distance from us the way I imagined kind parents with good boundaries might, even though we were all about the same age.

"How are you doing with your job hunting? Steve asked.

"Um, we're both looking," I said, although I had no idea where to look. My mind was running faster than I could, but I didn't know concretely anything to do.

A November darkness followed Luke to Cambridge like something ominous had attached itself to him. He'd been more somber at the end of our time at the Farm and became increasingly paranoid when he smoked dope. But something else was happening. He was down and withdrawn without any help from pot. My heart fell when I saw him so flat and pulled into himself. We were both flailing, but he took it harder than I (I tried to hide it from the Glicks by being especially cheerful).

My only perspective on Luke's mood was Dad when he stopped drinking. I was fourteen. Severe cirrhosis and what would be several surgeries to remove various parts of his stomach and intestines forced Father to get sober. He never drank or smoked again. That summer at the Cape, after a surgical close call when they couldn't stop some internal bleeding, he was reeling from alcohol withdrawal and his near-death experience.

I was a watchwoman following his every move. I stood on the shore of Pleasant Bay under a steel gray dome of sky. Father readied his twelve-foot dory, pushing the boat out from the shore where he'd anchored it in caked mud and seaweed at low tide. His German Shepherd jumped in and took his seat at the bow.

"Be careful Dad. The fog might roll in later."

He didn't respond.

I watched him pull the starter cord hard and quick to start the outboard engine. His legs looked so skinny and his belly protruded with excess fluid from the cirrhosis. He revved the motor with the choke out for a moment and then sat down in the stern. He pointed the bow out to the bay and motored slowly out from shore. He didn't wave or look back. As he went further out into the bay, he became a small spec on the wide water that bored a hole of terror in my belly. I might have gained some confidence when he returned after hours out on the water, but I didn't. I had to accompany him each day when he went down to the beach. I couldn't pull myself away. And I couldn't stop watching, as if only my fixed gaze could keep him alive.

A notebook sat on top of a pile of Luke's clothes on the floor by the pullout sofa. He was absorbed in writing poetry again, like he was when his Father called him back from Mexico. I felt him disappearing from me into some inchoate space that I couldn't see.

There is a shadow over my soul, he wrote, *and I cannot find my way.*

I had to do something. I had to save Luke from himself. I was afraid of what he might do, but I didn't know where to go for help.

Steve and Virginia left early in the morning for their respective factory jobs. Luke was still asleep. I sat in the living room after they left, at a loss, biting the inside of my mouth. The Glicks must have associated color with bourgeois frivolity because their apartment was brown in all its dingy gradations. It could have been nothing more than a lack of aesthetic taste. Either way, I was suffocating, as if I was becoming brown and dingy, dragging like Luke.

"Get up," I said and yanked Luke off the bed. He was a dead weight, drowning in his own darkness, and I was beginning to drown with him. I didn't have the energy to keep us both afloat. "Let's go outside."

He took a long time to answer. *Where is he? What is he thinking?*

"Mmm...no thanks." There were long gaps between one word and the next. "I think I'll sleep a little longer."

"It's eleven o'clock, Luke. Come on. You'll feel better if you move."

"I'm tired, Ali. It's like I'm moving through mud." His words dragged as if there was no beginning and no end.

"You're scaring me."

I gave up temporarily and left the room with a pit in my belly. When I felt scared, I got angry.

I was too worried to leave him alone for long. What if he did something to himself when I wasn't looking? My heart started beating hard when my mind jumped ahead with vague images of Luke dying. I went back in and tried again. I wanted to yank him up, pull his dead arm right out of his listless body. He got up reluctantly, and slowly slid his feet into his huaraches. He looked like a bum, unshaven, gray, someone starved of all light and hope.

"Pick up your feet," I scolded as he scuffed along the sidewalk. We slogged by the projects where the scene was enough to make anyone despair: no grass, no trees, a concrete jungle of dark windows in grungy apartment buildings.

As soon as we got back inside, Luke returned to his writing while chain smoking Pall Malls. "You're not supposed to smoke in here." I growled from the back of my throat. He put the cigarette out and lay down on the sofa. I said maybe it was all the pot we'd smoked that made him depressed. He said he didn't want it anymore.

"Obviously. You need a job, Luke, something to get you up in the morning."

"Doing what? I don't know anything but sales."

I was ready to scream as if he was doing it to me. But we both had a problem. It wasn't a matter of small obstacles thwarting us; we were in a total vacuum. Neither of us had a clue of what talents we possessed or who to speak to. I had no idea how to go about taking the next step for myself, but I focused on Luke's problem as if I couldn't go anywhere on my own.

"Look in the paper, take anything you can get for god's sakes."

"That's enough Ali. Leave me alone. Stop pestering me." He lay back down and turned his back to me.

***

"How about a bennie?" a fellow waitress said.

I'd gone back to my old job at Barney's. It was all I knew. They gave me the weekday lunch and Sunday brunch shift.

"Really? In the morning? Anyway, no thanks. I'm done with drugs. But has anyone seen my bike?"

"If you left it out back in the alley, it's gone," a busboy said.

"Someone could have told me. I didn't know that."

After serving a typical three-martini lunch for a table of Harvard Square businessmen, I said, "I feel like running after them. They left a two-dollar tip!"

"That's the way it is," the waitress who'd been there for life reminded me.

After my shift and free lunch with the staff, I walked the two miles from Harvard Square back to the Glicks grumbling about my stolen bike, which I couldn't afford to replace. My mind was bouncing from wall to wall, with no productive thoughts. Things were bad enough with Luke, but what was I going to do?

He and I had run through all the hippie options: boats and beach, itinerant travel, and communal living. And drugs. By process of elimination there was nothing left but work, work with a purpose. But what?

When I walked into the apartment Luke was sitting on the sofa, dressed. I'd only been gone a few hours. He looked different, less disheveled.

"What's going on Luke?"

"I got a job today. At Peter Bent-Brigham Hospital."

That's where Dad was when he almost died. I wondered if Luke would be an orderly or work for administration?

"One of the ladies in the autoclave department suddenly dropped dead."

"Oh… what's the position?

"Sterilizing the equipment."

"Huh."

"It's all women and I have to wear a hairnet. And it's in the sub-basement. That's lower than the basement. It feels about right for where I am."

At least he got a job. And a reason to get up in the morning.

***

Luke began talking again, at least to older ladies with hairnets. Apparently, they liked him.

There were still big spaces between the few words he shared with me. Either his gears weren't turning correctly, or he couldn't get his thoughts from his mind to his mouth. If there were antidepressants, he could have used them, but in 1972 that was nothing we knew about.

He had a funny story to tell me when he came home from work one afternoon. "I took an employee questionnaire on a machine. I was going along with the questions and then the question popped up would I want to see a psychiatrist if I could."

The world of psychology was foreign to both of us. We'd had no college courses in psychology and there was a stigma around needing psychiatric help. Even the word *psychiatrist* was spoken under one's breath for fear that someone else would hear. There were still expressions like *looney bin*, *wacko,* and *fruitcake* to describe crazy behavior. People were also *put away*—mostly women—and often never came back.

I sat down next to him and put my hand over his, trying to be patient, but full of dread. "What do you think that meant?" He pulled away. "I have no idea. Anyway, I pushed the *Yes* button."

12
CAMBRIDGE 1972

We were both nervous the morning of Luke's appointment.

I wanted him to make a good impression with the psychiatrists at Mass Mental, the Harvard Teaching Hospital. "Try to stand up straight, Luke, and try not to wander around with your words. I don't want them to think you're crazy."

I didn't understand that Luke couldn't help what he was doing. I was afraid they'd put him in a mental hospital.

Luke came home after the appointment looking dazed. He'd stood before five psychiatrists and psychiatric residents as they grilled him. He told me he'd tried to speak, but couldn't get the words out, and felt stupid.

"I passed with flying colors, Al. I'm seeing a shrink for five dollars a pop. I said that was all I could afford."

At that time, therapy was thought of as a crutch for the weak. Somehow, I knew that was wrong. Dad would have been better with therapy. I could use some help. And the people who were truly crazy were often the ones who thought they were fine. Yet needing help still seemed humiliating, and Luke already felt bad about himself.

Later that week, when I got home from the restaurant Luke told me about his first session with the shrink. He said Dr. Registein wore a Glen plaid suit with pants that didn't reach his ankles, had a pair of black rubbers by his desk that fit over his wingtips and a black umbrella, for rainy days. I made a face, but I said being weird didn't mean he wouldn't be a good therapist (I wasn't sure about that). Then Luke added that Dr. Registein didn't say one word the entire hour. Except to stop Luke at minute fifty on the dot and say, "Our time is up."

"Yikes," I said. "Maybe that's the way he begins. Maybe he'll warm up."

It frightened me to think of sitting in a room with a person who was staring at you silent as a stone and analyzing your every word. I told Luke he was brave, but secretly, I thought I would have quit.

***

On Saturday mornings Luke and I walked into Harvard Square for breakfast at Cardullo's. We had to thread a path through the Hari Krishnas who occupied the corner of JFK street and Brattle with their shaved heads and multi-shaded orange robes. They played tambourines and small drums, danced like crazy people flinging their arms and heads around and chanting maniacally. They swung themselves right up into our faces with their eyes swirling in their heads like bliss ninnies. We swatted them away and refused to give them any money.

Cardullo's had been in Cambridge for years. Sawdust covered the floor and for 99 cents you could get a full breakfast of eggs, bacon, and toast with a bottomless cup of coffee. The cooks were friendly, and all the Cambridge regulars went there: Harvard students, homeless people, stray hippies, and us. Cardullo's was a cafeteria style treat we could afford. Breakfast was my favorite meal. Coffee lifted my mood and I looked forward to conversation while we lingered over a second cup. Luke grew restless quickly and was ready to leave as soon as he finished eating.

I tried to keep him talking. "Do you like the ladies you're working with?"

"Sure. I like them well enough. They think I'm funny. I don't know why."

I knew why. Luke was an idiosyncratic character. Who else would wear lederhosen at the age of twenty-eight, even if he didn't wear the suspenders? Or a beret with a cape when he was sailing? He was in his own parade. All my friends said he was mysterious, almost inscrutable, which made them curious, but suspicious. When a person doesn't say much it's easy to imagine things about them that may or may not be true. I knew him—when he wasn't fending off a bout of depression—by the touch of his hands, the warmth of his body, the texture of his skin. I felt the opposite of suspicious. I trusted him, at least so far as I could trust anyone. My body let down in his presence, my blood warmed, my energy was enlivened. He's hard to explain because I knew him in my senses. The worrisome thing to me was that he was all alone inside, and he didn't seem to have an exit.

"You're probably unusual to them." I sighed. "On another subject, I'm working on figuring out what my purpose is in life. Do you have any idea what I'm meant to do?"

"That's a big question, Ali. Too big for me right now."

It could have been such a good topic for discussion if only Luke would join in. I glanced at Robert Lowell who was sitting by himself with a cup of coffee, buried in a journal of some kind, writing furiously. He was there when we came in and there when we left. I would never have thought of bothering him, but I imagined beautiful sad words piling up around him on the table.

By contrast all my words seemed to drop onto the floor with no one there to catch them.

***

Luke and I sat on zafus—little meditation cushions—together in Patricia's yoga studio on Marlborough Street. Patricia was one of handful of early yoga teachers on the East coast. She was attractive in a tight clear cool way, speaking carefully, never betraying any emotion or upset. She was amazingly flexible while I could barely touch my toes.

A small group was gathered on her plush Persian rug anticipating the arrival of Chogyam Trungpa Rinpoche, a young Tibetan whose lofty reputation among a long lineage of Tibet's revered lamas preceded his arrival in the United States. If my teacher Patricia believed in him, then I trusted him automatically.

Luke and I checked out everyone who came to town from the East: Maharishi, Muktananda, Rajaneesh, even Ram Dass who was American but converted. It seemed like there was a guru on every corner. The various swamis would sit in lotus position, unmoving, like potted plants, in front of mass gatherings in conference centers. Their primary devotees with shaved heads and robes sat next to them. Those of us in the audience would stare back in hushed devotion waiting for any drops of wisdom or taps on our heads with feathers. The closer you were to the stage, the higher up you might be and the greater the possibility of a personal blessing. Because I was one of Patricia's early yoga students, Luke and I were privileged to see Trungpa in an intimate venue soon after his arrival on the East coast.

The studio was a typical Back Bay living room with high ceilings, big windows, and graceful molding. The air in the room was cool and smoky with the scent of sandalwood incense. Candles burned in the dim light on lacquered tables in front of us. A small Tibetan gong sat at the ready.

"How long are we supposed to wait for this guy?" someone asked.

An hour had passed.

"Time is relative," Patricia said. She looked slightly offended by the question but remained her composed cool self. "Perhaps it means less to him than it does to the western mind."

"My western mind is getting grumpy," I whispered to Luke.

"Let's hold on a little longer, since we're here," Luke said.

By nine o'clock some gave up. Luke and I and a few others persisted. Trungpa arrived two-and-one-half hours late.

"Maybe this was deliberate," I said to Luke later, "to see if we were sincere in our search."

He was a short square man in a shiny expensive sharkskin suit flashing an oversized Rolex watch on his wrist. His fat fingers were covered with heavy gold rings. He looked more like a successful but shady businessman. He gave no explanation or apology for his late arrival.

Rinpoche's theme for the night was *spiritual materialism*. The American mind, he said, consumes the spiritual as if it's one more product. Was all his bling a statement about our own greed? He was smart and articulate. Luke and I bought two of his books before we left that evening and we began to practice Vipassana, a Buddhist form of meditation.

***

We pooled Luke's hospital salary with my waitressing tips and rented a two-bedroom apartment in Cambridge's Central Square for $110. Steve and Virginia were happy for us, and I'm sure happy we were leaving.

With nothing but a Salvation Army bed, a table, and a few chairs we focused on our meditation practice. The spiritual was what mattered, not our material poverty. We sat together once or twice a day, observing our breath moving in and out, in and out.

"If that dog doesn't shut up, I'm going to…" I got up from my zafu and yelled out our bedroom window, "shut up!"

Captain, a mixed breed hound dog, was chained outside, barely visible in the deep weeds behind our pink vinyl sided duplex. He barked all day and late into the night. I went downstairs and knocked on the landlady's door. She appeared after a long pause. Her hair was an uncombed mess and her eyes were wide and blood shot, like she'd been crying for days. An overheated musty smell wafted out into the small downstairs hall.

"Mrs. LaViguere, please, can't you make him stop barking? We're trying to meditate."

She was a new widow, worked long hours, her two preteen children were sad and obese, and she told me she had no idea what to do.

I felt sorry for her, but my bandwidth was overstretched by the dog. I was riled up anyway. (White House staffers had been arrested, and I was furious at Nixon. I knew before he was elected that he was disturbed and a crook. I hated him. There had been more anti-war protests and more arrests. I felt guilty that I was too afraid of the police to march.) I clomped back upstairs and sat back down. The barking continued.

"Now she's screaming, Luke. She's screaming at the dog! I don't want her to hurt him."

"No, I think she's screaming at the kids," Luke said. "Let's see if we can let his barking be like our thoughts and watch them go by like a river."

Like Luke was watching life go by him as he sat on the river's edge with nothing.

"Fat chance," I said, as I repositioned myself on my zafu.

***

Gregge (the second g and e added for numerological significance) Tiffen came to town and wowed our friends with charismatic penetrating *Life Readings*. Gregge was an ex-Army officer who'd spent some years in a cave in Tibet. Luke and I hesitated at first because he was expensive. But I thought it might help Luke. I mean, what was his purpose in life? What was he meant to do? I wasn't as worried about finding my purpose as I was about Luke finding his. I didn't think I needed a reading myself, but I was curious. It was difficult to get an appointment. Time increased our desire to see him, the way you might feel about grabbing the last shiny object off the shelf because everyone else had one. I anticipated a plan for Luke and a positive supportive reading for me.

Gregge had set up a temporary office in his room at the new Hyatt Hotel on Memorial Drive in Cambridge. We were given explicit written instructions when and how to enter the room for our appointments. I waited in the lobby until two minutes before the time. I rode the elevator to the tenth floor, opened the door and walked without speaking into room number 1033. I assumed the number on the door had some significance.

The room was dimly lit, the blinds were drawn, the air conditioner was on high. Gregge was standing with his back to me, looking into a mirror where I could vaguely see my reflection. He was equally tall and spare without an ounce of extra flesh. He wore black jeans and a fitted black leather jacket. When he turned to face me, I saw his closely cropped silver hair and ice blue eyes. He wore a wide silver bracelet on one wrist.

He turned the light up slightly and gestured me to sit down on one chair while he sat across from me at a distance on another. He began the reading in a low steady voice without inflection.

He said in my last life I'd been a Spanish soldier in the mid-1700's. I was a loyal follower of Junipero Serra, the Spanish Franciscan priest. I traveled with him north from Mexico and helped set up all the missions along the coast of California. I was Catholic and overly devout. My life lesson was to move past devotion, stop following other people, and develop an independent sense of self which Gregge said was clearly lacking at the present time. That was it. No questions permitted.

He stood up and opened the door and I walked out. I could feel my blood boiling, my face burning.

I returned to the lobby where Luke waited. He looked at me expectantly. I grimaced and told him to go up and good luck. I sat stewing, stunned by Gregge's reading. I'd always thought of myself as a definite person with clear thoughts and beliefs who knew exactly who she was. It was odd he'd picked up on Mexico since he had no way of knowing I'd been there. And the words *soldier* and *devotion* did ring a small bell, but I was incensed. Nothing could have offended me more than being accused of lacking my own self. I was sorry I'd spent $150, more than one month of rent. I concluded he was not only cold, he was off, way off.

Luke came down about thirty minutes later. He looked stunned too. Gregge had told Luke he was from another galaxy. I had to admit that explained a lot to me. And Gregge said Luke was here on vacation and he had no specific life lesson other than to take back all that he learned here to whatever galaxy he was from. And then he said something about Luke waking up at some later point near the age of forty-five, knowing something about light refraction.

The whole thing enraged me because it suggested Luke didn't have to do the hard work of living like I did. On top of that, for a reason only partially understandable, I felt panicky at the thought of Luke leaving me after death and going back to his own galaxy where I couldn't reach him. The devastating conclusion from the reading was that someday we would be separated forever, and I would never see him again.

Back in our apartment, Luke said, "Al, you're even trying to hold onto me after we die?"

"But look, considering we assume the existence of previous lives, it only makes sense that there's something after this life. If you're going back to your galaxy, you'll be in some distant place and gone forever."

Just thinking about it made me cry.

"And another thing," I said, "if you're here on vacation, why aren't you having more fun?"

"Maybe I haven't realized it yet."

Gregge's bit about light refraction was very odd. I wondered if he'd picked that up because Luke had once had a sales job in California for a company that sold bicycle reflectors. In other words, I was both doubtful about the readings and shaken by them because he seemed to hit on some familiar points.

I was furious with Gregge Tiffen.

Some of our friends returned to Gregge for a reading on *Circadian Rhythms*. Luke and I couldn't afford to go back, but I wouldn't have chanced it anyway.

13

I AM MY FATHER'S DAUGHTER

"Thinking about this is ruining my breakfast," I said as I poured more syrup on Cardullo's French toast.

Apparently, I'd been thinking by myself. Luke looked up at me startled, more focused on his eggs and bacon.

"My parents," I said. "I've got to deal with them."

I'd barely spoken to them since we left for the Farm nine months before in the spring of 1972. I wasn't thrilled about them seeing where we lived. The pink vinyl siding said it all. But they took care of that worry by refusing to come to our apartment because we weren't married. On the one hand, that hurt my feelings, but on the other, I dreaded seeing them. I knew nothing would be said about our last visit and the way Dad had hidden upstairs, feigning a headache, like a coward. And I wanted to avoid introducing him to Luke.

Luke put his fork down and said he'd go with me. I shook my head back and forth for emphasis. Nope. I should go alone.

"I've got to meet him some time," he said.

"Maybe if you shaved your beard or something."

"Ali. I am who I am. I'm not going to change. I'll neaten myself up. How bad can it be? Don't be so worried."

That was it exactly. Luke was who he was, and Dad was who he was.

***

When we got back to the apartment after breakfast, I gave up ruminating and called my Mother while the sugar and caffeine were still coursing through my system. Mum was cool on the phone. At least she was talking to me and I hadn't been totally cut off.

She said to come the following day for lunch. I told her Luke was coming with me. *Oh*, she said.

Luke and I went up the street that night to the Orson Welles Theater. My favorite date with Luke was supper in the little restaurant there and after dinner a film, usually a foreign one. Then I hoped we'd have sex when we got home.

After a supper of roast chicken and couscous with slivered almonds we watched *A Man and a Woman*, a French romance between two people torn apart by the woman's grief over the death of her husband. We held hands and I cried hard at the scene of the two of them driving, the windshield wipers moving back and forth in the pouring rain. They were silent, looking straight ahead, each in their own thoughts as terribly sad music played in the background. She hadn't been able to move beyond her loyalty to her dead husband. Love was unable to bridge the anguished pain of a separation between them.

I kept thinking about Luke being from another galaxy. Someday he'd be leaving me and going back there. The only thing missing for our situation was the theme music. I couldn't get over how painful their story was.

Then I wondered if my parents were pulling us apart, if going against Dad was an act of treason, punishable by something I couldn't even name.

***

"This was a stupid idea," I said, slamming down the word *stupid* as we drove out to Groton for lunch. I was shaking in my seat with a pain in my gut identical to what I'd experienced in teenage years the few times I brought a boy home. Dad got pompous and formal and I felt embarrassed for the boy. I was awkward enough myself and Dad ruined it. Afterward, I saw only the boy's flaws and lost interest in him.

"He's going to take one look at you and…" I gritted my teeth and let out a small growl. "I'm so mad. I want to turn around. I can't do it."

Luke turned the wheel sharply, pulling the car off to the side of the road and jammed on the brakes. I lurched forward. He turned to look at me.

"What are you so upset about? We're haven't even gotten there. Calm down. It'll be fine. You're getting yourself all worked up."

"Don't tell me to calm down!"

"Jeez Ali, don't be ridiculous." He pulled back onto the road.

"Keep the damn car on the right side of the road, Luke. God. You're a pathetic driver."

"You're acting like a baby. You're a grown woman. Act like one."

"Hell with you Luke. Turn the damn car around. I'm not going."

Luke swung off the road again, screeching to a stop. Cars rarely had seatbelts then and my head bumped against the window.

"Great. Now I have a lump on my head."

Luke took a deep breath and shook his head. "We're almost there and we're not turning back. Can it."

I could feel myself cutting off from Luke and like a magnet, being pulled toward my parents.

"I can't stand you," I said.

"Well I don't like you very much either."

I was spitting fire by the time we got to the house. We both slammed the car doors. Luke walked ahead of me toward the front door.

"Not that door Luke," I yelled, "*We* don't *use* that door."

I stomped in ahead of Luke, letting the door close in his face. *I hate all of you.* We walked up the small staircase into the wide hall. This time Dad came right out of the study, ready to greet us. I took it as a good sign. My heart slowed down a little. Maybe Luke was right, and it wouldn't be as bad as I was anticipating. Dad shook Luke's hand. I knew the handshake was a test. Was it firm? Was it confident? Was it brief and to the point? Dad wore his usual tweed sports jacket with a Harvard tie of red and navy stripes, and gray flannels. He was handsome, striking, with his intense energy, like a tight spring, coiled and contained, except for a look in his green eyes that was on the edge of wild.

Luke appeared small next to him and I saw him shrinking before my eyes. Dad stood ramrod straight, the Colonel at attention, his short dark clipped hair, his military pride, his authority over the men below him, his readiness for battle. Luke looked like he'd already received a dishonorable discharge.

Dad and I kissed, or rather, I kissed him on the cheek as I always did. I smelled his warm clean skin, his sharp aftershave. We didn't hug. That ended when I became a teenager.

Well, he said in small conversation, *your Mother says this, and your Mother says that,* as if I was only related to her and not to him.

Mum emerged, dressed in the female equivalent of Dad. A tweed skirt, round collared McMullen blouse, the WASP-wear of the time, with a gold circle pin, and a cable knit cardigan in a soft blue that matched her eyes.

"Let's go into the dining room for lunch," my Mother said, as if she was saying, "Let's get this over with."

She barely acknowledged Luke and I didn't get much more.

We could have eaten in the little dining room off the kitchen, but no, it had to be the formal dining room, as intimidating as possible. I could see where we were headed. It was sterling silver and fine china all the way. Each place setting had two forks, two spoons on the side, and a soup spoon above the plate. Luke looked confused as he sat down. I glared at him. At least look like you know what you're doing.

"This is very nice of you, Mrs. Thorne," Luke said.

"You're welcome," Mum said without looking at him.

Mother placed a shallow bowl of jellied consommé in front of him.

"Thank you, Mrs. Thorne," Luke repeated

"You're welcome." A back and forth, a mix of sniping and courtesy.

Luke glanced at the jiggling aspic, I thought, to ascertain if there was anything living in its translucent interior. Then he looked across the table at me with an unspoken question, *So far so good?*

I shook my head when he picked up the outside spoon. I held up the solitary spoon above my plate. Luke put his spoon back and lifted up the other spoon. The next trick was to spoon the soup from back to front and take in the broth without making any noise. I gave up on that one. I'd had a hard time myself learning that technique.

"Well. Tell us about your job," Dad said in that deep voice that suggested a possible turn for the worse at any moment. "Alicia says you're working in a hospital."

I glared at Luke with my teeth clenched. *Do not mention the sub-basement.*

"Yes. Right now, I work with an autoclave, sterilizing and delivering equipment. Uhh…it's a temporary thing until I decide what I want to do."

It sounded as menial and meaningless as it was.

"How old are you?" Dad asked. He cocked his head and looked at Luke as if he was an imposter.

My jaw began to hurt.

"Uhhh…I'm twenty-nine." Luke tried to bring the spoon carefully up to his mouth, trying not to spill. It looked like his hand was shaking.

"I assume you've been out of college for some time. Where did you go to school?"

"I went to the University of Hartford."

"I didn't know there was a university there."

If Dad didn't know it, it wasn't worth knowing. Mother took the soup bowls away and brought in creamed chicken in Pepperidge Farm pastry shells with peas.

First fork Luke. The one on the outside.

"At twenty-nine one would assume you'd have a good idea of what you plan to do," Dad said.

At twenty-nine Dad was a Lt. Colonel, had fought in the War and been wounded. Already a hero. Luke had missed Vietnam by joining the Airforce after high school because his grades were so bad. He'd served a year and received an honorable discharge for migraines. That wasn't information I wanted my Father to have. I waited for Luke to answer, to say something about his future, anything that would quiet Dad. But there was nothing. Luke was frozen in his seat.

"Dad. We're both working on it," I said. "I might go back to school."

"Well…" By that time Dad was conversing with his plate, clearing his throat, and wrinkling up his chin in that super-serious way of his. He didn't look at either of us. Luke was looking up at the walls, staring at the dead ancestors whose portraits in ornate gold gilt frames surrounded us on all sides.

"Beautiful paintings you have," Luke said.

"That man with the cane," Dad nodded, "is Alicia's great-great grandfather. He built the Charlestown Navy Yard. And that couple over there, her many greats, owned the Arboretum in Jamaica Plain. Mr. and Mrs. Bussey."

"Oh. That's very interesting. I didn't know that," Luke said.

"And, of course, he built the capitol building in New Hampshire," Dad kept going.

People who did something important. People with accomplishments. I could have said, *And what about you Dad?* But I didn't.

Endless moments of silence followed, laden with throats clearing while I helped Mum clear the table and bring in dessert, Lemon Snow Pudding and coffee. Mum was all business. I could hear Luke asking Father questions about the ancestors. The last spoon. We could go soon.

"Delicious, Mrs. Thorne, very light."

We had a short clippety-clop goodbye and walked out to our car parked in the circle.

"That's over." I blew a lot of air through my lips. It all had a bad taste to it.

"Wow. I've never seen so many spoons. It was like going to a foreign country."

"I have a bad headache." I rubbed my forehead and closed my eyes.

Luke had stayed calm and polite while Mum and Dad were cruel and contemptuous trying to squish him like he was an undesirable insect. But I didn't give him any credit. I hated all of them. We sat in silence staring straight ahead on the long drive back to Cambridge.

"I couldn't think of anything to say, Ali," Luke finally spoke. "I felt so small, like a boy instead of a man."

I cringed. "I wonder if they knew you're Jewish."

I'd never thought about how one would know if someone was Jewish. I looked at him as he was driving, his strong handsome profile, his dark wavy hair. I loved watching him when he wasn't looking back at me. Dad's profile was just as strong.

"Honestly, Ali, I don't think that's at the top of the list. There was nothing he could check off that was right with me. The way I look, the school I went to, the way I picked up the wrong spoon…"

When he got down on himself, I felt like quitting on him. As my Father would say, "To the victor, go the spoils." I needed a stronger man, someone who could stand up to Dad. *Should I pick one of the Harvard guys I went to school with*? Mum and Dad would have to treat a guy from my own background with more respect. He could become part of our family. And I'd dress like my Mother and I'd bring home a nicely dressed, nice-looking WASP banker type who wore the college tie and knew which spoon to use and they'd be happy. Everyone would be happy.

Now no one was happy.

We turned down Kinnaird Street and parked in front of our pink vinyl sided duplex that smelled of sadness as we passed the landlady's door. We walked up the stairs into our apartment with bean bags for chairs and our salvation army bed.

"I don't think this is going to work."

“You’re leaving me out to dry, Ali?”

Tied up in a tight knot, I had nothing to say to him.

LESSON THREE:

FOLLOW YOUR EXCITEMENT

14
SEARCHING

"You sure don't look like you're enjoying being on vacation Luke," I said one morning. I couldn't resist throwing Gregge Tiffen's life reading in his face. But it was true. Luke was a lot of things, but he was not having fun.

"Why are you so angry, Ali?" Luke's eyes were sad.

My nastiness came from a sour place in my belly and back up into my throat. "Sorry. I'm all stirred up and I don't know why. And I thought being in therapy would help you."

"Well, talking to someone who doesn't say anything back feels useless." Luke looked hopeless for a moment. "I don't know what to do."

I went into the bedroom to meditate. Recently, I was practicing moving energy from the base of my spine to the crown of my head. I'd stumbled on Kundalini yoga. As I explained to Luke, Eastern Spirituality was at the opposite end of the way we westerners thought about life by holding a bigger perspective yet working within. Westerners were all about action external to the self, trying to fix every little thing.

Luke came into the room. I opened my eyes and glared at him.

"Are you still doing Trungpa's method?" he asked.

"*No*. I'm focusing on moving my Kundalini from my root chakra to my crown chakra."

"Hm, that sounds interesting in a bizarre kind of way."

"I'm trying to find my power and creativity. Which I can't do if you're interrupting me," I snapped.

***

On my day for grocery shopping, I walked up to the co-op we belonged to in Central Square.

With almonds, tofu, granola, sprouts, and a bunch of swiss chard in my basket, I stood waiting and restless in the checkout line skimming an Esalen catalogue. Esalen was known for its courses in new age psychology and spirituality and its hot tubs overlooking the Pacific. I never imagined getting there because I couldn't afford to go to California, but a class that combined Western psychology with Eastern spirituality caught my eye. I took the catalogue home with me.

I stood at the kitchen table rereading the small blurb on the course. It was taught by a psychologist, Harold something. On a quick impulse I wrote to him at Esalen to tell him how interested I was in the very thing he was teaching. Strangely enough, I received a letter back within a few days from Somerville, one mile from our apartment. The teacher, Harold invited me to tea. I hadn't expected anything, but the universe had responded. I had a good feeling.

Late one afternoon I walked along a small side street on the Cambridge-Somerville line and into a three decker, one of the typical houses in Somerville. I climbed a steep staircase with several missing balustrades to the top floor. Either this guy didn't care where he lived, or he was frugal.

The man who opened the door looked older than his description in the catalogue. Harold was about my height, but slight. His rimless glasses and graying beard fit my idea of an old-world rabbi or philosopher, but I remembered reading he was only forty. A serious, even critical face broke into a warm smile and his small eyes brightened as I introduced myself. I relaxed some. Harold invited me to sit down, make myself at home. He disappeared into the kitchen to get the tea.

Smells of sautéed onion and garlic permeated the room. I stopped worrying about him and began to take in the space around me. Books filled every wall of the room from floor to ceiling. I sat on the edge of the chair and glanced at a small stack on a side table, all new to me. Suzuki's *Zen Mind, Beginner's Mind*, Alan Watts' *The Wisdom of Insecurity*, Fritz Perls' *In and Out of the Garbage Pail.*

He brought in a tray with a brown pottery tea pot, a jar of honey with a small wooden spiral honey spoon, and two hand thrown matching mugs. I could smell the peppermint as he poured the tea through a bamboo strainer and asked me about what I'd read and experienced. A moment became an hour. His workshop in Big Sur was titled *The Integration of Eastern Spirituality and Gestalt.* Why did that grab my attention, he asked?

I said I'd been meditating and experimenting with Kundalini yoga. He raised his eyebrows and said he'd heard that could be dangerous if too much energy got released. I told him I was expecting it to make me feel peaceful but instead, I was riled up. I was surprised at myself for confiding in someone I'd just met. His course sounded helpful. Harold asked me where my psychological understanding came from. I said from novels, writers like Henry James and D.H. Lawrence. I had no psychology in college.

"Well," he nodded with an encouraging smile. "Fiction is a good teacher about the inner workings of people. And it sounds like you're learning from your own experience."

"Yes, and especially yoga."

"I've never practiced yoga. Maybe I should try it," he said.

A quick spark in his eyes made me wonder if he was kidding or playing along. He said he'd been meditating too, and his practice of Gestalt therapy lent itself perfectly to the Zen Buddhist idea of being present in the moment. Gestalt focuses attention on physical sensations and used role playing to heighten awareness of the body and emotions.

"Awareness itself can be a spiritual practice," he said.

"Maybe I should try Gestalt," I said.

We both smiled. I felt playful with him.

"Well, let's see about that."

He was about to lead a Gestalt workshop at a retreat center north of the city. He told me he had an idea. In exchange for doing the food shopping and preparation for the weekend, he'd give me free participation in the workshop. Did that sound fair? I told him I'd love it. He sent me on my way with Perl's book on Gestalt.

My feet were barely on the ground as I galloped down the stairs and loped home to tell Luke. In fact, I tripped on the bottom step and got a big lump on my knee. I couldn't wait to sit down and read the book, already sensing it was speaking to me. My instinct had been good. I knew my meeting with Harold would take me a long way.

"This guy's exciting, Luke. He's doing something called Gestalt."

I dropped Perl's book on the kitchen table and pushed it over to him.

"Check it out! Totally different from Freudian. He meditates too. Some form of Zen."

"Good for him." Luke's voice was flat.

I felt bad being excited while Luke was struggling inside and holding down a job he didn't like. But I couldn't help that my future was unfolding before my eyes. I could almost see a path for myself.

***

Harold and I became a team, or rather, I joined his team and became his assistant. The day before the workshop I went to the Cambridge Co-op with his list for meals to serve twelve people for the weekend. I bought the Jarlsberg and Fontina that he liked, and I'd never heard of, the whole grain breads and granola, the fresh fruits and vegetables, the brown rice.

On Friday afternoon I waited at the window upstairs with my cartons of supplies. When I saw Harold's old Volvo sportscar pull up to our apartment, Luke helped me carry the boxes down. The two men exchanged a brief, polite hello. Bye bye Luke! I'd see him on Sunday! I kissed him quickly and jumped into the car before I could see the expression on his face.

Harold and I drove to the Merriam Hill conference center in southern New Hampshire, talking all the way about Perl's techniques and philosophy. I listed the food I'd bought. Perfect, Harold said. What an assistant I was! On the one hand

I was pleased with myself; look what I'd made happen! On the other hand, Luke's face popped in as I was talking, with his forehead furled, his mouth frozen, and I dropped down. I pushed his image away.

Group participants were beginning to arrive as we pulled up to the retreat center. I made myself busy, carrying in the boxes of food, setting everything out, organizing the kitchen for supper that night. The other group members must have been wondering who I was and why I had such an important position.

On Friday evening, I prepared a light supper of short grained brown rice with sautéed zucchini, carrots, and mushrooms. We convened briefly as a group after supper. Harold explained the purpose of the workshop was to learn how to diagnose character through the body.

"We'll be working in our underwear in order to better observe and read the body," he added.

A group shiver passed through, most everyone shocked as we looked at each other with eyebrows raised and small smirks. It made sense. Harold explained that the roots of all psychotherapeutic bodywork were the teachings of Wilhelm Reich. It was all new to me and I'd never heard of Wilhelm Reich. Someone suggested we were all donating our bodies in order to learn from each other. I wondered if I would rise to the challenge if I had to. What about my body? How did it look? And what about the very overweight man? What would it be like for him? Or the girl who had a rash on her face and arms? It could be all over her body.

That was it for the night, Harold said. We'd meet for breakfast at 8:30 the next morning.

I woke up at dawn and lay in my bed looking up at the cracks in the ceiling, imagining anonymous faces, then Luke's face again, wondering if he missed me. I didn't miss him, but I didn't want him to be angry with me. I wasn't paying for the workshop, so I told Luke I'd be more of an observer than a participant.

I got up at seven, dressed in my Navajo skirt and black jersey. I went out to the kitchen to brew coffee, heat water for tea, and put out the breakfast food: honeydew melon and papaya, an assortment of breads in thick slices with butter and jam, and bowls of yogurt with honey. As I waited for others to wake up, I leaned against the kitchen counter with my hands wrapped around a warm pottery mug full of coffee with milk. I occupied a special place and so I felt cushioned from the group anxiety. Still it was hard to eat anything with my stomach tight.

There was jittery chit chat and joking at breakfast about what was coming. Harold told everyone to leave their clothes in their rooms after a quick trip to the bathroom. I looked at him questioning. He nodded and smiled. "You too."

I went back to my room and took off my skirt and jersey. *Where is this workshop going? How did I end up here?* I'd chosen this without knowing what it was. Not unusual for me. But now I thought, *Who is Harold anyway?* No one I knew had ever heard of him. *Well, I'm here now, and I might as well go along with the group.*

We followed one another into the large workshop area. The room was surrounded by glass windows from floor to ceiling, too big to hold much heat. I noticed one woman wore a lavender lace bra and matching underpants. I realized I'd never paid enough attention to my underwear. My bra was old, and my Carter underpants were nondescript white cotton.

As I sat down in the circle, I noticed we were all looking furtively at each other while also bearing the gaze of being looked at. Arms folded across chests in the drafty room, everyone quiet and waiting, for what? Someone said this was ridiculous. Harold came into the room, sat down on the floor in the circle. He was fully dressed. He scanned the group and said now we'd begin individual work. One person at a time would volunteer to come before the group. We'd all look at the body in front of us and discuss what we saw. Then Harold would demonstrate his Gestalt techniques. After the session we'd reflect on the theory behind the work. The body reveals character, he told us. That made sense, but I didn't know exactly how. It sounded interesting. And clinical. We were going to learn a lot. He stood up and went to the front of the room.

"Who would like to work first?"

Of course, no one volunteered. I felt dread in the pit of my stomach at the thought of being stared at and scrutinized.

Harold smiled, his eyes twinkling. "Let's all stand up, feel our feet on the ground, take a deep breath."

A collective, audible *ah*... followed, but no one stepped up. Breathing was everywhere I went; yoga, meditation and now this. Harold waited a moment, then looked right at me.

"Me?" I pointed to my chest.

"Yes you. Thank you, Alicia for volunteering. Don't worry, I won't hurt you," he joked.

I walked slowly up to the front of the room and stood trying not to look at anyone as they all stared at my near naked body and thought better me than them. Harold put his hand on my shoulder and looked at the group.

"You can see that Alicia has some collapse in her chest."

"And her shoulders are forward," someone said with great enthusiasm.

I straightened right up.

"Correct. Good point." And gently turning me to the side he continued, "And we can observe that her pelvis is positioned forward as well, suggesting fear, perhaps of a sexual nature."

I collapsed at that comment. I already knew something was wrong with me. It was horrifying to think that it was obvious to other people.

"We can also assume that she has rage locked in her pelvis as well as fear. Would you say that's true, Alicia?" Harold asked.

"I don't really know what's in my pelvis," I stuttered.

"Now. What else do people notice? How is she standing?"

"It looks like her legs are locked," someone said. I wished everybody would shut up.

"And her head is sitting forward, almost as if she's expecting to have it cut off," another said.

That hit hard. Before I could catch my breath, the entire group became a pack of dogs chasing a bunny. No wonder I was feeling terrible, I had so many physical flaws: my rounded shoulders (like I'd been beaten), my tensed jaw (I must be angry), my unfocused eyes (someone said they didn't know what that meant). I was a piece of dead meat and everyone wanted a share.

"Exactly. Good points," Harold said cheerfully. "We see how the body reveals all. So, if we have Alicia bend her knees, pull her pelvis back, stand up tall…" and he repositioned me. "What are you feeling now?"

"I feel stronger." Partially true, mostly I was humiliated. I didn't want anyone to see the way my features were dissolving so that my whole face was crying.

Harold put an empty chair in front of me. "Tell us. Who's in that chair? Who are you angry with?"

I was silent. Frozen. I was angry at the group for picking at me, but I knew that wasn't the point.

"Who comes into your head?"

"You?"

Harold laughed. "Well, that wasn't quite what I was thinking, but all right, fine. Let's have you envision me in the chair. What do you want to say?"

He moved my pelvis back, like a weapon cocked, ready to fire.

"Just…I hate you?"

"Right! Say it loud."

"I HATE you!"

"Yell it out."

I looked at the chair and it was as if Harold really was sitting in the chair and I did hate him. So, this was Gestalt. I yelled and screamed at the empty chair, not exactly sure why I hated him, but knowing it was true. It felt good. My head was exploding until I broke into tears and fell to my knees.

"Wonderful, Alicia, so open and true." He turned to the group, "This is a young woman fully expressing herself. Thank you, Alicia, go back and join the others."

The others followed me until the room was filled with sweat, screams, and exhaustion. I was part of the group, settled in my body, breath moving through me, all new sensations that felt good. So, this was Gestalt, this was body work. Certainly, I'd been embarrassed, even humiliated. But I accepted it as a matter of course; the nakedness, the scrutinizing others' bodies, the screaming. We were pioneers on psychology's cutting edge, discovering and exploring the mind-body connection.

***

I came home after the weekend clear and emptied out, as light as I'd ever felt.

"I'm a group star," I told Luke.

"What does that mean?" He stood at the stove sautéing strips of chicken in a wok for a stir fry.

"I was the first to open up and I let everything out. Harold said I was one of the most open people he'd had in his groups."

"Well. Good for you Ali, fantastic." He sat down at our kitchen table. He lit a Pall Mall and took a long drag.

"I thought you'd given up smoking."

"I'm only having a few a day," as he blew out a long exhale of smoke.

He dipped zucchini, broccoli, mushrooms, and onions into a beer batter and sautéed them in our wok. He divided the vegetables into two large wooden bowls, added the chicken and a big spoonful of rice on top of each one. Soy sauce sat on the table. We ate quietly.

Why isn't Luke interested? I wondered if he was jealous. His therapy wasn't going anywhere, and his job was menial and grueling. I felt mean being so excited. I decided I couldn't show how hopeful and happy I was. And I stopped talking about Harold.

15
LITTLE LIES

Luke and I walked the ten blocks or so over to the Turtle Café in Inman Square. At nine, the place was already jammed with a steady line of people continuing to squeeze in. There were no empty tables or chairs. Luke pointed to a space on a windowsill. We grabbed it. We climbed up onto the ledge where there was just enough room for the two of us to lean back and let our legs hang down. We had the best view in the house, slightly above everyone else, able to look over their heads to see the band in the front of the room.

The Turtle was long and narrow, smoke filled, buzzing with excitement. James Montgomery and his band were hot, known for their raw, sexy blues. The whole room cheered as they began playing, all of us rocking and swaying in the groove of the sound. We drank beer and smoked, listening to a wailing guitar and thrumming drums that went right through my body. I grabbed Luke's thigh and we put our heads together, moving our shoulders against one another to the vibrating rhythm of the blues.

Luke squeezed my hand as we walked home, the night soft and still. "I feel happy," I said. The music stirred our senses. We fell into bed wrapped around each other. The bed collapsed. "That's what you get for twenty dollars," Luke said. We laughed, put it back together and continued along our sweet way.

The following morning, I was to be picked up by Harold to head for a workshop he was holding in New Hampshire. I could have told Luke earlier, and I should have. And it was for Saturday and all day Sunday.

Luke's face fell. "I thought we could go to the movies."

He hadn't been excited about doing much of anything for a long time, so it was a big deal that he wanted to go out twice in one weekend. I told Luke watching how Harold worked with people was an important way of learning. In addition, I stressed with a smile, I was getting free help with my own negativity, which I thought might make Luke happy.

I felt guilt lump in my throat, and I hadn't even done anything. I couldn't explain to Luke why I made myself available to Harold any weekend he asked for my help. And on top of that, I was accustomed to have Luke waiting for me on Sunday evenings. In that regard, his depression worked well for me.

He was always home.

***

I walked in the door Sunday night full of energy. Luke was lying on the beanbag in the living room reading a story about survival at sea. He was like a cat when it's been left and the owner returns, pretending he didn't see me. I poured a glass of water and planted myself in front of him.

"Do you notice any change in me?" I said.

Luke looked up. "I see what you're getting out of this," he said. "What is this guy Harold getting out of it?"

"I'm trying to learn from him, Luke. That's all."

"That's not what I asked. What is he getting out of it? Do you think he's helping you out of the goodness of his heart?"

"Well, yes. I think he's happy to talk with someone who's thinking like him."

"Jesus. You're either naïve or you're not telling me everything."

"Now you're saying I'm either stupid or I'm lying!"

"Well, she doth protest too much. Which is it? Are you playing dumb or are you messing with my head?"

"Wow. So that's what you think of me. You're the one messing with my head. Fuck you Luke."

I threw my glass into the sink. It broke. I stomped into our bedroom and slammed the door shut. "And don't follow me!" I yelled.

***

We never revisited the fight, but each time I got ready for a weekend workshop, we stopped talking to each other. I'd pretend a cheerful goodbye. Luke did not pretend. He barely spoke to me. He'd left the hospital job and gone back to sales ("I know how to do that," he said), but now he had to drive around the nameless midlands of Massachusetts selling long lasting light bulbs that no one was ready for. I felt depressed watching him go out each morning with the bits and pieces of a good attitude and come home at night with some small antique item he'd bought on his route, but no money.

"I couldn't resist it," he'd say, as he unwrapped some lovely object that he'd gotten a good deal on.

"I don't want to do it anymore," Luke said after a couple months with paltry sales.

"What do you want to do?"

A long silence followed. "I have no idea."

There were still big gaps between thoughts and words.

"What does Dr. Registein say?"

I already knew what Luke's therapist would say. Another long silence.

"Dr. Registein doesn't say anything, Alicia. That's the whole fricking point." Luke grimaced and shook his head. "That's what the Freudian method does for you. I feel worse than when I started treatment."

***

We lay in bed one night and Luke began moving his hand slowly across my belly. I turned on my side to face him. The bed collapsed.

We got up, rearranged the slats under the mattress as we'd done many times before, usually laughing together. This time it didn't feel funny. We climbed carefully back into bed.

"Where are you?" Luke said, as he put his arm around me.

"I'm right here," I said, "Where are you?"

"I'm right here," he said, but by that time the little fire we were stoking was out.

It was as if we'd argued back and forth, It's your fault. No, it's your fault. We turned onto our backs and stared at the ceiling. We were each throwing water on the other's flames. I felt a sadness in the pit of my belly.

The distance between us widened. I began meeting with Harold even when there was no workshop. Home was empty and nature abhors a vacuum.

***

Harold and I often met at the Blue Parrot, a small upstairs café in Harvard Square that served wine, coffee, and light food. Nothing like the combination of something good to eat and stimulating conversation. I couldn't help comparing my discussions with Harold to the way Luke and I talked. Or couldn't talk.

"It's wonderful, this ongoing conversation we're having" he said during one lunch meeting. "You have a natural ability to bridge theoretical boundaries. This is some of the frontier of psychological thought."

I sat across from him eating a baguette with melted cheese smearing a little Grey Poupon on top, an exotic mustard at the time. My role with Harold was familiar. I was the good daughter who listened and made the man feel good. It gave me a certain kind of power, as if by attuning myself to a man I could shape the relationship and the feeling between us. It was also true that I enjoyed making intellectual connections between different lines of thought.

As we talked, I thought I really should bring Luke and Harold together. I mentioned it to Harold. He said, "Hmm." It was obvious, he wasn't interested.

Harold told me more about Wilhelm Reich, a student of Freud's in the fifties who'd gone beyond Freud, developing a theory about energy that connected our individual bodily energy to a universal energy. He said Reich's brilliance was the foundation of body work. He suggested I read *Character Analysis* and *The Function of the Orgasm.*

First, I had never said the word *orgasm* out loud, much less heard a man say the word. Secondly, Reich sounded way out there. Harold held onto my eyes. I didn't like what I thought he might be thinking. But there was something about Reich that excited me. I wanted my small self to be connected to something greater, something to make me feel less lonely. My body could be the bridge to the spirit. The only reference I had for that kind of thinking was the novels of D.H. Lawrence. I'd written my senior thesis at college on his idea of the highest kind of love being the meeting of two separate and whole beings.

Harold's eyes were almost swimming as he looked at me. I dropped my eyes. Would he extract a payment for being my mentor? He had such a penetrating mind and I wanted to be able to learn from his innovative thinking.

I'd also never been close to a man who was safe to admire. All the men of Father's generation—Mr. Blackman, Mr. Kelly, Mr. Thompson—back from the War, they all drank which made them dangerous to young girls like me. I wanted to look up to Harold who was twice my age and that much more experienced. I went to the Harvard bookstore on the way home and bought Reich's first two volumes.

Luke didn't say hello when I got home.

He looked at *The Function of the Orgasm*. "So now he's talking about orgasms?"

"Who? Reich?"

"No. Harold! You're hard to believe, Ali. What the fuck are you doing with this guy?!"

"Oh." I began to babble, "It's not really about orgasms. It's more about energy and the way all things are connected, big and small through our bodies."

"Ohhh," Luke said, smirking. "Now I see. You're not discussing orgasms; you're chatting about energy. Very nice. Very nice." His mouth looked like he'd vomited.

***

I went to a women's workshop on feminist sexuality. I'd been reading Betty Freidan and was increasingly insecure and upset about my sexuality. I'd never considered my unhappiness had anything to do with being female. The leader said we needed to learn how to pleasure ourselves so that we could teach our partners how to give us pleasure. I froze. I wasn't sure I'd ever had an orgasm. Getting my body all wrought up at night as a teenager with my pillow, did that count?

"If you don't know whether you've had one, you haven't had one," one woman said.

"Oh yeah, I've been pretending for years," someone bravely admitted. "It's easy. You arch your body, throw your head back and yell, "Oh god. Oh oh, three times. Take a deep breath and then call out and sink back into the bed. Cry if you can. It makes a guy feel good."

It wasn't only me. Women lied all the time, I discovered, to protect their partners. And in turn, we betrayed ourselves. It was time we started to reclaim our bodies, and our pleasure.

"Better to learn what pleases you first then teach your partner. Take his or her hand and move it as you would your own. Go home and practice," were the facilitator's parting words.

I sent for a vibrator and checked the mail every day so that I could catch it before Luke saw the package. It arrived in brown paper with no labels. I practiced with it whenever Luke was at work. It was a little too strong at times, but I figured out how to use it with KY jelly to make it softer. The first time it worked I felt what I'd been missing. And how long I'd been lying, not only to men, but to myself. Now all I had to do was ask.

But that was the *hard* part.

***

The next time I had lunch with Harold he said, with a glimmer in his eye and a chuckle, that we had to stop meeting this way, as if he and I had an in-joke. I pretended he hadn't said it because it could ruin everything. I had so much more to learn from him. Had I seduced him by mistake? I could continue to pretend I hadn't understood his innuendos, but I felt confused. I didn't want him, but I wanted something he had. I wanted to pick his brain.

As I read Reich, I grew excited. He wasn't easy to follow but gradually I understood the way Reich thought, the idea that the human orgasm was a natural and universal movement of energy, that the movement of energy in my body was the same as the movement of energy in every living creature. I wanted to learn more.

Harold said if I was serious, that I should be in Reichian therapy, the best way to learn. He recommended Reuben Sontag, Reich's most direct descendent in the Boston area. "A mensch of a guy," he added.

Harold drove me home with the top down and turned the engine off in front of my apartment. Oh god. He looked deeply into my eyes.

"I'm becoming very fond of you," he said and took my hand.

I caught my breath. "Luke is upstairs."

"And we're down here." He gazed into my eyes with a dreamy smile.

I pulled my hand away, smiled. "Thanks Harold! I'll see you Friday at the workshop!"

I jumped out, slammed the car door, and ran up the stairs.

"Why are you out of breath?" Luke asked.

"I really need to stop smoking," I said.

16

REUBEN-1972

I stood in the front hall of Reuben's graceful Newton house with hands cold and clammy in my pockets as I waited to meet him for our first therapy session.

What will he be like? Luke's Dr. Registein in short pants with wingtips? What am I supposed to do as a patient?

Luke hadn't been able to figure it out in his therapy, but of course there was no one on the other side of the desk talking to him.

Shortly after 10:00am, a tall, dark skinned man in loose gray flannels and a crumpled white oxford shirt walked quickly down the wide curving staircase. I wondered if his wife ironed his shirts and then he got them messed up as the day went on. He didn't look like someone who cared the way he appeared to others. He looked at me from under bushy eyebrows, his eyes straining, as if his mind had been intensely occupied and now, he was trying to shift his attention to me. His voice was deep and distinct with vowels slightly rounded by his European accent.

He took my hand in a warm firm handshake.

He appeared cosmopolitan and sophisticated in a rumpled kind of way, nothing like Dr. Registein's buttoned up prep school look.

“Let’s go up,” he said, the sound of labored breath and the distinct smell of tobacco trailing behind him as I followed him upstairs to the third floor.

A Mozart piano concerto filled his cozy room under the eaves with a fluid limpid sound. I knew it was Mozart because I’d heard its melody in the Swedish movie *Elvira Madigan.*

“I like Mozart,” I said.

He nodded, smiled, and said his most moving works were the concertos numbered in the early twenties. This was the twenty-first.

The chair at his desk was pulled out as if he had gotten up hurriedly, a book was open, and papers were in disarray. He saw me looking and said he was working on a biography of his teacher, Wilhelm Reich. I heard his love for Reich in his voice.

He motioned me to sit down on the bed, pulled the chair over from the desk and sat at a distance looking at me. He said to tell him a bit about myself, why had I come, what did I want from therapy?

My head tilted down as I raised my eyes to look up at him and my voice shook as I told him my thoughts about integrating the east and the west. I said I’d been reading Reich, one book after another. Reuben listened carefully, nodding. I told him I wanted to learn more. He told me that no graduate school could teach me more than my own experience in my own body. For that reason alone, he said, one’s own therapy is the foundation for becoming a good therapist. Harold had said the same thing, but I had no idea what that meant. But after several workshops where members did deep emotional work, I could see that I was learning about body work through my own direct experience. That made Reich's difficult and dense theory come alive.

He asked me to take off all clothes, except for underwear, and lie down on the sofa. This was the way Reich worked, he explained. He left the room, like a medical doctor. I was prepared, but still, I was nervous being exposed. Workshops with Harold made it clear that I had many issues that I knew little about, all revealed by my body. What I was about to experience couldn't be any worse than the workshops.

I undressed and lay down, arms at my side, my heart beating fast and hard. I drifted off briefly with Mozart stirring my memory of the lovers in *Elvira Madigan* as they ran through a rolling meadow of wildflowers. I was startled when Reuben came in and pulled the straight-backed chair closer to the bed. I could almost hear my heart. Having a stranger so close, staring at me. The attention was nearly intolerable. He looked down at me, nodded, his brown eyes serious underneath the thick brows, his forehead furled, like a doctor who cared about me.

He told me to breathe, which I said I already was doing. But a little deeper, please, he said, which I tried to do… the breath caught in my chest. I couldn't go any deeper. He said that was fine as he placed his warm hand on my chest and pushed gently down, all the while looking off as if he could feel and hear what lay beneath his hand.

What was my body telling him without me knowing?

He lifted his hand as I breathed in, pushing down as I breathed out, in and out, in and out. His hand was big and warm, as if he was receiving my breath through his hand and holding it for me. I felt myself about to cry… *what is the feeling, I don't know, just sad, what's making me sad, I don't know...* He pushed down a little harder and I began to cry softly. He said that was fine, let it come out, very good, lifting his warm hand, sitting back in his chair, taking a breath, looking at me with kind concern.

I felt like a wild animal, one who was wounded, understood it had been captured in order to be helped, and yet instinctively would do everything possible to escape. He continued to look at me, not with judgment, but with curiosity and concern.

"I'm missing something. I'm missing a part. Something I need badly." I began to cry again. "And I don't even know what it is."

"'*The world is more full of weeping than you can understand.*' Yeats," Reuben said.

I thought that was so beautiful and true. I looked into his sad eyes and saw the reflection of my own sadness. His eyes rolled back, as if he was trying to reach something outside his grasp.

I sniffled. He offered me the box of Kleenex that sat on the floor beside his chair. I blew my nose in a honking sound.

"So, is this therapy?"

Reuben smiled, "It's part of it, a small part. You'll see over time as your experience unfolds."

"Is there something wrong with me?"

"Nothing is wrong with you, everything about you is good."

So different from the workshops where there was always a lot wrong with everyone. The goal of a workshop was more about learning about the body and character, not the same as therapy.

He looked at me from under his knitted brow. "I imagine you're carrying a lot inside and sadness may only be the beginning. Think of it as peeling an onion."

It was unnerving that a layer was so quickly stripped away. Although the light in my consciousness was dim, I could already see there was something ugly hidden underneath, like mud, thick and impenetrable, a dangerous territory to enter. I wasn't sure if it would be worse to show it to Reuben or to expose it to myself.

I headed home on the Green Line trolley and instead of changing trains I got off at Park Street and came up the stairs and out onto the street. I walked across the Common to the Boston Public Garden. I recognized the beginning of a journey, a feeling I knew from traveling across the country and in Mexico. I was a good traveler. I'd been many places alone, I'd been afraid, I'd taken risks, I'd been in danger, I'd made discoveries, I'd been weary but kept going, I'd waited without knowing what was coming. I knew a lot about traveling, but this was a different kind of journey. I couldn't get up and leave when I felt like it.

And I needed to place my trust in a man. I wasn't sure if I could do that.

When I attempted to turn inward and reflect, all I saw was darkness with unspoken warning signs that I had always respected. *Don't go there, don't look any further. Pretend that you didn't see it.* Beneath my sunny exterior there was something shameful and lonely that I'd lied about, jumped over or buried for so long that I'd forgotten what was true. The darkness was not about anything I'd done. It was about who I was.

I hoped courage would come to me. I hoped I'd be safe with Reuben.

I walked past the swan boats as they floated slowly, patiently through the water carrying tourists of all ages. The lagoon was shaped in a gentle curve. When I'd ridden in the boats as a child the journey felt long as we glided by lily pads with pink blossoms and a pair of swans, with weeping willows gracing the rounded edges of the lagoon. Now I saw only a small body of placid, murky water briefly stirred by the young men and women who pedaled the boats. I walked back up to Park Street and rode the Red line to Central Square then walked from the station to our apartment on Kinnaird Street.

"How'd your first session go?" Luke asked when I got home.

"Fine. I like Reuben," I said.

"That's it?"

"Yup. It was only the first time, Luke."

I picked up my zafu and headed for the bedroom. Luke followed me in.

"Could I be alone, Luke?"

I didn't want any more questions that might topple my precarious equilibrium.

"Sure thing. I'll just grab my book."

He gave up and closed the door quietly. It was easy for me to push him away. I began my meditation alone, breath in, breath out. My body wouldn't settle, my mind holding on to every thought.

That night I woke up at 3am with my head hot and splitting, a familiar kind of headache I'd experienced before I developed epilepsy and then experienced after each grand mal convulsion. While the seizures seemed to have mysteriously disappeared when I left home, the headaches continued to come on fast and strong. I got up and put a cold washcloth on my forehead. I sat in the darkness of the living room holding my head, crying. I stifled the sobs because I didn't want Luke to wake up. I didn't want him to see me like this.

I couldn't get away from the pounding. I just wanted it to stop. The sensation felt dangerous to me, something pushing and explosive pressing up against the walls inside my head.

So, the journey had begun. The only instinct I had was to hide the secrets of myself (at least so far as I knew them) from Reuben. And from Luke.

17

DENIAL IS NOT A RIVER IN EGYPT?

I had three goals for my therapy. The first was to be a good patient, the way I was a good student or a good daughter. I knew how to give people what they wanted, and I worked overtime not to annoy them. The second goal was to prevent Reuben from seeing what lay underneath the sadness he'd so easily uncovered. And the third was to learn about Reichian therapy without exposing anything about myself.

As I read more of Reich, I liked thinking about other people and analyzing them. Every person had a story and it was interesting to see how people figured out ways of living within their own story. Both Harold and Reuben were encouraging when I spoke to them about becoming a therapist. Although direct experience was the best teacher, they acknowledged graduate school was necessary to become a credible practitioner.

I applied and was accepted at Goddard College and began a low-residency master's program in Clinical Psychology. The concept was new: a university without walls that allowed students to work and study off campus.

As I took courses, I tried on every diagnosis I read about. I could see that Luke's Freudian therapy was not working. It was too cerebral. Reich's holistic theory included the whole person and made intuitive sense to me.

Reuben and I agreed on one session per week. The reality of looking at myself, translating exciting thoughts into my own feelings was hard. It wasn't long before I began dawdling at home on my therapy days, always finding something else I needed to do so that I left late and had to run from the trolley to his house.

One day I arrived with only thirty minutes left for our session. Reuben remarked that this wasn't the first time I was late. Why? I thought he might be just the tiniest bit frustrated and I said I had no idea, what did he think? He thought there was something painful I didn't want to talk about. I joked that maybe I was a little chilly lying there every week in my underwear. He replied that was not what he meant. I'd annoyed him. Could he see through me? I avoided his eyes. He placed his warm hand on my chest, pressing gently down, reminding me to breathe, in fact, constantly telling me to breathe.

"I really don't get exactly why it's so important to breathe."

"The breath is the vehicle for moving energy in the body, and the movement of energy allowed feelings to move." Reuben looked extremely patient. I worried I was tiring him out.

"Right. Of course, I knew that," I said. I didn't say that was exactly why I didn't want to breathe.

More important to me was the fantasy I'd been having that Reuben was in love with me. It started when he looked directly at me and I looked back at him and I felt the look in my body, in my belly. It felt forbidden. I thought he must have sexual feelings for me and just looking into his eyes stirred me. A delicious disturbing obsession developed that I kept secret, a repetitive series of thoughts that preoccupied me. I imagined our looking at one another would intensify look by look, stirring our bodies until he couldn't help himself from bringing his head down to mine and kissing me, which would then have led immediately to lying down with me and having sex leading to unavoidable romantic feelings that we were unable to resist. The fantasy only grew stronger as it repeated in my mind until I couldn't stop thinking about him, about us together. Our age difference of thirty years was unimportant. His dark look and elegant speech became movie star handsome as I thought about him. I thought about him day and night.

I felt guilty being around Luke when it was Reuben who was in love with me. Luke's therapy was obviously not working, and he remained withdrawn. My own mind was better company because he hardly spoke at all. My thoughts were so permeated with Reuben that I began to feel like something had already happened between us.

At the end of the session, after I had continued resisting any expression of what I was feeling, he looked at me and asked, "What are you thinking?"

"I can feel your attraction to me." The thought burst out of me before I could stop it. "Embarrassing," I said quickly.

Reuben nodded and smiled, "No thought is ridiculous." He looked at his watch, took a deep breath and said, "We'll talk more about this. Time to stop for today."

I was taken aback that he didn't extend the session to make up for the lost time.

***

My obsession with him was so strong that I only saw love in his eyes when I looked at him, love for me. He didn't deny it, and for weeks that's all I saw and all I thought about. I continued to arrive late. Reuben repeated his thought that there were more difficult feelings inside me. He kept pressing me. I didn't understand what he was getting at. What I did feel was gypped at the end of each session when he didn't give me extra time.

Then one day he responded. "You are a lovely person. But unfortunately, I am your therapist and there are boundaries to respect. I want you to have someone in life who is available and ready to have a relationship. Perhaps that's Luke or perhaps there will be someone else."

My heart fell and embarrassment filled my face. Reuben looked at me kindly as my cherished thoughts collapsed in a humiliating heap between us. He must have seen it in my eyes, how ashamed I was to be so stupid.

Reuben explained *transference* to me, the idea of displacing feelings onto one person that were intended for another. I had transferred feelings on to Reuben that could have been more about Dad or love that I wanted and couldn't have.

Dad? I was stunned at the thought. We weren't even on speaking terms.

When I mentioned Reuben to my friends who were in therapy, they admitted they also had fantasies about their therapists. In fact, there was one well-known therapist who had sex with one of my friends. So, I wasn't special. I was right out of a textbook. My face flushed just thinking about how dumb I'd been.

I gave up and began arriving on time. A faint awareness crept in that I'd been avoiding myself.

Reuben continued to press and probe. It was like being at the dentist's office with the sound of the drill in my mouth bouncing off the dark corners of my psyche. Reuben wondered what I was guarding so fiercely. I didn't have a clue. I had no fantasy left, Reuben was just Reuben, rumpled and smelling of cigarette butts, having a hard time catching his own breath, and talking constantly about Father and all my difficult feelings for him. It was disappointing and irritating.

When I thought about Dad, if he ever spoke to me again the mere idea of looking into his eyes made me shake. His eyes were crazy, and I never knew what might come back at me. I didn't get what Reuben was getting at, what I was guarding against.

I only knew it was dangerous.

***

One night following my session, I went to bed deflated. Reuben had repeatedly turned our conversation to my guarded self. I became afraid to think about what was inside, what I really felt about Dad or Luke or Reuben for that matter; they were all risky ground better kept buried. I woke up in the middle of the night with a blinding headache and a memory.

I was little, five or so, sound asleep upstairs in my grandmother's house. I might have heard commotion that frightened me coming from the kitchen downstairs, shouting and glass shattering. The kitchen was far away from my bedroom and the voices were like nothing I'd ever known. The grandfather clock that usually comforted me with its serene tick-tock, now bonged a sinister warning several times on the stairway landing. I heard heavy footsteps and a strange muttering. Father came into my room and picked me up out of bed. He reeked of whiskey, a smell I already recognized. He carried me down in my nightie into the glaring lights of the kitchen and out the back door into the dark night. He put me in the back seat next to my ten-year old brother Johnny who was in his pajamas. Mother sat like a stone in the passenger seat.

"Where are you taking us George? In the middle of the night," she said. Later I learned that midnight rides were all too familiar to her.

Dad got in the car, turned the key, and pushed the gas pedal to the floor. He revved the engine, put the car in gear and stalled.

"God damn it."

He was growling. He started the car again and we lurched forward, bucking as if he'd forgotten how to drive.

"You're going the wrong way, for god's sakes," she said.

We headed off the driveway into the fields behind the house, the car pitching precariously as we tumbled up and down through the vagaries of the lumpy meadow until we came to my grandmother's apple orchard. Dad began racing the car up and down the narrow lanes between the trees, flying up over mounds and rocks. Gnarled black branches leered at us, scratched our windshield, thudded against our roof, and threatened to crash inside of our car. My brother was silent, holding on with both hands to the leather strap above his door.

Mother screamed, "George!" at one point which made me cry out, "Daddy!"

Mum measured my fear for me. When she began to cry, I knew to cry.

"Let us out of this car! Right now!"

"Shut up Eleanor! If you know what's good for you!"

The car rocked from side to side until I thought we'd tip over. The rocks scraped the under- carriage until I thought the bottom would fall out.

Father kept going as if we were escaping an enemy greater than him and in a race against time. Our trip ended when Dad felt like ending it. Johnny and I returned to our beds. Nothing was ever spoken about our midnight journey.

***

Reuben sat in the straight-backed chair looking down at me, as if he knew what I was thinking. Once more he asked, what was I guarding against? To *guard* is a military term. I answered his question as a soldier would answer his commander, with carefully scripted obedience. I remained guarded. I gave Reuben only what I thought was necessary to stop his relentless questions.

"Did you read the book *Helmet for My Pillow*?" I asked.

"No, I didn't."

"It's about the War in the South Pacific. Dad. He was on the front lines of Guadalcanal." My voice grew unsteady. "And even though the War had ended the year I was born, it was still going on at our house."

Reuben nodded and sat back in his chair.

"Everything was about the War; our TV programs like *Victory at Sea*, our movies-like *Mr. Roberts* or *South Pacific*, the childhood games I played with my boy cousins. They were required by my uncle to dress in khaki, like enlisted men."

Reuben nodded with a small smile.

"Dad and I used to march together. 'Hup two three four, hup.' When he looked sad, I wouldn't say, don't be sad, I'd sing the Marine Corps anthem to him and march in step. My birthday is the same day as the Marine Corps birthday. We celebrated them together."

"I understand," Reuben nodded, "I'm sure that made you special to your Father. World War II was hanging over all our heads."

I was breathless, trying to explain myself. "I know," I said as Reuben reminded me to breathe. He placed his warm hand on my chest, pushing gently down each time I exhaled.

"He told me he never slept in a bed during the War, that a good soldier could sleep standing up."

Reuben raised his brows.

As I exhaled, tears came. I tried to stop them. "I tried to be brave. To obey. And especially, to be loyal. Semper Fi. That's the oath every Marine has to take."

My jaw was locked, my teeth grinding. I was hot. We were headed into dangerous territory.

"That makes sense. You don't want to be a traitor."

A therapist always respects the defenses of the patient. I learned later they are there for a good reason. His look was serious and at full attention. But his understanding was a trap.

"Thank you," I said. "That means everything to me. People think I'm a wimp, that I can't stand up. But it's not true. It's just that I'm loyal to the end."

I thought we should end the session right there. I started to get up off the bed.

Reuben had one more question.

"And what is the end for you? What would be the point when, as a soldier, you had to make a decision not to obey?"

I looked up at Reuben and stared at him for a minute. For the first time, I could look into his eyes without flinching because what I was saying was true.

"A Marine doesn't make that decision himself. That's why they're so tough and they're the best soldiers. I'm not free to make that decision either."

Reuben hugged me before I left.

"You are very brave," he said. "But there's a price for being special. There comes a time when being loyal can turn into a betrayal of one's own self."

I walked as fast as I could to the T stop. My head was splitting.

***

Every Thursday that year—in addition to my Tuesday therapy appointment—I took the train to Reuben's house for my 4:00pm slot in the Orgone Box. The Box was an experiment of Reich's that he built to demonstrate the presence of orgone, the energy that he believed was present in all of creation. A peculiar little gray box sat in the middle of Reuben's driveway. I often ran into one or another of his patients coming out of the Box as I went in. Did he love them as much as he loved me?

The Box was what made some people think that Reich (and by association, Reuben) was a quack. I didn't know who built it, but I was sure Reuben had no ability in that area because he wasn't a practical man; he was a visionary. It must have been some other patient. In the back of my mind I understood I wasn't Reuben's only patient. However, I discounted the rest of them and concluded one was weirder than the next, all of them obsessed with Reich.

On the outside, the box resembled an outhouse with a door and no windows. The inside was what was different. The walls and ceiling were lined with strange brillo-type coils that collected Orgone, Reich's term for the energy that infuses all living things. Reich had invented the Box in the 1950's as an experiment. He claimed it could help patients whose energy was blocked by depression or disease.

Because it wasn't FDA approved, the FBI arrested Reich for transporting the Box across state lines. He died alone in prison. I believed in Reich's overarching theory of one universal energy that was in the air, the trees, in me. He just happened to call that energy *orgone*. So, the idea of collecting orgone made sense to me. Beyond that, I didn't fully grasp how these coils were working.

I didn't like being lumped together with Reuben's other patients. I'd noticed in workshops that body-oriented therapy attracted some strange people. But, where the Box was concerned, I thought of us as a small select group. On Thursday afternoons I sat in complete darkness on a stool in the center of the Box surrounded by steel wool. The space was tight with very little air as I breathed in the orgone energy, waiting for sensations in my body. It wasn't easy sitting there for half an hour. Was I really experiencing more energy or was I making it up? I felt something, a tingling of my hands, goose bumps on my legs.

The Box was so well insulated that the interior was silent. It was like being in a time capsule of Reich's 1950's mind via Reuben. I was carrying his legacy. I got warmer as I continued to sit, but whether that was the result of an increase in energy or simply from being closed inside a small space, I couldn't tell. My body was supposed to feel energetically charged by the end of a session, like a battery.

When I stepped out into the bright light after a half hour, I did feel a buzz, although that could have been from getting back outside and breathing fresh air. I'm prone to claustrophobia.

The truth is that I would have lived in a tree or rowed through crocodile infested waters for Reuben. I liked to think that Wilhelm Reich was Reuben's deity and Reuben was mine.

***

It took most of the first year to face the reality that my relationship with Reuben was not what I'd been expecting. Yes, my therapist cared about me and wanted the best for me, but he was not and never would be in love with me. I was cold and shaky, skating on the surface of my being. Thoughts and images of Dad forced their way in and out of my mind. It was too disturbing to think of him for long.

That left me looking at Luke. What did we really have together after three years? I was determined to fix us. In the dog days of August, most Boston and New York therapists famously adjourned to the town of Wellfleet on Cape Cod. Dr. Registein was among them. Even Reuben was gone, although he didn't say where. I had a feeling he didn't socialize with most of his Harvard peers. As patients we were forced to get along without therapists and try hard to have fun on our own vacations. I imagined they all hoped we wouldn't call them.

Money was tight for Luke and me, so we planned a camping trip to Nova Scotia in our '50 Desoto. It was a hopeful sign when he agreed to do something together. We bought some new camping gear – a pup tent, sleeping bags to replace the old ones from our time in Mexico, and Boy Scout cooking gear. We headed north.

After endless thick forests in Maine Luke commented on all the open land as we drove through New Brunswick and crossed the border into southern Nova Scotia. All I saw was empty space. Land so bleak that it felt desolate with the wind blowing across purple and brown moors that stretched all the way from the road down to a cold sea. My heart sank. We'd chosen the wrong country. Nova Scotia refused to hold us. It was a BYH land: bring your own happiness.

The food was as bleak as the landscape, mostly fishcakes or Hodgepodge which was overcooked potatoes, turnips, carrots, and peas in a smoky bacon cream sauce. Luke usually ordered both, but we didn't want either one.

It was a long drive to Cape Breton, our destination in the northern most point of Nova Scotia. The Cape was stark and striking with thick stands of dark pines, clear fast running streams alongside narrow winding roads. It was lonely country, as if time had passed it by and gone on to more promising places.

Luke and I stopped at the first seaside campground we saw and set up our pup tent on the beach. We raced against the dark. The ocean was black as coal except for the white caps of the crashing waves. We took off our pants, keeping sweatshirts and socks on, and climbed into our bags, tired from ten hours of driving.

I hoped something would happen between us, some spark from the cold sea air, but no. Luke gave me a quick kiss goodnight and turned his back to me.

I didn't know how long I'd been asleep, but I was woken up by the sound of a woman crying out. As I listened, it became apparent that she was not in pain, but in pleasure that seemed to rise and rise as she grew increasingly excited until she let out a scream. I tossed and turned for the rest of the night.

***

On the last day of our vacation, we drove up to Cape Breton's highest point, winding up and down the narrow highway over mountains rounded and worn with age. We parked the Desoto at a lookout and ate an early lunch of Jarlsberg cheese and crackers with apple cider. We stared at the valley below, pretending to share an awesome sight.

Luke said we should head down if we wanted to have any chance of getting home to Cambridge before dark. I said fine. At this point who cared when we got back? Let's just get out of this sad place that called itself a country. We began the descent.

"Ah Jesus," Luke said, as we rounded a sharp curve. "I have no brakes."

As he pumped the pedal it went to the floor. The Desoto was running away with us. She was so heavy that we picked up momentum quickly. His hands were white on the steering wheel as if trying to slow us down with his bare strength. The car went faster and faster as we tumbled down the mountain road.

"I want to get out. Let me out," I said.

"Ali, shut up."

Luke was clutching, down shifting, clutching, but we continued to roll faster and faster. I saw the headline in a Boston newspaper: *Young couple on idyllic romantic holiday in Nova Scotia drive off mountain cliff in fatal accident.* No one would know the truth.

"Do something," I screamed. "Oh god."

Luke grabbed the emergency brake in the center console and pulled it up slightly. Later he admitted he'd never used it before and didn't know if it worked. We felt the car respond but we continued to roll like a barrel down the hill. Luke had his right hand on the hand brake and his left hand navigating the hairpin turns. I put my head down and covered my eyes. Dad always told me I was useless in a crisis.

Luke pulled the brake up a little at a time until the car miraculously began to slow down. He pulled it further up and up until it was completely engaged. We continued to roll but we were approaching the bottom of the decline. Several hundred yards later we coasted to a stop with the smell of burning rubber. Luke pulled over, put his head back and let out a long breath that filled his cheeks.

"That was a close one," he said.

Even the car had turned against us.

"We'll get them checked when we get back." He looked over at me and frowned. "Next time, don't try to bail out in the middle of an emergency."

"Sorry," I said.

It was a perfect ending to a bad trip. It seemed like everything in my life was falling apart. Reuben didn't love me in any special way. I couldn't look at Father, much less get him to speak to me.

And Luke.

I had to make things better with Luke. I had to. He was all I had left.

18

SEMPER FIDELIS

Reuben arranged to meet me at the T stop in Harvard Square and walk up Cambridge Street to the hospital where he was presenting a case to the psychiatric staff at the weekly Grand Rounds.

As we walked along Harvard Street, he told me the Harvard cabal considered him to be a brilliant kook. A wonderful consequence of my nascent plan to become a Reichian therapist was that Reuben thought of me as a student as well as a patient. “Tell me how I do,” he said with a mischievous glint in his eyes.

Cambridge City was a teaching hospital and the auditorium was packed with psychiatric residents, psychiatrists, and staff. The psychiatrists were lockstep loyal to Freud. In their tweed suits, brown wingtips, and tortoise shell glasses, they represented the kind of man I couldn’t stand, aloof and cerebral. They considered Reich to be a traitor to psychoanalysis.

Reuben told me there would only be a handful of women scattered among the men, one or two of them psychiatrists, and the others nurses.

We entered an amphitheater-style auditorium with banks of seats surrounding a small dais. It was crowded that morning. A circus atmosphere pervaded as if we were about to witness a high-wire act with no net and the audience half expecting but never admitting wanting the performer to slip and fall to his death. The auditorium quieted as Reuben walked up to the front and took his place behind the microphone. He wore a dark suit jacket with gray flannels. I noticed his bright white shirt, probably ironed by his wife, was already untucked and his tie was crooked. I wanted to run to the stage and neaten him up.

Reuben looked out at the audience, smiled, and thanked everyone for coming. He said it wasn't often that Harvard Medical School opened its doors to alternative thought.

I admired how cleverly he presented himself, how he cajoled them while simultaneously giving a little poke. He was used to being in this position, proud of being an outsider. He joked how lucky he was to have their sincere attention. He sounded breathless.

Some mild laughter followed. Reuben was self-deprecating, even apologetic, but he became acutely definitive as he laid out systematically the way Reichian theory advanced Freud's thinking. I watched a relentless condescending grilling coming from the audience.

"So, you're actually attributing the resolution of this woman's melancholia to her expanded chest," one psychiatrist questioned in mock seriousness.

Right, you idiot. I knew from my own experience that sadness was often buried in the chest and I'd learned about melancholia, a kind of depression that could become intractable from an untreated grief.

"I'm sure it did expand with your hand on it," another called out, as they all snickered.

I glared at the cocky young doctor who obviously knew nothing about Reich, and worse, had no curiosity to learn. The Freudians were a bunch of talking heads, like Luke's first therapist. Anything to do with the body or the idea of energy terrified them. Reuben encouraged them to look at the patient as a whole person, a microcosm of a universal macrocosm, all sharing the same life energy.

As they continued to mock him, I leapt up inside and imagined myself yelling at them to shut their arrogant mouths.

Dad would have felt the same way. He taught me to protect the underdog. My parents gave me *The Diary of Anne Frank* for my eleventh birthday. Her story settled like lead in my stomach as I felt the terror Anne endured while her family hid in their little attic. I didn't make the direct connection to the nights I hid in the dark at the top of the stairs while Dad raged below. Life was black and white for Dad, and so it was for me. There was a lot of evil in the world, Dad had told me. While Reuben's family was German and had mostly escaped the Holocaust, suffering was part of his soul. Dad and Reuben would have a lot in common.

After his talk, we walked back to the Harvard Square train.

"Reich had a term for those doctors in there." He seemed weary, his feet scuffling along the sidewalk. "He called it the *Plague*; the need people have to destroy whatever threatens them. They drove Reich right to the edge in the 50's. The FDA harassed him and pursued him for years, until they got him."

Reuben's head dropped as he thought about an odd invention causing so much suspicion. "I've always believed he died from a broken heart."

"That's a tragedy," I said.

"That's the Plague."

I wondered if Reuben's heart might have been broken, but I didn't know how. He coughed and coughed. I could hear the phlegm trapped in his chest. And he lit another cigarette.

"You've got to stop smoking, Reuben."

I thought of Dad and his whiskey. I used to ferret out his stash stuffed beneath the dirty clothes in the laundry hamper, cooling in the toilet tank, hidden behind Winston Churchill's book *The Gathering Storm*. I emptied bottles down the drain thinking because he couldn't see me, he wouldn't discover I'd done it. He never said a thing about it.

"You're absolutely right," Reuben said, as he took a long drag and then stamped on the butt.

He was as loyal to Reich as I was to Father. It was no wonder that he understood how torn I felt.

***

Shortly after the Grand Rounds at Cambridge City, Luke and I sat eating supper at our newly constructed kitchen table. Luke had found a discarded electrical spool. We used a wine barrel as a pedestal. We bought two stools. The tabletop tended toward splinters and it collected crumbs in its ridges.

“Society is filled with the Plague,” I said, making conversation. “Vietnam, Civil Rights, feminism, it’s all about resisting the Plague. That’s how Reich describes it, you know.”

The Plague was a helpful way of looking at everything in the world that made me angry.

“Yeah, I know Al, Velma talks about the same thing.”

Velma was a young Reichian therapist Harold referred Luke to. Luke was becoming more articulate about his feelings. Finally, he had a therapist who talked to him instead of remaining silent.

Ironically, it didn’t work in my favor.

“Velma says the Plague is also in all of us, in our negativity,” Luke said.

It grew ominously quiet except for the clinking of our forks as we idly pushed our rice and beans around our plates.

“This isn’t working Ali,” he said. “I don’t think I can do it anymore.”

He spoke looking down at the plate. Our orange tiger cat Willy rubbed up against my calves and I reached down to run my hand along his back as my throat dropped into my belly. I couldn’t have heard him correctly.

“Can’t do what?”

“Us,” he said. He looked at me with his forehead furled, his eyes sad.

“Oh, come on, Luke, you can’t do this to me again.”

Just like in Mexico the bottom of me was falling out.

"I've found an apartment. On Inman Street. I can move in at the end of the month."

"That's the day after tomorrow! You went behind my back!"

My supper rose up into my throat. He'd ambushed me, no time to protect myself. "You traitor. I hate you," I screamed. "Hate you! Bastard!" I spit the words out.

I threw my plate, the sound of stoneware bouncing and shattering on the floor. Willie tore out of the kitchen with his ears back.

I threw a wooden serving spoon at Luke. He put his arms up and ducked. "Jesus, Al. Watch out."

"I fucking hate you! I hate you!" I pounded my fist on the table. The spool jiggled on its base.

"I'm really sorry. I need to be on my own. And we're on a sinking ship, Al."

"That doesn't mean you get to jump overboard like a rat." I shook from head to toe. I sputtered, "You are unbelievable."

Luke came over toward me with his arms open.

"Get the fuck away from me," I screamed. "I never want to see you again. Ever."

He was always kind, even as he was rejecting me. It made me feel pathetic, as if I was something delicate that could shatter, and he had to take care of me in order to abandon me. As he treated me with respect, I only felt more humiliated. He went into the bedroom and shut the door carefully.

"Come back here. I'm still talking to you!" I yelled.

I couldn't control anything. Luke had more energy than he'd had in months and he was turning against me. I put my head down into my arms on the table and wept.

***

I woke up bleary eyed at daylight having lain awake most of the night in a fury of hot rage about the way he'd been sneaking around. He should have kept me up to date on his plans for leaving. He was giving up on us, on me. What was I going to do all by myself?

I lay in bed and watched him packing his clothes, unable to grasp that he was really leaving. He took some old newspaper and wrapped the antiques he had bought on his sales route. The Asian dishes, a Japanese tea set, an Indian pipe. All the beauty was leaving with him.

I began to shake. "When am I going to see you again?"

"I don't know, Al, I can't say."

His head was down, carefully folding his clothes and laying them in a suitcase. I dressed quickly, wondering who would get Willie. The doorbell rang. I'd forgotten Harold was picking me up to make plans for his next workshop. He stood at the bottom of the stairs looking up while Luke looked down at him, scowling.

Over the past months a thick layer of tension had grown between them covering over a cursory politeness. I felt it but did nothing about it, either by reassuring Luke or making a boundary with Harold. I'd been enjoying the competition. Being desired made me feel more of a woman. I had something to offer, something of value.

They had nothing to say to each other. I looked down at Harold and stood in the hall with Luke. It was too little too late. Luke put his arms around me. He held me tight. I didn't want to let go. He pulled my arms off him and held my hands as he kissed my forehead. I was crying as I went downstairs and got into Harold's car. I told him Luke was moving out. Harold said he was sorry, but I thought he looked pleased.

LESSON FOUR:

FOR NOW, YOU SEE THROUGH A GLASS DARKLY

19
THINK LIKE A MAN

I woke up, looked around the room and froze in place remembering I was alone. When I rolled onto my side, the bed creaked its warning sounds of impending collapse. My heart pumped hard and fast. Captain—the mixed breed hound perpetually chained outside—was already at work in the back yard, barking his loneliness and frustration.

Breathe in, breathe out.

Luke was across town in his new apartment with his new roommates.

Are any of them women?

I pictured him happy and busy without me. His parting words were, "Better if we didn't talk for a while."

How long was a while?

I lay back down and lit a cigarette. Marlboro Lights had given way to Benson and Hedges, the extra-long cigarettes with an elegant woman advertising them. The V of my fingers and the bend in my wrist as I held my cigarette didn't make them taste any better. I'd painted my bedroom floor Tibetan orange, hoping the Buddhist color might give me enough courage to get myself up in the morning. I squished the butt into the ashtray by my bedside. The ashtray smelled like some bad night before. I rolled out of bed and put my feet on the cold floor. A zafu waited at the foot of the bed. I positioned myself cross legged on the pillow to meditate.

I tried to breathe. Captain barked and barked.

Help, please help me.

I couldn't get enough air and the pressure on my chest filled me with dread. My anxieties were a secret I kept, even from Reuben.

***

A pal of mine moved in and took the extra room. We had things in common, boyfriends who came and went, heartbreak that left us each crying in our rooms. It made me feel better when I heard Janet crying too. "This sucks," we agreed.

Janet was a graphic artist drawing all the newspaper ads for Gilchrist's department store. She brought home delicious oversized chewy macaroons in wax paper slips that Gilchrist was famous for. I continued to work lunches and Sunday brunch at the restaurant, while writing my master's thesis on the psychological components of epilepsy. I remained a mystery to myself and I thought my seizures held a clue.

We ate our suppers together, although I did most of the eating. I would never have thought of mushrooms on toast. They tasted delicious. It was also one of the few things Janet would cook, much less eat. "Especially sautéed in a lot of butter," she said. After Luke left eating became my favorite past time.

"You eat like a little bird, Janet."

"I don't feel like eating since Alan and I broke up."

Janet didn't eat when she had a new boyfriend either. When Buddy came along, she was too excited. She collected boyfriends and when she left them, she kept them on as friends who functioned as advisors for the new boyfriend. She had long red hair and a readiness for sex. Janet was an inspiration to me.

"I should practice my powers of seduction," I said. There had to be some technique besides a Daffy Duck imitation. I wanted to learn to think how a man would think, that is, who could I seduce and how little could I care?

"Let's go on a hunt together!" Janet said.

She needed to cement her relationship with Buddy. And she'd ask her pal Larry for me.

We'd make dinner. Or rather, I'd make dinner. I had a gourmet recipe from The Window Shop on Brattle Street. The restaurant opened in 1939 to assist Germans and Austrian immigrants fleeing Hitler and was now run by Hungarian refugees from the 1956 rebellion against Russia. (Reuben's wife was a refugee from Hungary; she was very sophisticated). The chicken Marengo was the most elegant dish I'd ever eaten, calling for mushrooms, black olives, and white wine.

"Good idea, Al, we'll serve the guys a meal, plenty of wine and then we'll go in for the kill."

***

I was not a hunter of men by nature. I needed a glass of wine before the guys arrived. Buddy came first. He was droll giving every statement a funny twist. Larry arrived a little late. I'd already had a second glass of wine. He was a friend from Janet's teen years, sweet with frightened eyes and a broad smile. He seemed blissfully unaware that I was gunning for him. It felt like I was taking advantage of a minor. We laughed a lot at dinner, Janet was fun when she drank. We discussed Tibetan Buddhism.

"Trungpa is a big drinker, I hear," I said.

Trungpa Rinpoche had moved on to a larger audience since Luke and I saw him at the yoga studio. He was in the process of establishing Naropa University, a spiritual school in Boulder that combined Eastern wisdom with Western scholarship.

"God. They all end up being drunks, don't they? Or claiming to be celibate while having sex with their disciples," Janet said. "I still want a guru, though. I really think enlightenment is possible."

"I'll drink to that," I said as I drained my third glass of wine and poured a fourth with a big splash. "Woops. My cup runneth over."

"Enlightenment is all the rage now," Buddy said. "Good food someone cooked. I know it wasn't Janet."

"I know Trungpa's got troubles, but he's a wise man even so," Larry said. "Look how cool his writing is."

"I painted my floors Tibetan orange in his honor. Want to see them?" I asked. It was important to seize the moment.

"Sure," Larry said.

He had no idea what was about to happen. Janet's eyes moved back and forth from me to my bedroom, egging me on. Wine spilled from my glass as I led him into my room.

I sat down on my bed, my wine glass in one hand, patting the space next to me for Larry with the other hand. I was moving like a hot knife through butter, although I had a little worry about the bed collapsing when we had sex, which—my confidence had soared—was imminent.

"I like that color," Larry said, looking at the floors.

He seemed a little dazed and stared at the orange floor instead of me. He wasn't going with the program. I sidled up a little closer so that our thighs were touching. Usually that gave a guy the green light.

"How's your meditation practice going?" Larry asked.

I turned to look at him and noticed the room was starting to move around him, like a merry-go-round as it starts off slowly, gradually picking up speed. I leaned back as the room began to spin. My head was whirling. I patted Larry's knee and put one finger in the air.

"Give me a quick minute," I said. A trip to the bathroom. When I got up, I threw up. Yellow vomit all over the bed, splattered onto the orange floor.

"Jeez," Larry jumped up. "I'll get some paper towels."

It was the most excited he'd been all night. He rushed out of the room.

"No, no, I'll clean up," I called, although I could barely stand up.

"Don't worry about it," he said.

I was too embarrassed to look at him while he helped me cleanup, a sour expression on his face as he tried not to breathe. He seemed relieved when he said good night. The evening was a letdown for me, but Janet had possessed her next boyfriend, Buddy. I told her I wasn't really attracted to Larry anyway.

***

"Don't give up, Al," Janet said, a couple weeks later, as I packed my bag for the Goddard Symposium. "Think of all the possible guys who will be there looking to have fun,"

Twice a year, graduate students gathered for individual sessions with our advisors and to meet the classmates we never got to see because Goddard was primarily a *university without walls*. The students came from all over, having created alternative programs to earn a master's degree.

Thinking about being trapped at Goddard with all those new people made my heart pound, but I had to go because I had a meeting scheduled with my advisor. I drove to Plainfield, Vermont, in Janet's car. The college had a funky campus looking out over a bucolic vista of rolling farmland, Vermont's special summer beauty.

The first evening was a kind of meet and greet, with about one-hundred grad students crowded into a gymnasium, milling around, introducing ourselves to each other. A feverish excitement hovered in the air. The students were like hawks flying around scouting for prey, although that might have only been me. Bouncing from one person to another was infectious. Then I bumped into a guy who was electric. He looked like he'd found gold.

"Hey!" I said, looking back at him. I was burning up. "I'm Ali. Is it hot in here?"

He pulled his head back and took another look. "Hey to you, I'm Judah."

Judah's wild wooly hair looked like he'd lost his comb and didn't care. His smile was crooked, and his clothes were stained with all colors of paint.

"So, what are you studying?" I was fishing, like Janet had coached me, my pole back, my line thrown out into the water.

Judah was a painter on campus for a few weeks finishing his portfolio.

We stared at each other and made funny faces and started giggling. And me? I told him I was studying Wilhelm Reich. *The Function of the Orgasm*. He nodded. We couldn't stop laughing. I wasn't sure if he knew who Reich was, but he certainly got the part about the orgasm, not that I'd had one recently.

"I'd be interested in seeing your etchings," I said, grinning.

He threw his head back and laughed. Okay, okay, he told me to follow him. I'd caught him and he was flopping helplessly on the deck. We left the gym for a brisk walk across the campus to his dorm room. I briefly admired the wild murky abstract paintings that lined the walls of his studio, although they were muddy and ugly. All I liked so far in the art world was Salvador Dali and the Impressionists. We waded through piles of dirty underwear and socks. Everything stank of turpentine.

He tossed some sketches off the bed and we lay down on his dirty sheets. We couldn't get our clothes off fast enough. Even his underwear had paint stains. He climbed on top of me as if I was a horse and we were about to gallop away together. The sex was so fast and frantic that I was left behind, but fun because we were both so excited.

We repeated ourselves as soon as we woke up the following morning and that was slower, better, I could keep pace.

"Let's go for a swim," he said afterward.

We got dressed and walked to a quarry where we swam in deep cold green water. We had sex high up on the rocks by the quarry where we spent the day sunning naked and skinny-dipping, even though there were people down below who had us in full sight. I could have been playing marbles or jacks. It was plain old fun. We had happy sex back on his dirty sheets again that night. I thought how much fun I was having, reassuring myself that being with Luke before he left me had been no fun at all. Judah was so much fun in fact, that I almost forgot my advisor meeting.

At the end of the weekend, we made plans to see each when he got back to Philadelphia or, I said, he could visit me in Cambridge. But that wasn't the point; it had already been a successful weekend for me. My confidence level had soared.

It wasn't so bad being alone.

But I was very sore.

20
A DARK BLANKET

I waited upstairs in my apartment looking out the window for Mother's car to come down Kinnaird Street.

Before Luke moved out, I'd invited my parents for dinner to cook for them and show off our new apartment. They refused. They had no problem visiting my brother and his wife, but a clear *no* followed my invitation. We weren't married. I'd mentioned the idea of marriage to them sometime after we left the Farm. They answered with a stony silence. Luke and I gave up.

"You're wearing that awful scent again, Alicia," Mum said as I got into the car.

"It's the Patchouli still in my clothes, Mum, I can't help it."

"Is this a safe neighborhood? I saw some unsavory types as I turned down your street."

"Leaves a bad taste in your mouth, huh?"

I rolled my eyes and resigned myself to a long day as we drove out of the city. A day familiar in the way old shoes fit when all the support is worn down. Mum seemed stuck on the surface of all things, the way they smelled, the way they appeared, the way other people might see them.

I didn't tell her that Luke had left me. I was afraid of her lack of sympathy.

The house was like a museum when I walked in. Quiet and still, nothing to disturb its ordered beauty. Nothing except me.

Mother wore a sleeveless vest inside. 1973's OPEC oil embargo had raised oil prices sharply. She told me they kept warm in the print room where Dad always made a fire. As far as I was concerned, the house would never be warm again after Nanny died.

In the summer of 1960 when I was fourteen, we returned to Massachusetts from Pennsylvania, hoping to live with Nanny again. Dad's attempts at a new life had failed. Seven more years of drinking left him unable to function and had lost him his job. I overheard my Aunt Edith speaking to my Mother before we left Lancaster. "I never thought I'd say this Eleanor, but maybe you need to think about divorcing George. God knows we've all tried to help him." I didn't hear Mum's response. Aunt Edith's words were too horrifying. No one I had ever known had divorced parents.

We had nowhere else to go and so we returned to Groton in shame, just as we had left Groton seven years before. I remember there was a house on Farmer's Row that we had arranged to rent so maybe my grandmother said, "No, you can't come here."

But unexpected coincided. We were in Chatham in our summer cottage. My bedroom was on the bottom floor below the first floor in one of two bedrooms lined with pine walls, damp, but with a smell that was comforting to me in that it was familiar. We played Canasta at night, we went crabbing early in the morning in Brewster's shoals, we bounced in the waves at Harding's beach when the wind was southwest, we ate three-D burgers at the Howard Johnson's on the rotary. Dad was drinking heavily. Nanny was with us stationed in a deckchair on the small terrace during the day in her navy-blue silk dress with white flowers. Her soft plump body and thick legs in matching espadrilles would have withstood a great wind. I kissed her when I left and again when I came back into the house.

Three things happened, in which order I don't remember: I had a bad seizure and wet the bed for the first time. Mum and Dad scheduled me for a spinal tap at Boston Children's. Dad began to get very sick and bleed internally. And Nanny developed Pneumonia, was admitted to the Cape hospital. I didn't even have the time to wonder when she'd come home; she died within a few days.

We left the Cape and returned to Nanny's house to prepare for her funeral. I went into the print room and stared at her empty chair. The house was filled with silence. Now we didn't have to rent; we could stay there, but what difference did it make? Nanny was gone. Mum and Dad bought the brothers' shares and the house became theirs.

But who cared? Without Nanny the house was a shell.

On the day of Nanny's funeral, Dad was in emergency surgery for cirrhosis and bleeding ulcers. I should have been more sympathetic to my Mother for all that she was suffering. But I felt only for myself. I had lost the one person who loved me without condition.

As I took my coat off, I looked across the wide hall to the library. I imagined a velvet museum rope cordoning it off unless you had a special pass. I followed Mum through the formal dining room and down the long narrow pantry, cabinets with beveled glass doors on both sides heavy with sets of hand painted dishes sent back by Great Aunt Eleanor from Shanghai in the early 1900's.

I stood in the kitchen with Mum while Dad came down by the back stairs to join us. He looked as he always did, held together by tweed and military manner. I inhaled his crisp after shave as I planted a dry kiss on his cheek. We sat down at the small table in the breakfast room. It was my first visit with Dad since the fiasco of his introduction to Luke six months before.

"Thanks for the money, Dad. It helps."

He nodded. Seventy dollars a month. "Until you finish school."

Dad had made a winter squash soup, rich with cream, and pieces of toasted buttered pita bread. He was a good cook and didn't need recipes. But my stomach was nervous. I dreaded a fight. We almost got through lunch without incident simply by avoiding Vietnam, Civil Rights, and Luke. I didn't say a word that Luke had left me. Dad would have said I told you so.

"Delicious soup, George," Mother said. She didn't compliment him often, but I knew she loved his cooking.

"Doc says I'm labile," Dad said.

"Uh hunh. What did he mean by that?"

"Well, my moods go up and down. He knows me. A good doctor."

I wondered for a brief second if he was trying to explain his behavior to me. If only we'd understood the true diagnosis which was confirmed many years later as bipolar hidden by alcoholism. It might have helped me be more sympathetic to him. Maybe labile was the best word available for what he experienced inside. Any of my friends who knew him agreed he was a lot more volatile than a little word like labile could encompass.

"That's good, Dad."

"Now. I know you don't want to hear this, but I'm going to say it anyway." His voice deepened and his mouth went into his neck. "You are going to be sorry if you stay with that young man. You don't know what he's after."

Mum was silent, her agreement with Dad unspoken.

A chill wind blew into my bones. After what?

"Come on, Dad," I sighed and shook my head. "I'm not stupid."

"No. But you're naïve. You don't know what he's really about."

I thought about one summer on the Cape when Dad had tried to come in between me and a guy he hadn't even met. It was as if he could smell my desire and said in a voice full of foreboding, "Beware of propinquity." I had to look up the word in the dictionary.

"He's not after anything except a relationship with me."

"He's taking advantage—"

"Of what? It's not like I have a trust fund. He's not after seventy dollars a month."

Mum shifted her weight in her chair. "I wish you'd go through your closet, Alicia, and see what you want to keep. I'm about to throw everything out."

Leave it to Mum to bring the conversation back to what was truly important. I already had my own thoughts that something was wrong with Luke and that was why he kept leaving me. I gave up. We cleared the table and I went upstairs.

The afternoon sun poured into my old bedroom flooding the dry air with yellow light. I could smell the lilacs outside my windows even though they weren't blooming yet. The soft blue and gray flowered wallpaper resonated with the scent that permeated my room every spring. The white mantel piece was still occupied with my china animal collection, the fireplace empty and clean. I picked up my old stuffed Snoopy dog that lay plopped across my pillow and held him in my arms for a moment. There was no difference between me and the room that I could ascertain. It was as if the boundaries of my body dissolved into that space and I should give up knowing anything more about myself.

I carried Snoopy downstairs. Mum and Dad were sitting in the print room by the fire. Mum was leafing through an issue of *Ladies' Home Journal*.

"That's all you can think of to take with you?" she said.

"That's all right now." All I knew how to do was disappoint her.

I looked at Father. "Dad." He took his eyes off his book and looked at me with some effort. "Dad, I can make up my own mind about Luke."

"It's my duty to warn you. You're making a big mistake and living with him is an even bigger mistake. A woman's reputation is all she has. There's such a thing as damaged goods you know."

Why bother defending Luke when he'd left me? Again!

"Beware the forbidden fruit," he said as I hugged him goodbye. He put a twenty-dollar bill into my hand in the same way that he'd sneak extra money in tipping a waitress, so that Mother wouldn't see. I knew why he gave waitresses money. Mum was Scotch and didn't believe in big tips. But sneaking money to me? I took it. I always took what Dad gave me, but there was a string attached, something like, *I will love you more but don't tell your Mother and do what I say.*

There was a time long ago, before I was ten, when I worshipped Dad and trusted him with my whole heart. We could be together, sit and talk about things that were too grown up for me, human suffering, and the War. I could love the loyal Marine and be his loyal lieutenant. I could keep him afloat. But his drinking and the bipolar illness I had no name for weighed on me. As my fear of him grew my heart had to hide.

***

I rode the Green Line out to Reuben's the next day. It was the first time I'd met with him so soon after seeing Father. I was heavy inside, moving only with effort through something thick and muddy, my new permanent altered state. No feelings, only a constant sensation of having to plow over something unnamed in order to get through a day. I lay down in the office, relieved for a moment to remain unconscious. Maybe Reuben would let me sleep. Was my therapy helping me? I felt worse off after every session. I closed my eyes.

"I want to go back to what we were discussing last week," I heard him say. "Let's think more about what you might be guarding against."

I yawned, squeezed my eyes, and scrunched my face trying to loosen my jaw, struggling to remain conscious. Reuben's eyes were on me. I lay still and silent for a moment. Reuben stayed patient.

"Dad's trying to get me to give up on Luke. For my own good he says."

"Right, I wonder how loyal he is to you."

I hadn't thought of that. I only knew my own loyalty.

"He doesn't want me to stay with Luke. But so what? Luke doesn't want to be with me anyway."

"What's happening in your body right now?"

"My jaw is clenching up."

I wrinkled the skin around my mouth, my teeth were aching. Reuben told me to growl, which I didn't want to do. It felt stupid. He put one arm in front of me with his fist clenched.

"Push," he said, "push against my arm," which I did. I heard myself growl, louder and louder until I was a cornered animal ready to attack. I was dangerous.

"Get away from me."

I was pretending for Reuben, but gradually, I wanted to yell. I was mad at everyone. I was being strangled, I told Reuben.

"Okay, who's strangling you," as he put a hand around my throat.

I couldn't breathe. Reuben was leaning with his other arm right up against my face.

"Get away. Back off," I yelled.

"Good. Louder."

"I hate you, Dad. You bastard."

His name slipped out. The sound grew louder, as if it wasn't coming from me. Father had me with a noose around my neck. My body began writhing on the bed. My legs kicked and slammed down on the mattress like they had a will of their own, and I couldn't do anything to stop them. My fists pummeled the air, my yells became screams for my young self at 7, at 10, at 20, for all the times I'd stuffed my terror and rage into a bottle's neck and corked it with shame.

"You don't deserve my love."

"Keep kicking, Ali, let it come out."

My head rolled from side to side, my jaw throbbing, my murderous teeth grinding as the sound threw itself up into my throat. I felt the heat rise in my body, into my torso, up into my throat, spitting bile.

"You're trying to scare me to death," I screamed.

My eyes opened wide.

"You don't love me."

I began to sob. My heart was shattering. In that moment I understood that what Dad was doing was for himself, not for me.

Only the pounding in my head made me stop. I rolled over on my side and looked up at Reuben. He sat back in the chair and nodded. He was with me. I was clammy and my underwear felt damp. The air smelled of old sweat, like rotten fumes from spoiled food that has been forgotten in the refrigerator.

"There's a fierce bite behind loyalty, if you feel betrayed," Reuben said.

"Yuck," I said. The room stinks. It's me. But I feel like I can breathe, like a weight has been lifted.

I was exhausted, like after a long battle, but I already knew there was more to come.

"I need to go home and shower."

***

I went back to the apartment, lay down for a moment. The room looked brighter the shapes more defined, the edges of the furniture sharper, the light clearer.

Therapy had pulled me deep down into a swamp of anger. Billy Goat Gruff, who I'd been afraid of as a child, had reached up and grabbed me from his hiding place beneath the bridge. Something had shifted. That night as I was trying to get to sleep, I remembered a dream that had repeated in my childhood. A tall man wearing a black morning coat, white gloves, and a white hat silently approached the piano in the library. I only saw him from the back. I never saw his face. The dream was filled with dread. My dark unknowable friend.

As I was dropping off to sleep the familiar heavy dark blanket of terror came over me, no thoughts, my jaw locking like an iron gate, slowly, steadily coming down on top of me, grinding shut… the aura that preceded my seizures. I woke up on the floor with Janet cradling my head.

"Oh Ali, oh god."

Spittle dripped down. "You scared me," Janet wiped my mouth. I'd wet myself.

"Sorry," I mumbled. "I should have told you what to do. I guess my seizures aren't over."

My seizure was too close to my visit with Dad and my session with Reuben. Even my master's thesis consisted of my theories about the roots of my seizures, why they began when I was nine, and what they meant. I used my own experience to study the direct relationship between mind and body.

For the first time, I saw the connection to Dad. I thought Dad could kill me. His own rage was that big. That crazy and wild. What I hadn't realized was that over time my rage had grown to be as big as his, as ugly, as threatening, but also as powerful.

21

THREADS OF CONNECTION

How was I supposed to have one-night stands with guys if there was a chance of me having a grand mal seizure while we were going to sleep? Potentially humiliating.

It was risky, but I was enjoying myself in a perverse sense of freedom by having mindless sex with men who meant nothing to me.

There was a guy I met in a Harvard Square bar. He had long wavy light brown hair and wore wire rimmed glasses. I had the idea that men with wire rimmed glasses were good, bright, and serious. We stood at the crowded bar side by side flirting, hardly able to hear each other over the other alcohol amped voices and throbbing music from the Rolling Stones. It was more of an inner experience. Did I even take a good look at his face? Did our eyes ever meet? I felt the whiskey sours heating my blood, I sensed his growing excitement, I was confident and certain where we were headed, enjoying the ride. Feeling my own power, getting that swelled head Mum had warned me against. Near closing time, we walked in loopy form from the bar to his apartment on Putnam Avenue, laughing at nothing. The sex was good enough and I was enjoying doing exactly what I'd been taught not to do.

The thing was, when I woke up in the morning and turned my head to look over at him, I thought, *who is this and what's my point?*

I met another guy on Commonwealth Avenue in Boston where I happened to be walking on a sunny afternoon and he happened to be riding by. We went on his motorcycle for a day trip into Vermont. We found a stream alongside a back road, rushing over mossy rocks with birch branches bending down low over the water. We bought oversized sandwiches at a general store nearby and sat eating them splashing our feet in the cold water. The simple beauty of the place pushed up against my regret. We seemed to agree that we had nothing to say to each other. We did have obligatory uncomfortable sex on the rocks, but I thought he seemed angry by the end, as if he knew we would never mean anything to each other.

Seduction was starting to feel more like a job than a hobby. "Don't you get tired of the hunt?" I said to Janet.

"Not really, it's always so promising."

Yes, but also disappointing.

***

I called my parents. When my mother picked up the phone I asked if I could come out and spend the night. She said, of course.

I'd been working on my feelings about Father in therapy, week after week. I'd been angry, sad, raging, sobbing, hurt, guilty, always exhausted after a session, wondering if my injured self was a bottomless pit of pain that would never heal. I wasn't sure what I wanted from Mum and Dad, and I told myself I didn't expect much.

I took the commuter rail out to Ayer, a dreary outpost of a town with a small army base. She was waiting for me at the station lot.

We drove along Farmer's Row, a stretch of road with lovely New England homes, blue hills off to the west, then passed Groton School where the air always seemed thinner.

"I had a seizure the other night," I said.

"I thought you were over that," Mum said.

"Well, I'm not."

That was the end of that conversation. As I said, I'm not sure what I expected. I wondered what it had been like for them when they saw me convulsing. They never said and I never asked. I wonder now if they were ashamed. Although they never said I couldn't speak about it, my epilepsy was our secret.

"How's Dad?"

"Fine."

Jeez. So far, nothing coming my way. Why bother? Mum pulled the car up at the kitchen door where the purple and yellow pansies planted twenty years before by my grandmother persisted in blooming every spring. I used to think of them as clueless, the way they popped up so blithely cheerful with no idea what was really going on inside the house. I took my bag up the back stairs to my room and then I went out through the library for a walk before supper.

At the far end of the library three sets of French doors opened onto a stone path that wound around the back and side perimeter of the house. A set of wide granite steps, cracked and irregular, went downhill bordered by snow drops in the early spring snow and now by trailing English ivy. The steps led down from the stone path to a white arched gate that opened onto the remains of a formal garden. A stone angel with a few chunks of her wings broken off sat on a pedestal reaching up from the ruins in the center of the overgrown area. Spring crocuses surrounded her, persisting even after years of neglect.

At the end of the garden directly opposite the gate, was an identical archway with an arbor thickly covered with Concord grapes and benches on either side. Mother used to sit there with her dog when she was young. I sat down and tried to imagine her, ten years old and alone, her Father languishing on the sofa in the library dying of Bright's disease, the name for kidney failure back then. A hole bore into the pit of my belly. Her dog Dukie, sitting at her feet, her hand gently scratching his head while she stared off. There was a convent next door and from her post under the arbor she peeked unseen through the hedgerow and watched the nuns playing baseball, shouting and running the bases while holding up their long black habits. The power of the past was as present as anything that was happening in our family now.

I climbed back up the granite steps and circled the house on the path until I came to the kitchen door. Mum was baking pork chops covered with tomatoes and sautéed onions. She wasn't a gourmet cook, but I liked her food. Dad was quiet at dinner, even pensive as we watched the American exodus from Vietnam on TV, the frantic scrambling to get on the planes, the scenes of desperate women and children begging the soldiers to take them. All the men who'd acquired Vietnamese wives during the long war and then left them behind. We were witnessing a funeral for the death of a country.

"Those poor people," I said.

"We should never have been there in the first place," Dad said. "We can't even take care of our own."

I couldn't believe my ears. We were agreeing. I stayed quiet.

"I've got a guy at work who's in trouble," Dad said.

Father had a personnel job with the Defense Department, his first job in seven years after cirrhosis. Money left by my grandmother's death supported him during those years of sickness and recovery.

"What's wrong?" I asked.

"Alcohol," Dad said. "I hate to fire him. Poor guy."

I couldn't remember Dad and I having an adult conversation.

And it wasn't a fight.

It was about real things.

I recognized the familiar sorrow that lay at the bottom of his alcoholic well. Only now he was feeling it for another human being. I loved him for that. Yet one week ago in therapy I hated Dad and wanted to kill him.

"You're not eating much, George," I said.

I had never used his first name before. He didn't blink an eye. Who was I to him? And who was he for me? I tried to step back and see Dad, but my eyes remained clouded.

He had a bowl of canned peaches in heavy syrup and some saltines on a small plate.

"Not much of an appetite," he said.

I took that to mean Mum and I should be concerned. Dad depended on us worrying for him.

After clearing the table, I went upstairs early to read. It had been a long time since I'd slept in my virginal bed. It was narrow and high off the floor. I felt the old family tug on my heart. Dad's pull was stronger than Luke's, stronger than any man. It only required a few kind words from Father to reel me back in. It was as if I knew him in some other way, some other time, as if I'd always known him, and there wasn't any room for Luke, or any man other than a superficial meeting.

The next morning at breakfast, Mum and I sat watching the yellow finches and chickadees at the feeder as we ate our soft-boiled eggs and English muffins with bitter orange marmalade.

"Nanny loved the birds," Mum said.

"I remember."

Breakfast took a long time. Mum ate slowly and there were many cups of coffee to be had.

"You can come with us to the Groton Woods to walk," she said. "We'll take the rhododendron path. They should all be in bloom by now."

The three of us walked quiet and steady in the woods by the Nashua River, companions admiring the generous pink and white blossoms on either side of the path. I could see myself between them, each of my hands in theirs. We continued down along the river as far as the Groton School boathouse and then turned around. They took that walk every day, but today Dad was a little winded.

We had a small lunch and Mother drove me to the station. We hugged goodbye. I was okay with them. I was safe again.

***

The following week, Mother asked me to go to a concert with her. Mum and Dad had season tickets for the Boston Symphony in Row D where old doyennes sat with elderly husbands who slumped down in their seats and nodded off by the second movement. Mum said Father didn't feel well. We had lunch together in the Colonnade Hotel. I told her Luke and I had split up. She took a sip of her Dubonnet on the rocks, looked at me straight on, and said she was sorry. She told me that when she was my age a boyfriend had left her, and she had lain on the guest room bed and cried for twenty-four hours.

"I know how that feels," I said.

It was a fleeting moment with Mother. She landed near me ever so briefly.

I cried during the Emperor Concerto's adagio. Its tenderness, like the ache in my heart, like an ache Mother once had.

22

DON'T FENCE ME IN

I rode in a van with seven other mental health workers out from Cambridge City Hospital to Westborough State for our initial visit to its inpatient chronic ward.

For my first job in mental health I joined the Ambulatory Community Service, an innovative project to empty out the state mental hospitals. I was ready to get to work, to help the people who needed it. In fact, I'd been ready six years earlier when I graduated from college and became a member of the Teacher Corps. I was placed in the Detroit ghetto soon after the riots of 1967 and nothing had gone as planned. The black community resented all the young white do-gooders with our unconscious white guilt and worse, we were paid almost nothing to replace black teachers. However well intended, we were used. I hoped that the Westborough patients would be grateful to get their lives back after their long hospital imprisonment. I sat in the back anticipating using newly acquired psychiatric tools like empathy and attentive listening to help people who'd been dumped into institutions so long ago. My blond hair was cut very short and close to my head. I was thin, dressed in bell bottoms, but conservative bell bottoms- no embroidery or hip hugging waist. I had a white cotton scoop necked blouse that reached below my hips and a long necklace with African beads that I'd made in a make it yourself shop. I thought I looked presentable and yet still myself.

We turned off the highway and entered through high, wrought iron gates onto a long straight narrow drive lined with high dark pines. A spooky castle-like building that looked like it had been built in Jane Eyre's time sat on lovely mowed grounds apart from the outside world. I thought of Mr. Rochester's wife Bertha locked in the rear wing upstairs, cut off from the rest of the house and the world, raving in a hopeless madness.

I don't know why I assumed the patients would be thankful for our intervention. In recent weeks I'd been feeling kind of cocky. Most weekends I was in training workshops run by men who were like celebrities in the world of body workers, and I was a star. Various leaders and participants alike praised me for my openness and emotional depth. In groups, I was often the catalyst for others to break down and open to their feelings.

Other than winning sprints as a young girl because of my long legs, emoting was the first thing I was good at and it gave me some confidence. Even if I got bad headaches after each cathartic explosion, I thought the praise from others made it worthwhile. And it was new to me to be special, although I had to remain vigilant not to get cocky.

And then there were all the random men I'd picked up under my spell.

On top of all that, I'd completed my master's degree and had a job in my field.

It was all promising.

***

The resident psychiatrist came out to meet us. She was young and striking. I noticed she drove a ritzy Datsun 240Z, which told me she made a lot more money than our minimum wage. She led us through thick wooden doors, down a low-ceilinged hall opening upon another set of doors onto the chronic schizophrenic unit where heavy metal doors closed automatically and locked behind us with a finality.

As we walked down the corridor between walls painted a flat nauseous green, a sickly musty smell entered my nostrils and stayed there. I wanted to gulp in air, but when I breathed it was toxic. I felt woozy. We weaved in between patients aimlessly slogging with their sad jerking gait, the trembling movement of the chronically overmedicated. Nurses carried medicine on trays like efficient waitresses, dispensing the thick orange antipsychotic liquid in tiny pleated paper cups to those patients sitting on the floor and hugging the walls. Other men and women sat slumped in chairs with their heads down and chests concave in front of a TV no one was watching. These were the patients who were docile enough to exist in the halls, the ones we'd be liberating. Orderlies popped in and out of individual rooms with closed doors that I had no desire to open. Each door had one small window at the top for the staff to peek in on the patients without having to go inside.

The psychiatrist gave us a lengthy introduction to the unit followed by a pep talk (we could feel proud of what we were doing) and the appointment of our patient groups. We adjourned to have lunch in the cafeteria. The food tasted like the hospital smelled. I gagged on the blond asparagus that came from a jar and the creamed something or other. What was it like to be stuck there for years? It could have been Dad if we hadn't pretended there was nothing wrong with him. No cleanser, no disinfectant could mask the odor of hopelessness that permeated the unit.

After lunch we were each given a room to meet with our prospective groups. I entered a small windowless space, its odor like my idea of a Motel 6 room with carpets holding the dead smoke of lonely traveling salesmen. My six patients had been coaxed into a circle waiting to meet me. My first therapy group ever!

I felt shaky, my body tingling. Six seemed like a manageable number.

"Good-afternoon." I smiled a new therapist's smile, trying to appear as warm, positive, and unflappable as possible. I looked directly at each person. No one had cautioned me that making direct eye contact constituted a major threat. Three of the six turned their chairs and faces to the wall. The other three stared blankly, one man with his head down, spittle running down his chin. Everyone did their best to avoid looking at anyone else.

Our team was to spend two days a week getting to know our groups in order to prepare them for the world of 1974 in Cambridge, Massachusetts. I told my group we'd become acquainted in the hospital before they were released and then I'd support them in relearning how to live in their hometown of so many years past. Things had changed since the 40's and 50's. I couldn't explain exactly how they'd changed but we'd adjust together. I felt like a miracle worker.

As I talked, a fourth woman turned and faced the wall. Legs jiggled causing the chairs to bounce on the linoleum floor. A man tapped his chair with a pencil. Smoke hung heavy in the dank room. There was some talking in the group. I was heartened until I realized they were not talking to me or to each other. They were talking to themselves. I'd read a lot of material on schizophrenia, but it startled me. It was as if I wasn't in the room or was speaking to the walls.

I already had my own problems about claiming any ground for myself. I felt like I was disappearing. I wished I'd been given a few pointers as to how to talk to people who were so severely withdrawn into their own world. They might have been frightened by me or were hearing competing voices in their own heads or were simply unable to concentrate on what I was saying. In RD Laing's book *The Divided Self* he claimed to understand the schizophrenic mind and how to reach them with empathy, but his method of stripping naked and rocking in order to mirror one of his patients was frightening.

I plowed ahead and said I'd be helping them finding an apartment or room of their own. Maybe the women would welcome the freedom I was supposed to offer them. Maybe they only needed an escape hatch, like I did. Virginia Wolfe's *A Room of One's Own* was the first book that gave me any hope about becoming an independent woman. But no one in my group looked at all excited.

We'd go to a grocery store, I said, and I'd show them how to shop. That didn't go anywhere either.

I caught one man's eyes and he jerked his head away. His shoulders froze and his head shook, as if he'd seen a vampire. My confidence slid down from a ten to a three. They were Rip Van Winkles, long asleep, on the precipice of a dangerous awakening. It felt mean. I couldn't tolerate any more.

"Okay!" I chirped and said, "That's it for today. Thanks for coming!"

The meeting, scheduled for half an hour, had lasted twelve minutes. My patients remained immobilized in their chairs, some continuing to mumble to themselves as I flew out of the room. I retreated to the nurse's station, the long crescent shaped desk behind a glass partition where the sane could take shelter from the insane. I was suddenly overcome with exhaustion and put my head down on the table.

"Wake up, Alicia," one team member said, with a gentle hand on my shoulder. "We've got team meeting."

I lifted my head, thick and dizzy, and said, "I couldn't even get their attention."

My co-worker told me he couldn't get his patients into the room and one had to be taken to solitary. What had I gotten myself into?

When I got home at the end of the day, Janet said that there was a message from Luke. My heart knotted. Six months had passed, so long that he was safely stored in the back of my mind. When I listened to the message, I heard excitement and determination in his voice. It made me laugh, an angry little laugh, like Mother's. All of a sudden, *I* was supposed to call *him*? There were more flings to be had, more guys to meet in bars or pick up on the street. And there was nothing to lose. I could do whatever I wanted to do.

"What do you mean, *what should I do*? Call him back." Janet snapped her fingers. "Right away. Check it out."

"I don't trust him."

Janet shook her head. "Sometimes I think you were born with a gene missing, Ali. That's not the point. He must want something."

Yes, but what did I want?

I didn't tell Janet or any of my friends that I'd casually ambled by Luke's apartment several times over the past months, wondering which window was his and whether he might be thinking about me.

Curiosity got to me. I called him back. I heard his low soft timbre over the phone, a velvet cord drawing me in. "Ali. I want to see you. Cook for you. Soon." Sounded a bit desperate to me.

"I'll think about it." I hung up victorious and confused. Did I want to punish him? Or play with him like a hysteric would, as Harold had described me. Pull him in then cast him out? Did I love him? It felt good that he wanted me. At least it sounded like he wanted me. But why did he want me and why now? What had changed? I wasn't ready to admit that I had any interest in him.

I couldn't wait for my session with Reuben. I called him at home, crossing an unspoken boundary. As soon as I heard his voice, I got my breathing back. I apologized and said I was confused. I said it felt risky to see Luke again, much less to let him back into my heart.

As usual, Reuben directed the conversation back to Father, to how dangerous it felt to love him.

There were ways, Reuben reminded me, that Luke had something in common with Dad.

I thought of Dad with his black cape galloping bareback on a black stallion. And Luke with his cape and beret sailing in stormy seas. Dad had chosen a life of the sword over a boring office job, he always said. Luke had left the business world for life aboard a boat. They were both dangerous. What should I do?

Reuben told me to follow what felt right to me, not what he thought. I knew he'd say that, but I needed to hear it.

Reuben rarely mentioned Luke or commented on him when I brought him up in our sessions. Usually, I was complaining. He always turned the subject back to Dad.

I continued to ask everyone I knew what I should do. Harold pointed out that Luke had never been someone I could count on but of course, he allowed, the decision was up to me. I heard him implying that he, on the other hand, would be someone I could always depend upon.

Friends warned me repeatedly that Luke wasn't strong enough for me, he couldn't commit, they didn't trust him. However, they only knew the information I fed them.

Janet said I had to give him a chance. I didn't know if it would be strong or weak of me to call him. I felt suffocated.

When I thought about Luke and a real relationship with him that would carry over time, I worried that I was walking into a trap and might disappear.

23

CHOICES

My thoughts reached a dead end and I ran out of people to ask for advice, which left me to check out Luke myself.

I called him and said I would come for supper.

The next evening, I put on my Mexican uniform of peasant blouse, Navajo skirt, and knee-high moccasins, as if putting on armor before going into battle. It was what I'd worn when Luke first met me in Mexico four years before.

I sat immobilized for a moment. If this was a game, I had no idea how to play. "Maybe I should have an escape route if it doesn't feel right," I said to Janet.

"Just go. Feel your way, respond in the moment."

Where did she get all her savoir faire about love?

His apartment was no more than a mile from mine. My thoughts scurried faster than I could walk, scrambling for some ground within myself to stand on. When I rang the buzzer a heavy-set guy with a bushy red beard opened the door, one of Luke's two roommates. He called for Luke who came to the top of the stairs and stood beaming down at me.

When he reached the last step, he hugged me like I'd only been away for a weekend.

"Wow, you look great Ali, I'm so happy you came." He stepped back and admired me. "Let me show you my cave."

He introduced me to another roommate who was reading on the living room sofa. The communal part of the apartment was neat, but dingy with furniture rejects that might have been picked up on the street at garbage day. Luke led me by the hand down a narrow hall to the back of the railroad apartment. His room was long with a mattress against the far wall. Luke's energy filled the objects in the room.

I could have been back on Destiny.

I didn't need to touch him. I could feel him as my body grew warm. Polished stones, hawk feathers, quill pens, black ink, Japanese prints… all spontaneously placed, Luke's artwork all over the walls.

I picked up a pottery vessel that was either a vase or a pot. The shape was almost liquid, and its glaze shimmered in irregular splashes of yellow and chartreuse.

"Did you make it?"

Luke nodded. "Raku, an old form of Japanese pottery."

"It's unusual, it looks just like you."

Luke said he had been throwing pots at Mudflats, a co-op pottery studio around the corner, and he had a new job working at Earth Guild Grateful Union selling everything to do with weaving and crafts. The people were interesting. All, except him, members of an urban commune.

We talked briefly, Luke gradually moving us toward the kitchen as he told me he'd started to do massage. He said it came naturally to him. It was not a surprise to me. I felt the warm healing touch of his hand on my back.

Everything in Luke that had been stuck when we were living together was now moving.

He opened the refrigerator and took out a fresh piece of bass that he had bought from a new store called Legal Seafoods. He threw it into a hot fry pan with a chunk of butter and a little olive oil. He added salt and a sprig of Rosemary. Rice steamed slowly and a green salad waited to be dressed. He sprinkled the fish with slivers of toasted almonds. He held the cast iron pan with his strong graceful hand and served me. He lit a candle then poured me a glass of Mateus from a straw covered green bottle.

I looked down at my plate, the food so pleasing and appetizing. I had forgotten what a good cook he was.

We raised our glasses and looked directly across the table at each other, like we had only been recently introduced. I was shy. We talked about this and that. The restaurant, my decision to begin a doctoral program, his pottery. He told me about his landlady downstairs who banged on the ceiling with a broomstick waking them up at two in the morning because she thought they were doing laundry. Captain was still barking all day in the back yard. We laughed, always some crazy neighbor.

I found myself smiling and softening. It was curious that Luke did better when he was away from me.

"Here's what I'm thinking," he said. "I want us to see if what we have will work or not. So, I have an idea. I'll convert a van into a camper, and we'll go back to Mexico and travel together."

"So that you can break up with me in a dusty Mexican village again?" I pointed my finger this way and that. "And then I can go on a bus all alone and cry for days and then finally I recover and then you can get me to come back to you and then you can leave me all over again? You mean something like that?"

I glared at him. I didn't realize I was still so angry and hurt.

Luke looked pained. "No, I don't mean that."

"Well, that's what I mean." I laughed a snide little laugh and bared my teeth like a chimp who was about to attack and rip off his face.

"You know what, Luke? I've been fine, in fact, more than fine without you. I've been thinking like a man. Some fun, some good sex, and then goodbye, toot aloo! Oh! Then I say,"— I put on a sad face— "I am so sorry I hurt your feelings. Yadda yadda, I didn't mean to."

Luke's face crumpled. And looked a little scared of me. Good!

I continued, as the delicious dinner fermented in my stomach. "Give me one good reason for trusting you. God, Luke!"

"I guess that's what the trip to Mexico would be about. Seeing if we could live together. I don't blame you for being mad."

"Well, good for you."

A fire in my belly kept me going.

"You have no idea what it was like to be put on a bus and sent away. Oh, and whatever way you choose, I'll choose the other way." Then I imitated his sorry voice when we separated in Puerto Escondido, "Poor little you, poor Ali."

"All right, Ali, I get the message. Please."

I looked at him.

My flare up dissipated.

I saw the face of a gentle soul, the kind of soul who would not want to hurt any living creature. My belly began to soften. I was confused. I sighed deeply.

"I really have been having fun Luke, a lot more fun than I had with you."

I held back tears. "I don't want to get left again. It's too painful."

Luke reached across the table and took my hands, just like he did when he was saying goodbye.

"It wasn't you, Al. It was never you. It was me who had to work something out. I don't think it'll happen again."

I rubbed my forehead and scratched my head. It hurt to think about it. Returning to Mexico was something I had always wanted to do, but it was the scene of the first rejection!

Yet, when Luke put his energy behind an idea, it was contagious.

It was a second chance.

More like a third chance.

I looked at him, at his golden eyes, startling when they looked directly into my eyes.

"I need to think about it."

"Sure. I'll call you tomorrow."

"Tomorrow? That's not much time. I have to think."

He was in a hurry as if all the momentum would stall if he didn't act right away.

He walked me home that night hand in hand like we used to stroll in Mexico when we first met; before we got confused. He kissed me gently at my door. I gave into his lips so soft and warm with the familiar sweetness to them. I floated upstairs. Janet was sitting at the kitchen table having a smoke.

"So? How was it?"

I sighed and lit a cigarette. I blew out the smoke slowly and watched it drift across the room.

"He wants to go back to Mexico."

"See? I told you." Janet laughed.

One thing continued to nag at me. It was true that I had been thinking like a man for the last six months. To me that meant I kept my heart in one compartment and sex in another. I felt strong and free, but only if the two remained separate.

I did not know if I could ever bring them together.

There might be better options, guys who were more dependable, more confident than Luke. I had enough trouble with my own insecurity. I didn't need to be with someone I had to prop up.

On the other hand, Luke was different from six months ago. He was standing on his own and he was surer of himself.

I knew how to begin with a man. Flirting, playing, drinking, and sex in that order. I also knew how to end with my own style of *thanks for the ride, see you later buddy*. What always stumped me was the middle part, the making a good relationship, the learning how to love, the getting over hurts, everything that Luke might be promising.

The road with Luke looked difficult with a lot hard work. What would I get out of it?

The following night, before Luke had a chance to call me, I went to the Paradise on Fenway with a guy I'd picked up at the Hay Penny in Harvard Square. The club was one big strobe light flashing, changing speeds and colors, exploding the cavernous dance floor with constantly booming light and swirling color. He (whatever his name was) and I were dancing to the Eagles' *Peaceful Easy Feeling* in the middle of the crowd, waving our arms, swaying, and singing along. I felt pretty and happy.

I heard the DJ yelling, I started to get dizzy and then I began to whirl.

"I have to get out of here," I said.

"What? Why?" he said.

"My head. I'm being squeezed by a boa constrictor," I mumbled. "My head."

The air grew thick and heavy, the walls closing in, the lights blinding, throbbing. I swirled and fell into him. He backed up and I went down hard on the floor.

I opened my eyes to a circle of nameless faces staring down at me in horror. I was drooling. I'd had a seizure.

That was the last time I saw him. I figured he had no interest in someone who wasn't quite right in the head. I shrugged him off. He was probably on his way to becoming alcoholic. Big drinkers were a magnet for me. They all wore signs with big letters over their hearts: *rescue me, love me, I can't help myself, but you can.* They got adrenalin going in me that I conflated with love.

Luke drank nothing more than a beer or two. He didn't even like to go to bars like the ones I'd been hanging out in for the last several months. In truth, I wasn't crazy about bars either. They were too loud with the stench of too much alcohol, everyone hopeful and hopeless all at one time.

But Luke was a little boring.

24
CLARITY

When Luke phoned the next day, I told him I needed more time.

He told me to take all the time I needed, but I heard the disappointment in his voice. It made me feel good. I did not mention that I'd had a seizure. I worried that epilepsy was a put off for everyone, Luke included. What was I supposed to do about his plan? And what was I supposed to do about him in general?

I put my decision away for the time being to savor the feeling of being wanted without having to give anything back. I liked having some control. I could only focus on one uncertain thing at a time and my job was proving to be challenging. My patients were not cooperating.

Margaret was the first of my group to be discharged from the chronic unit at Westborough State under my supervision. She had been in the locked ward for thirty-two years, longer than I had been on earth. How was I supposed to help her, much less manage her return to the world? I met up with her in the Cambridge office of the Ambulatory Service.

I almost said out loud *You're free, Margaret!* Instead, I said, "I know how big a change this is, Margaret."

She said nothing. Her eyes were frozen. (Now, I think she was mostly in shock.)

"It will take time to get used to your new life. Let's go grocery shopping."

Margaret did not respond.

This summed up my communication with Margaret and it never improved. I could smell the fear in her sweat whenever we entered a grocery store. I imagined the lights, the merchandise, the customers, the noisy ambience of a public marketplace, all of it a flood of stimulation. I didn't think about how overwhelming it was to face all those choices or how ridiculous it was to think that springing that kind of unknown freedom on her was helpful.

When she had to make a choice, I watched her choose Pringles, Coke, and Newport Cigarettes. I realized the capacity to choose and to choose well was a necessary step toward adulthood, something that was forever stunted in Margaret.

Why didn't anyone prepare us for helping our patients? A job that began as an exciting new development in mental health quickly became unworkable. The patients were unable to do any of the menial tasks that we tried to teach them. Even being responsible for their antipsychotic meds was outside of their capacity. The system had permanently disabled them and suddenly they were expected to become functioning adults.

"I don't know how to do this job," I admitted to my co-workers.

"I know. It feels cruel to push such tender souls to live on their own," one of them said.

The grumbling spread and intensified in my team. We concluded we were part of a cynical ploy to close the state hospitals. In a strange way, Margaret and I were in a similar position. We were the pawns of a hierarchical whim, neither of us were recognized. Nobody thought through what it would like to return to the world as a Rip Van Winkle. And nobody valued me enough as a mental health worker to help me do my job. They stuffed us into a tiny office in the back corner of the hospital with no instruction and no desire to know how the plan was proceeding.

The other patients fared little better than Margaret. The concept of freedom had no place in their psyches. I took freedom as my right, in fact I felt entitled to it and I was determined to protect it, even from Luke.

With my pick-up and drop-off sex I had no ties, no one mirroring back to me who I was or was not. If I said yes to Luke, I would have to deal with his wants and needs on top of my own. Acting like a guy was heady. I had power. And I could be selfish.

Why should I give that up?

***

One evening my mother called. Would I like to go to the Boston Flower Show with her? It was unusual for her to be asking for my company. But since splitting up with Luke, things were going better with Mum and Dad.

"Sure, Mum, I'll go with you." It was a change of pace. Free lunch.

April winds were gusting that Friday morning when she picked me up.

"I love the sound of the wind," I said as I got in the car.

Our mutual pleasure in nature was usually something I could count on sharing with her.

"I don't like the wind," she said. "Especially in the pine trees. It's a sad sound."

I drawled in Bill Monroe's mournful Appalachian twang, "In the pines, in the pines where the sun never shines…"

Mum gave a small smile, but her sadness sat heavy and gray between us. It was not new, but she could never speak directly about it. It was always something outside of her, in the trees, in the wind. The weather was always wrong.

I thought of Margaret, how impossible it felt to communicate with her, how she couldn't speak about what she felt, and the way I took it as my failure that I couldn't get through to her. It might be Pringles and Newport cigarettes with Margaret and Tomato aspic and Dubonnet with Mum, but it was all the same. Everything was outside of them, nothing within.

Mum and I walked through the exhibitions at the show in the Hynes auditorium. All the Garden Clubs around Massachusetts had entered their own garden designs, each in a twelve-foot square space. Mum's club had made a lovely pond with lilies surrounded by blooming yellow forsythia and lilacs in lavender and deep purple, a true spring scene. There was a red ribbon hanging from a branch. Their display had won second prize.

"That's so pretty, Mum, it looks like something you would do."

"Well. It certainly wasn't all me."

I felt as helpless with Mum as I did with Margaret. Nothing I said or did seemed to help. I wanted to boost her up, but she was stubbornly insecure. On the drive back to my apartment, I took a chance, "Who was Ted, Mum?"

I saw her hands grip the steering wheel.

"What do you mean?"

"You mentioned him the other day when we were talking at the Colonnade. Remember? You said he left you and you cried all day and all night."

It was something that she had let slip on our visit, but she had never mentioned his name.

I only knew a Ted existed because I had secretly read her diary years ago. As a teenager I often lay on my parent's bed at night simultaneously doing my homework and talking to my cousin Rozzie on the phone while we listened to the same radio station playing non-stop Beatles. One night I went snooping in Mum's bedside drawer while the Beatles were singing: *I want to hold your hand.* Mother was a complete mystery to me, so when found the diary I didn't feel guilty. Her entries were terse and superficial, like her conversation, but there was a lot of mention of Ted. I had not thought of Ted again until this moment.

We drove down Bow Street right past Adams House where Dad said he had lived while at college.

"He was your Father's roommate at Harvard," she said.

I tried keeping it light. "Wow, you had two boyfriends at one time."

"Not really." She took a deep breath and exhaled. Her mouth was set. "I went out with your Father mostly after Ted left me."

"Why did he leave you?"

"He'd graduated, he didn't have any job prospects, he said. We were going to be married."

"I didn't know that."

"Well, that's that."

End of conversation.

But it was not the end for me. Was she resigned? Did she regret marrying Father?

Dad was her second choice, a consolation prize. When I got out of her car, I looked at her differently, with sympathy.

As I walked up the stairs to my apartment the furniture of my parental alliances began rearranging in my mind. Suddenly my parents were two separate people. I did not know where that put Dad, but he was moved into a smaller room while I changed chairs and pulled up closer to Mother. It was as if I couldn't hold both parents at the same time. But then I felt sorry for Father. My thoughts began to ping pong between Dad and Luke. For the first time, Dad was not impervious. And Luke appeared stronger in my eyes. I bounced back and forth, yes, no, Luke or Dad. I had to choose.

I took the *I Ching* down from the bookcase in my bedroom. It was Luke's copy and had seen a lot of use. Luke and I consulted the *I Ching*, not to tell us what to do, but a way to understand and deepen our questions. I sat on the bed and thought how to phrase my question so that it would not be too specific. The *I Ching* is not a Ouija Board, it is not a yes or no game, it is an ancient wisdom text to be studied with care. We treated it with respect, as we treated our use of LSD.

I thought about the acid trip Luke and I took at the Farm and the confidence it gave us about a future together. So, I asked the *I Ching*, what should I do about my relationship with Luke? I threw the coins on the bed six times creating the hexagram. I drew number 30. Each hexagram had an extensive explanation.

Hexagram 30 was Clarity and one of its commentaries was luminous love. The reading continued, "Does the fact that the sun has spots mean that it should be removed from the sky?"

I lay down and thought about that. I understood it to mean we all had flaws and yet we could be forgiven. Luke was not perfect, but I did not have to think of him like my Father. It occurred to me that one day I might forgive Dad, not that he was not responsible for himself, but that he could not help who he was.

Dad's father was a bastard, he had told me. I remembered sitting with my grandfather in the room they called the parlor as he worked on his stamp collection in a house that smelled of Polly, the fifty-year-old African parrot who lived in the kitchen. Skipper wore a black morning coat that looked like he'd been living in it since the Victorian era. He was unshaven and his bottom lip was full and wet. He sat sullen, brooding, no movement in his body except his hands.

I wanted to feel the rice paper that protected the stamps, but I knew not to touch anything. He was taciturn, almost silent, ready to snap at one wrong move from me. Picking up one stamp or another with tweezers, he stopped only long enough to roll another cigarette with his yellowed fingers and long nails.

Sitting with the *I Ching* was the first time I thought of Dad as a small boy, Skipper's middle son. That strange forbidding man was his Father.

Love was stronger than human frailty.

I lay on my bed grateful for books of wisdom from teachers wiser than myself.

I called Luke and I said yes, I'd go with him to Mexico.

25

THE THREE S'S

We drove down the Massachusetts Pike to West Hartford, my first meeting with Luke's parents and our last obstacle before we left for a year in Mexico.

It occurred to me that they might not be any happier to meet me than my parents were to set eyes on Luke. I was clean with my hair in a neat braid, but I knew my Mexican uniform was unacceptable. I only wore it for protection.

I felt more confident about myself in relation to Luke's parents, than with my own. Luke had already assured me that he was not in danger of being swayed by his parents' disapproval. He stood up to his parents, so they didn't try to manage him. Whereas I collapsed under the weight of Mum and Dad's disapproval, which only fueled my parents' doubts and fears. But as we got closer to their house, I began to question myself. I fingered the long tight pleats of my skirt, trying to make them orderly.

Luke said it would be fine, he would take care of it.

We entered the city proper and drove through an African American section where his family lived when he was young. They had moved to the suburbs as part of white flight from city living. We passed through an area of stately older homes and tall trees like my grandmother's property and then into a recently developed section of split levels.

The Fine's house was in a neighborhood of ranch style homes with a small square of lawn in the front, a weeping Japanese maple on one side planted by his Father. Low hedge bordered the edge of the property and in the back yard a large maple tree separated their house from the neighbor's. Luke's Dad grew roses which were planted along the sunny side of the house. The house stood in stark contrast to my grandmother's grand colonial in Massachusetts, but it was much bigger than the garage-sized house Dad had built for us in Pennsylvania in my middle years.

Our seven years in Lancaster, Pennsylvania, was our Elba, a temporary exile caused by Dad's illness where we just seemed to slide down a steep hill just as other families appeared to be rising in stature. I was painfully aware as a young girl of eight to thirteen that most of my friends were wealthier than us with bigger houses, country club memberships, and healthier parents. Yes, Dad became an executive in a young boat company along with other young fathers who were recruited to manage other young companies as part of Lancaster's boom. Capitalism in the 1950s was a young plant beginning to blossom with shoots and flowers breaking out in the bright colors of money and success. But Dad could not keep up. His illness worsened and eventually they let him go. We had gone from the ancestral home to a tiny house and then back to the ancestral home; moves following Dad's rise and fall.

The turns in our fortune left me comparing my family with Luke's, which meant I ended up either inferior or superior, one side feeding the other. I was just confused.

"Well, well," Luke's Dad said as he opened the front door to welcome us.

He had a smile on his face, but I saw a knowing smile. I imagined he was thinking Luke is with this girl for sex, or something like that.

I tried to feel aloof. I was taller, blonder, and Waspier, (everything I had been trying to escape after growing up with other tall blond Wasp people). Luke's was the first Jewish family I had met so I decided to be curious like an anthropologist entering a new culture. Though, I lacked the neutrality of an independent researcher.

Lou was courteous and formal, not so different from Dad if you took away Father's affected accent. Luke's Mother was in the kitchen. She came out briefly in her apron and gave both of us a cool hello, like Mother. She was a striking woman, not much happier to see Luke than she was to meet me.

"Ohhh…," she said, in a way that sounded more like *Ewww...*

Parental disapproval could be a kind of validation for me, helping me define myself as a rebel. But I shrank beneath Anne's critical gaze. I could tell she would not pretend anything she did not really feel. I was not what she wanted.

The mood shifted when Luke's fourteen-year-old sister Abbe ran into the room. She grabbed Luke around the waist and hugged him tight. "I've been counting the days to meet you"—she turned to me with a sweet smile.

Luke stood back holding her hands as he took her in. "Wow you've grown, little sis."

He went out to the car and got a big box out of the trunk that he carried into Abbe's bedroom. We three sat down in a row on her pink quilted bedspread as Luke opened the box filled with traditional dresses and blouses from the Yucatan. He held up different pieces in white cotton with colorful embroidered flowers across the bodice. She exclaimed that they were so pretty. Luke told her to take anything she wanted.

He had bought them to sell but gave several of them to his sister. It was like him to do that. Luke was a collector, but suddenly he could give it all away. Everything in my family had historical significance and was to be kept forever.

Mother had often said, "Neither a borrower nor a lender be." I was baffled by those words, but I took them to heart and held on tightly to everything I had.

As we sat down in the dining room, I compared the glassware, the china, the flat silver to my parents'. Ours was older and more valuable. However, Anne was a better cook than Mother. Observations, evaluations, and judgments rushed into my mind, everything black and white. I prided myself on being different from most of my circle growing up, who were all about what their fathers did, where they skied, and where they summered.

I got the feeling that Anne and Lou did not like me.

Lunch dragged on. Anne barely sat in her chair, running back and forth to the kitchen for the next course. I thought about Mother who sat so comfortably at the dinner table, taking forever to eat her meals, as if she was still being waited on by an imaginary maid.

"Can't you sit down with us, Mom?" Luke said.

"Don't even try. She has to do it herself," Abbe said.

She gave me a smile that said, *I'm with you and my brother.*

Luke's Dad dominated the conversation. It turned out he was, like me, a familial anthropologist, also lacking neutrality. We were studying each other. He peppered me with questions about my family as if I was a foreigner. Where did I come from? What did Father do for work? Nothing for the past seven years because he was so ill. *Hm hm... Where did my people come from?*

He told the story, familiar to Luke, about their people from Russia and Poland, his Father's refusal to step off the sidewalk when a Russian soldier came by, his arrest and emigration to save his life.

I said my ancestors were stonecutters for the king of Scotland. For. The. King.

The first course was matzo ball soup. I tasted a flavorful chicken broth, made with Anne's grimmitz, which Luke said was a concentrated mix of onion, garlic, and chicken fat. There was a giant matzo ball in each bowl that was delicious.

Lou put his soup spoon down on the plate. "So. Did you hear the one about the shiksa?"

"Dad. Come on," Luke said.

His Dad shot him a warning look.

"What's a shiksa?" I asked.

Lou looked at me with a mischievous smirk. "A goyim. We have a lot of Yiddish words to say what we feel."

"All right Lou, let's eat," Anne said. Her expression was frozen, but I saw her mouth tighten. She had a few sips of her soup before returning to the kitchen. She seemed in a hurry to get on with it. Serving the meal was a job not a pleasure, yet it went on for a long time.

The entrée was white fish and a spinach Kugel. The Kugel was yummy, and I complimented her on everything we ate. She warmed a little, but mostly ignored me.

"We're known for our food," Lou said.

"I think *we're* known for our cocktails," I countered with no idea why I had to say that.

Luke looked at me. I shrugged. His father nodded as if to say he already knew that.

"How about when the shiksa met the schvartsa?" Lou looked at me with a twinkle in his eye. He might have winked.

"What's a schvartsa?"

We never got to the punch lines, but I played along as if I was Gracie Allen to his George Burns.

Luke bristled. "A black person, Ali, that's enough Dad."

Lou got up and took out a bottle of Manischewitz from the credenza. "Our traditional wine," he said, and poured a small glass for everyone.

Abbe's entire face scrunched, like she was about to gag. It was the sweetest most disgusting wine I ever tasted.

“You don’t have to drink it Ali,” Luke said, as he put down his glass.

We had fruit cocktail and Rugelach for dessert.

“I love these pastries,” I told Anne.

When the meal ended, Lou got up and said, “You come with me, son. I want a cigar.”

Luke mouthed *Good luck* as he followed his Dad into the den. My eyes asked him, *What do I do now?* Luke gestured to Abbe.

I helped her clear the dishes off the table and then we stood together in the kitchen while Anne put on yellow rubber gloves that went all the way up her arms like she was preparing for surgery. The foul smell of cigar wafted its way into the kitchen.

“Ach, what a stink,” Anne said. As if the odor of cigar in the den had never happened before

Every piece of china and glassware was methodically rinsed with soap and water, completely cleaned, before it went into the dishwasher. I put a dish in. She took it out immediately.

“Never mind, thank you. You don’t know my system,” she said.

“It’s all right,” Abbe said, “I don’t know the system either. Mom has her own way.”

We stood for what must have been thirty minutes waiting for the occasional serving dish that did not go into the dishwasher and needed to be dried by hand. Anne answered me when I asked a question, but with as few words as possible. I was not needed, and I had nothing to offer.

Luke came into the kitchen to rescue me and we went outside with Lou to admire his roses.

"We're going back to Mexico in the fall, Dad. I'm planning on making a camper for our journey."

"I see. Did you tell your Mother?"

"I was hoping you'd tell her."

Lou nodded. He seemed to have given up. Our news was nothing more than additional proof that we were not going to amount to anything.

***

"They'll get used to it with time, Al, don't let them get to you," Luke said as we drove home.

"I felt like your Father could like me. But your Mother... whew. Chilly. I already know that routine."

"You have to remember, Ali, they don't have any friends who aren't Jewish. They have socialized with the same eight couples for over twenty years. They don't know anything else."

"Well, they're not happy about us."

"No, but they're not about to sit Shiva either."

"What's that?"

"That's what happens when you're dead to your parents even though you're still alive. They kill you off. It happens if someone dies, but also if you marry out of the religion. They would never do that to me. My parents are too secular."

I was learning a new language. Everything started with *s*.

I was not sure I could have the same confidence about my own parents. I did not trust what Dad would do if I actually wanted to marry Luke.

26

THE VAN 1974

My boss scowled from behind his desk when I gave him my resignation.

As a young psychiatrist climbing the ladder of Cambridge City's hierarchy, he had a lot to prove. The success of our program was crucial to his advancement and he took my quitting as a personal affront. Why would I leave and disrupt what was already a difficult transition for my patients? He did not need to remind me. I already felt like I was abandoning them.

On the other hand, over the course of an entire year none of them demonstrated that they knew who I was.

I told my boss I was leaving the country. He grimaced. I scowled back at him. I wish I'd told him that the ACS plan to release chronic patients into the community was thoughtless and patronizing. And that it was unworkable and cynical at its core.

When I mentioned Mexico was my destination, he raised his eyebrows and pulled his head back. What did I expect from traveling in a third world country? It was not worth explaining. I added him to a list of people who were disappointed in me.

I sat squirming in my chair beneath his condescending disapproval. My heart's beating was audible as he signed my work contract release then handed the paper to me across his desk with an abrupt goodbye.

"The job will not be here for you when you return."

"I wouldn't plan on returning anyway," I said.

I left my patients to another naïve mental health worker. I hoped they would not register or care that a new person was working with them, but I did not understand the schizophrenic mind and made excuses for bailing out.

I left Cambridge City that afternoon and a heavy weight lifted from my heart. I breathed in the crisp autumn air as I walked to Luke's apartment. The familiar sensation of a successful escape encircled me like a cocoon, protecting me from any second thoughts I might have about leaving for a year. We had both struggled to find a place for ourselves in the working world, to find a purpose and now we were disconnecting again. My reasoning was that I'd learn and grow as a person, that travel always widened one's perspective. But would this growth be something I could bring back and apply to the world?

Luke said our trip was to help us as a couple, to see if we could live and face challenges together. We had not been able to sustain a relationship before, but he said that was his fault. I appeared to be better put together than Luke, but underneath my façade I did not believe in myself. The problem was that I did not want to see my flaws, so I had no idea what to do to change myself.

So, what difference was a year in Mexico going to make?

The leaves were beginning to fall as I scuffed along the sidewalk like I was ten years old again. I was going to Mexico, the land of unexpected joy and challenge. And I'd been freed from a job that left me feeling badly about myself.

That is what I knew to be true.

***

Three years had passed since I began therapy with Reuben. My departure for Mexico presented us with a natural stopping place. In therapist jargon we were *terminating*, which usually meant a final goodbye. When the therapy relationship ended, the premise of the relationship also ended. Terminating was a stilted word for a complex goodbye.

I dreaded saying goodbye. It felt unthinkable to lose Reuben.

The sessions had taken a turn as I became more conscious of my relationship to Father. It was not all better, but I was not stuck anymore. I could feel and experience my own energy and feelings. Most important, I felt a new freedom to express my rage.

The morning I told Reuben I was leaving I didn't lie down on the bed. I sat fully dressed in a chair and we talked face to face as we had when I came for our initial meeting. I was as nervous as when I began my therapy.

"Maybe we can continue when I get back," I said.

Reuben tossed his head back and forth. "We'll see. I think you've done the work on yourself that you needed to do for now."

"My seizures may be gone. I've only had a few lately. I have you to thank for that."

"You're a brave woman, Alicia. It's frightening and painful to confront dark emotions. You can feel proud."

"I love you, Reuben."

"I love you too."

"Even if you won't marry me."

We laughed together.

I told him I had delayed my doctoral program for a year. I had chosen an alternative school, the Humanistic Psychology School in San Francisco to do a theoretical dissertation involving Reich. I told him I could do anything with his support. I hugged his warm bear-like body. He had given me unconditional love and respect, something I had never known before. I wanted to stand on my own, but I still felt stronger with him standing behind me.

Reuben was clear about the line between therapy and collegial friendship. We had to complete the patient-therapist relationship and then he looked forward to being colleagues and friends. Our relationship was not over after all. It was entering a new phase.

I floated out on a cloud.

***

Luke was outside when I got to his apartment. A hulking dirt brown Ford Econoline van sat in the driveway. He had bartered the Desoto and gotten an equal exchange. The Desoto was so dignified, and this hulking vehicle was pure ugly. Luke agreed, but wait until I saw what he would do with the interior. He was making us a house. He had two wooden horses set up in the driveway, sheets of plywood, and a power saw ready to construct closets and cabinets.

"I can't wait," I said. I threw my arms up into the air. "Whew, I'm free!"

Luke squeezed me tight.

"This will make a perfect home for us, Al." He opened the rear door then sat and lit a Pall Mall. He blew out the smoke. "Let's quit before we leave."

"Great idea," I said as I lit up.

I peeked inside the van. Luke said the van had potential. He had said the same thing about the Farm. Nothing much came of that potential. I told my friends that Luke had potential too. If you need to talk about potential, it usually means jumping over whatever is inadequate in the present.

My voice echoed in the empty dark interior. I said I could not see anything cozy coming out of it. He said it was hard to picture it because it was all in his head. One thing I had learned about Luke over the years was that he was unpredictable. One day he would be painting, the next day throwing pots, the next day weaving, all of it beautiful, but I had a hard time trusting that he'd create anything practical.

"Hand me that board," he said.

I watched Luke measure and cut, beginning to put together a small cabinet.

"For the kitchen," he said. "A place for everything and everything in its place. Just like my boat."

He said, our home would be nearly complete by the end of the week.

***

It was easier for us to stay living separately until it was time to leave on our journey, like a bride and groom before the wedding. At my apartment with Janet, I had my own job preparing for our trip.

I had taken on some shifts at the restaurant, again. The salad man saved the empty five-gallon pickle jars for me. I made batches of granola with oats, seeds, nuts, raisins, and honey. I filled five jars. I bought enough short grained brown rice to fill another four. And I filled the last two jars with coarse ground coffee to make a cowboy style brew. I bought two wooden bowls and two wooden spoons for our meals and two tall pottery mugs for drinks. Luke gave me dimensions and Janet made yellow calico curtains to cover the side and rear windows and a dark green duck cotton cover for a thin foam mattress. I bought a carpet remnant for the van's floor. I left it all at the apartment and at the end of the week I walked over to Luke's excited to see his handiwork.

It looked like he had been living outside for the past week. The driveway was covered in sawdust and there were nails and screws and scraps of wood littering the space. Luke was sitting at the van's side entrance smoking.

He grinned. "Come look inside."

I peeked in and saw a complete living space. He had built the kitchen cupboard just as he said into the side wall behind the driver's seat with shelves for spices and condiments. The cupboard sat directly over a countertop with a two-burner propane stove. There was a cutting board that fit perfectly over the stove and had its own place at the rear of the cabinet while we cooked.

Below the stove was another cabinet with a shelf for pots and pans. Behind the passenger seat was a table for two that folded into the back of the seat when not being used. That was the kitchen. Going further back on the driver's side a six-foot sofa bed lined the left side wall. That's where the mattress would go. Underneath the mattress was a storage area that went the full length from the van's back door to the kitchen cabinet to hold all our provisions and dishes. The sofa and mattress in the daytime opened to a double bed for sleeping.

On the opposite side of the van, he built a long closet with a rod for hanging clothes and bins on the bottom for shoes and whatever other possessions we took with us. He'd cut out a space for a louvered side window over the bed and two sun lights on the roof, so that we could have air and privacy at the same time. Every pine surface was stained a cherry wood color.

"This is the best little house I've ever seen. Fugly on the outside, but warm and cozy on the inside."

And everything was a tiny bit off center, like Luke. Luke's red thread began to be visible to my blurry perception. On the surface he was everchanging, unsure, but he constantly surprised me with what was underneath: beauty and creativity and a steady goodness.

He looked proud.

We had our last cigarettes together two days before departure. I jumped up and down in Luke's driveway with nicotine withdrawal as we stored and organized our few possessions in the van. I mixed a jar of cashews with raisins for us to snack on when the craving got bad. We'd saved $2,000. for the year. Figuring on $1100 for gas, that left us with approximately $2.50 per day for everything else. We hid the cash in the storage locker under the bed.

There was one small item to take care of before taking off: telling my parents. I thought of telling them often, but…I didn't mention anything until two days before our departure. They rolled their eyes and shook their heads in tandem.

"It's ridiculous that you're taking off again. I'm disgusted," Mother said.

"It's irresponsible, more proof of my suspicions," Dad said. "For god's sake the man is thirty-three years old."

They didn't bother trying to dissuade me. Like Luke's Father, I think they had begun to give up on me. I was relieved to put a few thousand miles between us, at least for a year.

On a golden morning in early October, I called Rozzie to say a last goodbye. I told her to write to me general delivery at one of the several Mexican towns we planned to stay in. Sooner or later, something would get to us.

Janet came downstairs to see us off with a hand painted metal box of treasures for us filled with candies, band aids, toothpaste, birth control foam, and Suzuki's *Zen Mind Beginner's Mind.* We were both teary. We had been good roommates, she said.

We drove slowly down Kinnaird Street and then headed west on River Street. I held onto Luke's thigh with my left hand and stuck my right arm out, letting my hand wave in the wind as the currents sent us gently on our way, the two of us together with nothing but a promise lying ahead.

LESSON FIVE:

MAKE AS MANY MISTAKES AS POSSIBLE

27

ATICAMA

Early on in our trip we paid a nostalgic visit to Mazatlán where we had met five years before.

Outside of town we found a newly tarred area right on the ocean. A resort or hotel was about to be constructed, but nothing had begun other than the parking lot. I rode the waves, we read and talked, thinking back together to the serendipity of our meeting when Luke limped into the harbor on Destiny after a hurricane at sea.

And me biding time for weeks in Mazatlán with no reason for being there other than the fact I didn't want to go back east.

We agreed it was our destiny.

Tall lights came on after dark, shining on the parking lot and inadvertently into our van. After a few days, we took stones and threw them at the bulbs knocking out the lights. We both took rules and laws as suggestions. While tending to our renewed relationship, our own peace and privacy seemed more important than lights that had no purpose.

By the next day, the ocean changed its mood from relative calm to heavy chop and high rolling waves. In a matter of hours, the waves moved from rolling to crashing onto shore, and it was too dangerous to swim. When a young boy came to the van late that afternoon and warned us that a *cyclone* was on its way, I translated the word to mean storm instead of hurricane.

"Let's stay parked up here so that we can watch the storm," I said.

The ocean was beautiful when she was angry.

"That was not a smart move," Luke said later, annoyed that he'd allowed me to override his own good sense.

A Category Four (we learned afterward) Pacific typhoon thundered in and raged throughout the night. Our heavy van began to rock precariously in the darkness as the hurricane lashed it with screaming winds that sounded like a train roaring over us. We huddled together inside the van drinking shots of tequila and peeing into a bucket. With the growing intensity of the driving wind and rain, water began seeping in through the side doors and soaking the carpet. Luke tried to move the van in quadrants, to follow the circular course of the storm, he said, and keep us headed into the wind.

At its peak, the force of the storm was so strong that pushing the gas pedal to the floor was not powerful enough to move us. I am sure we went onto two wheels at one point and it appeared we might tip over or plummet off the cliff. The tequila was helpful in dulling my fear, but I had to pee frequently, and it got harder to hit the bucket.

Emergencies were familiar to me, but I had no idea how to get out of them.

When the hurricane wore itself out by dawn an eerie silence sat on top of us with the soggy salty smell of wet carpet mixed with muggy hot air. I opened the side door and dumped the pee bucket into knee high water. I lay back, hoping to catch my breath, but Luke said we didn't have that luxury. He said cholera would breed quickly with the sewage flooding into the streets.

He turned the key. We were lucky that the van started. He accelerated the gas as we plowed through engine high waters over barely passable roads swerving to avoid downed palm trees, deep holes, large rocks, and shattered glass from blown out hotel windows. There was no stopping. Luke gunned it and kept his foot on the gas to keep us from getting bogged down in mud and high water. I trusted him to know how to keep us safe.

I tapped the dashboard of the van. "Look at her go. We're so lucky to have our home with us."

I felt a familiar heightened relief of having escaped complete disaster, like the mornings after Dad's rampage finally wore itself out.

We had to get some distance from Mazatlán before leaving the detritus of the storm behind. I tried to relax as Luke's hands gripped the wheel. I looked out at partially cultivated land sprinkled with dusty roadside pueblos, untethered burros, skinny horses, goats grazing on the edge of the road. Gradually the landscape emptied itself of all animals, people, and dwellings.

We were quiet as we drove and drove and the day moved on, swerving to avoid potholes the size of gullies and random fallen rock. It appeared that we'd gone off all maps, caught between thick jungle on one side and random clusters of shacks here and there on the edge of the road with rusty signs advertising Coca Cola and La Rubia es Mejor, blond is better, cerveza.

The sun suddenly disappeared below the palms like a ball dropped by an invisible hand into an abyss. We were nowhere recognizable as a town. Luke said we had to stop while he could still see. He worried about bandidos, or Federales, for that matter. It was hard to tell the difference between the lawless and the law since they each had weapons, used blockades to stop cars, and extracted bribes. Luke had a heightened sense of danger, where I tended to dismiss it.

I remembered lying in my pajamas in the back of the family station wagon on the Jersey Turnpike as we rushed like emergency responders from Pennsylvania to Cape Cod to be in the center of Hurricane Carol. She was heading right for Chatham. Dad had said we needed to protect the cottage, but I could tell he just wanted a reason to be in the storm. My little body flooded with adrenalin as Dad courted danger like a good Marine.

When Dad sensed danger, he ran into it while my excitement bordered on panic. Luke avoided danger but if it found him, he grew noticeably calm. And so, with Luke I found a way to be afraid but calm all at one time. We found danger many times that year, yet with Luke's support I remained strong in its face.

At dusk Luke pulled abruptly off the road. We will sleep here for the night and decide what to do in the morning. We each had a bowl of granola with ripe banana, pulled open our double mattress and fell into deep sleep.

***

I pushed the calico curtain aside and peeked out through the slatted side window above our bed in the van. The sun was beginning its climb, a mixed blessing of light and stultifying heat.

We were wherever we ended up when darkness forced us off the road. I could see we'd parked on a bright green grassy area that bordered the ocean. A shoreline of fist size stones extended all the way down to the water. A few tall palm trees stood between us and the beach, emerald green slightly swaying at the top, brown fronds dropped on the ground. Opening the side door on the opposite side I saw a hard-packed dirt road. I could hear the faint lapping of the ocean with a backdrop of soft ringing in my ears.

In the sliver of time between dawn and morning the sun turned hot and the air settled in for a long dormant day. I announced I was going for a swim, talking only to myself since Luke remained in a heavy deep sleep. It had been an exhausting few days, and I hoped he'd feel more relaxed when he woke up.

I put my suit on and walked across the grass until I reached the beach. The stones made for rough going, even with huaraches fortified by tire tread soles. When I got to the water's edge, the bottom was still stony, and the water remained shallow. I could sit down on rocks in the water, but any thought of a real swim was hopeless.

I made my way back. Luke was hunched over in the van making our cowboy brew boiling water and adding coarsely ground coffee. I watched the mixture sink slowly to the bottom of the pot and breathed in the chocolate and caramel of the dark

Oaxacan blend. We added milk that came in a box. I was suspicious of milk that required no refrigeration, but it was all we had. Luke took a few sips.

"I'm not feeling too good," he said.

"Not again," I said.

When he glanced at me, I could see his eyes were glassy. He drifted off.

I knew from our last year in Mexico that all Mexican sickness started out the same way, but it varied in its intensity. It was unlike anything we experienced back home. We were ill equipped with medicine and knowledge.

Now I wondered where Luke's present bout came from. Was it the greasy tacos (old oil that was used over and over for cooking)? Or the strawberries in the licuado (berries washed in dirty water before they were blended)? Maybe it was in the air after the storm. By this point, who cared?

He sat on the edge of the bed holding his head in his hands to keep it from falling off, he said. Very quickly he soaked through his shirt and shivered violently even as the heat was suffocating. By mid-day Luke was spitting up bile and could not move. Whatever it was, it was something more than Montezuma's Revenge which would rush through the body in a matter of hours.

"Maybe I'm dying," he said, softly moaning.

If I thought he was being overly dramatic, I soon thought twice. Luke collapsed and slept. He woke up periodically for a mouthful of brown rice before another bout of diarrhea or vomiting. Everything was flushed out as quickly as it came in. He needed my help to squat in the area we had designated for our bathroom. He wiped himself with a palm leaf and rinsed off with sea water that I had carted up in a bucket. He grew woozy. In a matter of hours, he became dead weight, unable to support himself at all.

I wiped him down. He dry-heaved. His shit turned to water. I brought bucket after bucket of sea water to clean the bed. I sat beside him and put wet washcloths on his forehead. I tried to be a good nurse. I remembered Father in his bed, home from the hospital, yellow and swollen with cirrhosis like a pregnant woman, and then rushed once again to the emergency room; images as repellent as they were frightening.

Was it cholera? We knew mini-cholera and amoebic dysentery from our first year in Mexico. This was much worse. Was he dying? The thought floated in my head with an unreal feeling of helplessness. There was nothing to be done. Or maybe there was something I could do but I was unable to think and act. I became immobilized, watching Luke helplessly as I had often watched Father sick or drunk, as if everything was out of my control. Tepic, the capital city of Nayarit was three hours away. I could have gone, but it did not occur to me. If Luke died, I would have done nothing to prevent it. Now, I think I was frozen in old childhood terror unable to act when my action was needed.

Mexico was full of surprises. I had expected balmy days by the ocean, a backdrop for Luke and me to renew our love, held by the warm salty air. But a hurricane and a violent illness in the first month?

We were not going anywhere any time soon. I turned the van around as carefully as I could not to disturb Luke. I sat at the side door, took out our box of watercolor crayons and drew what I saw, palm trees on a grassy knoll, cerulean sky, and a glassy sea in the distance. I dipped the crayons into water and moved color and shape with a watercolor brush. All was quiet except for the soft rumble of Luke's snoring. Even the hot ocean had dozed off.

I had slowed down so much that the simple act of looking and seeing a tree grounded me.

I finished a sketch and moved to a shady spot under a palm tree. I had two used but new to me paperbacks. Small collections of books in English were traded by fellow travelers in most towns. A miniature library might appear in a small restaurant or a bar, sometimes in a casa de huespuedes. I had exchanged my copies of *Bleak House* and *Lolita* for the only two books in San Blas, French novels by Balzac and Stendahl. I sat in the shade and read *The Red and the Black* with complete attention, a book I never would have chosen, savoring every word. Who knew when I would come upon another novel, certainly not in Aticama.

I was alone, my thoughts at loose ends. Each hour passed slowly. Later that day I sat on the floor beside our bed skimming a chapter on Erikson's stages of development. It was the only psychology book I had with me to remind myself that a Ph.D. program was waiting back in the states. Otherwise, I never would have thought about my future. Mexico had a way of demanding that I stay present. As I read, I got concerned about myself. I could not wait for Luke to wake up.

"You won't believe this," I said as soon as I saw his eyes open. "I've actually failed in every one of Erikson's stages. I didn't realize I was such a mess."

I thought that might make him smile. It did not.

I continued, explaining Erikson's theory of psychological development as stages to Luke. Each stage presented the individual with a challenge, such as infant trust vs. mistrust, toddler autonomy vs. shame and doubt, latency initiative vs. guilt, adolescent industry vs. inferiority, etc. One stage did not have to be mastered to move to the next one. I hoped not because if mastery was necessary, I was in trouble.

Any stage that was not successful could come back to haunt the individual.

I was haunted.

It was a familiar syndrome of the psychology student convinced she had every psychiatric illness she read about. I went so far as to worry I had schizophrenia because I made loose associations in my mind and easily hallucinated with psychotropic drugs.

But I believed Erikson. Why was I so deficient and behind?

I was determined to figure it out.

"Which stage are you failing at now," Luke slurred. His eyes were closed, his arm hung limp off the side of the bed.

"I'm at the young adult stage. Intimacy vs. isolation. Do you think we're intimate?"

"Not lately. Oh god, I have to shit again. Help me up."

I was joking, but intimacy remained a mystery. I was taking care of Luke. I was learning about *in sickness and in health* and it was not all pretty. In fact, loving was something hard to do, something that meant I had to hold a lot of different feelings all at one time. Is that intimacy?

I did not know if I was capable of this type of complicated intimacy. I was an either/or person.

There had been little that was romantic or sexual between us since arriving in Mexico. I blamed it on the hurricane, sickness, travel stress. Sex remained hidden, hard to get to. I wanted it and did not want it. Sometimes I felt like I returned to my virginal state as quickly as possible after we made love. Yes, there would be that time just after sex when I felt like a full woman, whole in my body, confident with my desire. But then I grew separate and chaste and alone, and I did not want anyone to invade my bodily integrity. It was one thing to have sex with someone I did not know and had no reason to trust. Lust was easy. If I did not climax, I kept it simple and lied.

But when I looked into Luke's eyes and felt him looking at me with longing or want, it gave me a shyness so deep I was not sure I could overcome it. Or that I wanted to. I might disappear. I might lose a self I barely had hold of. Sex was easy as an act. Loving sex was something else. I needed time, lots of time, a slow opening, peeking out, checking for danger.

And I was not confident that Luke was drawn to me. He was not affectionate, and he seemed to be waiting for me to pull him out and what was I supposed to do? I wished someone would have taught me how to be more of a woman, whatever that was. Was I supposed to wear fancy underwear or parade around doing a strip tease? I felt like a failure.

I sighed. None of this was relevant now. There was no need for me to be shy and no chance to be sexual. I could not look into his eyes. He was completely spaced out. I squeezed the water out of the washcloth and put it over his forehead again.

"Thanks, Al."

He gave me a small smile, the first one in days. I was desperate for him to come back to me, even if I did not know what to do when he was there.

***

After two days, when the vomiting and diarrhea had let up, Luke felt well enough to get out of bed for a few hours at a time.

We sat on the edge of the van's side door after supper, dangling our legs, staring out to the flat sea as it melted into the horizon. I anticipated some cooler air when the sun went down, something to help take up the moldy smell of damp carpet, but it did not happen. I thought dark should be cooler than light, but any tiny breeze from the day came to a complete stop at night. Nothing moved and the air sat like a dull weight on top of us.

We got a friendly competition going in Cribbage. We pulled down our small table from the rear of the passenger seat, opened a pair of fold-up canvas seats, and played a few rounds every night while we drank our evening coffee. We complemented each other because Luke liked to win, and I did not mind losing. In fact, I felt a little guilty whenever I did win.

One evening a young man approached the van. He moved slowly and cautiously across the grass with a guitar in hand. He was handsome in a slender and guileless way. He said his name was Pedro. He spoke no English.

"Where are your children?" was one of his first questions.

"Oh, we're not married," I said.

"My wife and I have *too* many children," he laughed. "Seven!"

He was twenty-nine, a year older than me and four years younger than Luke. He had many questions about the states. Did everyone have a car and a large house?

"This is our house," Luke said with his hands open, "casa."

"How interesting," Pedro seemed surprised. "I dream of a better life for me and my family."

He said it was difficult feeding so many. And one child, Rafaela, had recently suffered polio.

"I'm sorry. I thought polio was wiped out. We have a vaccine," I said.

"Ah, that's not something we have here."

No medical help existed for the villagers other than might be found over the mountains at Tepic, the capitol city. It was a three-hour drive and who had a car? We had not seen one vehicle pass by in the days we had been there. Pedro explained we were in Aticama, a tiny village so far off the map that no one visited, not even the government, he laughed. Tourists might drive through on their way down the Pacific coast, but they never stayed because the beach was impassable.

“They’ve forgotten us,” Pedro said. “You’re our first visitors.”

There were countless forgotten pueblos in Mexico, but this was the first one we had stayed in. I was excited to have Pedro as our friend. It meant we were truly living in a Mexican community.

The next morning, I took a walk down the dirt road into town. I saw a ghost of a village, clusters of small shacks, a few mangy dogs, some chickens, a pig. I discovered the shelves of the only grocery store were mostly bare. Food was scarce and jobs must have been non-existent. Life was about subsistence.

My huaraches were covered with dust when I got back to the van, my throat was parched, and I was worn out. I lay down next to Luke and dropped off to sleep.

Ordinarily we would have moved on when we discovered there was nothing in a village, but with Luke so sick, we had no choice but to stay for as long as it took for him to recover.

28

ATICAMA - THE BIRTHDAY PARTY

Luke and I developed a routine with Pedro. We looked forward to his visits every evening at about the same time, whatever time that was (we had no clock). After a few moments of conversation, he would take up his guitar, sit on the grass by the door of the van, and serenade us. I translated the lyrics for Luke, but it was not necessary to know Spanish to hear the melancholy as Pedro sang to the night sky with an unquenchable longing that I could recognize in my heart. And deep in my belly where romantic love melted into sexual desire, a confusing pair of feelings.

One night he brought us a bag of raw oysters. I had never seen so many at one time. How would we eat them all?

"I dive every day," he said.

"What a luxurious treat. And so many," I said.

I happened to mention my birthday was coming.

"You must come to my home. Meet Cande and the children, have dinner with us, we would welcome you with a special meal for your birthday."

"Pedro, that's too much. You have enough mouths to feed."

I tossed the words off politely, as I'd been trained to do, having no idea what my words meant.

"I insist. You must come. We'll kill a chicken."

After Pedro left, I began dreaming of my birthday supper. And a small dream about Pedro. He was dark skinned, angular, slender, and lovely while Luke looked gaunt, sallow, and sickly.

"I can't wait to have an authentic Mexican meal," I told Luke.

***

The following evening, Luke dragged himself out of bed to get ready. He was weak, but it would be an insult to Pedro to decline the invitation. I lumbered across the stony beach and filled yet another bucket with sea water. We washed ourselves as best we could. Our skin remained salty and sticky, but at least we did not smell. Luke was haggard beneath his surface tan and his cheekbones were prominent.

I imagined roast chicken or enchiladas de pollo, both of which were in stark contrast with our meager meals that varied little from day to day. We had our $2 a day allotted for all expenditures. I relished every supper of brown rice with an undersized zucchini or some carrots and onions we would buy from the few women who sat cross legged outside their shacks with vegetables on their skirts. Even if we could have afforded chicken, there was not any available in Aticama's meager market.

We walked into the erstwhile village at dusk. Pedro had said to come after the sun went down. Luke shuffled like an old man. His frailty scared me. I commented how bleak everything was as we turned down one of the few dusty dirt roads. Homes built from tin, closet like, the size of sheds on an American property, like what we would order in a catalogue to house our tools and lawnmowers. Yards were powdery dirt with chicken droppings if families were fortunate enough to have chickens. Mexico's third world did not appear to have progressed at all.

Luke and I were not progressing either. The trip was supposed to be a romantic journey of learning and sharing the adventures of traveling together. Instead, I was a nurse. I could have had a lot more fun at home where I did not have to stay with a guy who was down for the count. I was being asked for too much and there was too little in return. Life was disappointing and I was still too selfish to understand that the nature of being alive was getting past disillusionment and learning to appreciate what was in front of me.

I was still grumbling to myself as we walked back in from the shore to the edge of the meager development that could be called civilization to the lush tropical bush leading up into the hills. Luke was struggling to keep up, dragging his feet, breathing hard.

Pedro had made a point of telling us that he owned two banana trees and one cow in those hills. Cande sold ceviche in small glasses from a cart using Pedro's oysters, although who could afford to buy her ceviche was not clear. Yet, relative to the other townspeople they were wealthy. At least I would get a break and we would have a delicious supper, a little celebration for my birthday. Some ceviche or fried oysters would be perfect.

Pedro told us we would recognize his house, the first one in his pueblo to have a concrete exterior. We saw him standing in the doorway waiting for us and beckoning, a couple of hens in his yard pecking for grubs.

We walked into a small dark space with a floor of hard packed dirt. I could barely make out Cande and the seven children all crowded inside waiting to meet us. The second and only other room had a bare mattress on the floor where four of the kids slept feet to face. The three older kids slept on pallets next to the mattress. Pedro and Cande slept in the front room on a straw mat, I assumed. During the day, the room functioned as an eating area.

He presented his children to us as a nameless group, all of whom stood politely staring at us, their noses running, their feet bare. Not a toy in sight. Cande and the children had sallow skin with dark circles around their eyes.

"Oh, let me present Rafaela to you," Pedro said.

He ushered her forward holding her arm as she limped and dragged her atrophied right leg. Her little face was dominated by huge brown eyes with thick lashes. She looked up at us with raw need. My heart went to my throat.

He pulled a string and two bare bulbs gave off a harsh hot light that surged and dimmed with the fitful flow of electricity, a new development for the town.

"A wonderful thing," he said. "Sit down, my friends, please."

He took on a more formal air as he gestured to a crude wooden table with three chairs. Luke and I sat down with Pedro. Cande and the kids remained standing, watching us, anticipating our enjoyment of the meal, which was their gift to us. Everyone was quiet as Luke and I waited at the table.

My birthday supper was chicken broth and warm Coke. Cande served us large bowls of bouillon with the bumpy feet of the chicken hanging over the sides.

"The flavor is in the feet," he said. "Feel free to," and then he tunneled his lips and pulled air into his mouth.

I knew he meant suck on them. My stomach knotted. I could not touch the feet, much less suck on them. I knew I was wasting something of value, something the children might have eaten if it was not for their dinner guests. There was no meat in the soup, no vegetable. No sign of oysters or ceviche. The children did not get soup or Coke. I forced myself to eat, which meant to drink the broth and Coke. I worried that my face gave away my disgust at the chicken claws.

"Our main meal is in the middle of the day. At night, the tradition is to have coffee and cookies," said Pedro.

"The children must love the cookies," I said.

What a stupid thing to say. When cookies become your meal, it's because something better is not available, which removes them from the treat list.

"Muy rico," I said. I tried to express my appreciation for the meal.

Luke nodded and said gracias several times.

Pedro walked us home after supper. He stood at the door of the van as Luke and I climbed inside. He lingered in an awkward silence before he spoke.

"I cannot care for Rafaela as she needs. I cannot get her a brace or proper crutches." He looked down at the ground and paused. "I wonder if you would take her with you when you go. Take her to America where she can get the help she needs."

I could not grasp what he was saying. He seemed to be offering to give us his child. I could not believe that a family was so poor that it was better to give a child away. Rafaela had no brace and depended on a crude wooden stick to get around. She was scrawny and weak, unable to keep up with her siblings who looked unhealthy as well. She looked hungry for love and attention. *Her life must be a misery.* Who would marry her? How would she have children and care for them? I looked at Luke and my eyes widened. I wanted to rescue her.

"Tell Pedro we are so sorry," Luke looked at me sternly, as if he did not trust that I would quote him accurately. "Tell him yes, our country is richer, but you and I have nothing of our own. Tell him we have no job or house, only this van."

I stared back at Luke, my eyes pleading. In Pedro's eyes we were wealthy with our clothes, our pots and pans, and our van. Luke looked distressed.

"Tell him," he repeated.

"Luke is saying to let us think about it," I said.

"Of course, of course, I understand," Pedro said.

"Okay, now. Really tell him. I know you didn't," Luke said.

I had forgotten that even though Luke could not speak Spanish his passive vocabulary was strong.

"I only told him we'd get back to him," I said.

"We don't need to get back to him. We cannot do it," he said emphasizing each word.

We thanked him repeatedly for my birthday meal. Luke was too weak to stay angry and fell back into bed. I was still hungry. Who ate the chicken? Did the children get any of the meat? Caffeine at night took the edge off their hunger and their tummies were filled with lard and sugar. But it appeared everyone had gone without for my birthday party so that Luke and I could eat.

I lay down next to him and looked in his eyes. "We could still take her, Luke, we could do it if we wanted to."

"Ali. No. We cannot do it. Think."

Luke appeared to be using all his energy trying to make me understand. He closed his eyes.

"We could give her so much. Even crutches would help her."

I thought of my pal Ruthie who'd almost died of polio in the 50's and now, with a brace and metal crutches, could not be held back and lived a full life.

"Use your head. I don't even have a way of making money. We barely have enough for ourselves while we are here. I know you mean well, but it's a ridiculous thought." He shook his head, "Anyway, you can't just up and take a little kid out of Mexico, away from her family."

"I almost feel like we're obligated. We have so much more than they do."

"Put your heart back in a box and let it go, Al."

It was not only my heart; now I see it was my wish to make the world after my own image. I had never felt so rich and so poor all at one time.

***

The following day I made Luke walk to town again. It would have been better for him to rest, but I could not tolerate seeing him so sick. I had to make him move, as if that would mean he was better.

The tortilla ladies had adapted to our presence and made enough extra so that we could get a supply each day. We walked slowly, Luke scuffing his feet under an oppressive blanket of heat and humidity. We made it to the tortilla bakery and bought the last dozen. Luke collapsed on our way back and said he could not go any further. He sat down on the side of the road with his head in his hands.

"Shit, Al, I feel like shit."

I had heard those words before. He could not get any more specific. It was my fault. I made him come. I was selfish. I was childish. How was I going to get him home? I sat down beside him on the scrubby roadside grass, angry with myself for pushing for what I wanted. I was at a loss. The sun pounded down, relentless. Luke was sweating. I put my hand on his forehead. I felt the zig-zaggy vibration of fever in my own hand. Was I killing him by dragging him around?

Like a mirage, a brand new shiny white pickup truck came slowly toward us from town and pulled over in a cloud of dust. The driver offered us a ride and told us to climb into the back. A picture of Luke pushing me up from Destiny onto the dock when we first met came to me as I was now having to push Luke up because he did not have the strength to pull himself.

The passing of any vehicle was unusual, much less one so shiny and new. But the bigger surprise was what we saw when we went to climb in the back. A dozen adults and children squeezed together along either side of the truck's bed with a huge bunch of white tuber lilies between them. At first, I did not see the tiny coffin that sat beneath the flowers, as glossy white as the new truck.

They were on their way to bury a young child.

Everyone pushed tightly together to make room for us. A young man said that for the love of god the baby had been called back. He smiled sadly as he kept one hand on the casket. I imagined they had pooled money together to rent the truck for the funeral. Generosity was second nature to them, even in their sorrow. I looked at the miniature coffin, a sparkling whiteness glinting in the sun, and I shivered as if death was contagious and I had no antibodies.

Wherever we went in Mexico there was help if we needed it. In the most rural areas people seemed to appear from nowhere. Although we did not know it in Aticama, our alternator was damaged in the hurricane. We would break down several times that year, usually far from the reach of any mechanic. It never failed that someone would rescue us. A family chugging along in an old beat-up car, spewing exhaust, a man on a burro carrying mesquite branches, a farmer who fixed our engine with a paperclip, someone would stop and offer help.

I knew I'd received something much greater than a ride. If I'd been wondering what intimacy was, well, this was an example. They went out of their way to take us home. They knew where we lived, all the villagers did. Then they turned back to take the road up into the hills where they would say goodbye to their baby.

I could not name what made it intimate, other than to understand that it had something to do with a loving presence. Was this a sign that Luke and I should be loving and present for each other?

Is this what sex was about, not games of seduction or conquering, but to be present and fully alive with one another?

***

We prepared to leave Aticama. We had been there for a month, every day feeling longer than twenty-four hours. I had explained to Pedro that we couldn't take Rafaela. He said he understood, but I knew he didn't. I was not sure I understood either.

Pedro had asked us to get him birth control. He and Cande were so afraid of having another baby. It was the least we could do. Luke and I said we would make the trip to Tepic.

I drove the three hours up into the hills and across the mountains with Luke lying in the back on the bed, holding on to the thin mat beneath him as we bounced along. The roads were rugged, and pothole ridden. The glaring fact that I would drive to Tepic for Pedro but was unable to go for Luke eluded me. I did think of driving Dad when he was down for the count, even though I was years too young to have a license. I felt important to Dad as I handled a tough situation. Maybe I was too angry at Luke for being sick. Maybe I thought I would get more credit from helping Pedro than I would have caring for Luke. Either way, it does not speak well of me.

I was determined to do something for Rafaela, even if that meant without Luke's knowledge. Luke was pragmatic. Sometimes that was right, and I was dreaming when I should have been awake. But sometimes I had to follow my own instinct. I reasoned that Luke and I could not think the same way about everything. Our mission was to find contraceptives in a country where they were still illegal in 1975. But I had Rafaela on my mind. The pharmacist looked at me with disgust when I mentioned birth control, reluctantly offering me foam and condoms. When I asked for crutches for a child, her expression softened. She showed me some small adjustable crutches, crude but better than Rafaela's one stick. I did not have quite enough money.

She agreed to sell them for less because I told her a child had polio in Aticama.

I asked for medicine for Luke with little hope that there was anything for him. Strangely, she knew right away what he had, although I did not understand the name of the sickness. It was not cholera, but it was more than dysentery. He was not going to die. I put the crutches under my skirt as I went back to the van. Luke was sleeping and I hid them under the front seat. When he woke up, I gave him two pills. He felt so much better by the time we got back to Aticama that it seemed miraculous.

I cannot answer the question of why we allowed Luke to suffer for so long. It was also true that we did not know how to take care of ourselves. I accepted that we couldn't take Rafaela, but at least I did something for her. I hoped Luke would not miss the money.

We gave Pedro a month's supply of foam and as many packages of condoms as we could afford, but he had no way of getting any more. We left him and his family with promises. We would send dishes and eating utensils, clothes and toothbrushes, paper, and pencils.

Even as we swore our promises. I came to understand that life is full of broken promises. Even then I wondered if we would follow through and if anything would ever reach them. They did not read and there was no post office. Our hearts were heavy when we said goodbye.

It was all inadequate, nothing was enough.

29

THE REAL WORLD

I stood leaning forward on my grocery cart at the checkout counter of the Puritan supermarket.

Why did we need all this food?

We'd spent several more months in Mexico with too many adventures to relay here. Luke recovered well. I got sick a few times, the van broke down repeatedly. Luke took care of me and I recovered well also. Living alone in a small space agreed with us. We grew closer. We laughed a lot. We ate sparingly, but we were not hungry.

At about the time our money was running out we had a serendipitous happening. We were parked on a small beach in Puerto Angel a fishing village way down the Pacific coast. Above us on the hill was an expensive inn. We could hear glasses clinking and men happily yelling late into the night. One morning we walked up to sneak into the inn bathroom before anyone got up. Wads of pesos were strewn along the pathway. We were like the Publisher's Clearing House winners. We clamped our hands over our mouths, picked up dollar by dollar and ran back to the van where we sat and counted and giggled. Seventy-five dollars was a windfall and it kept us going until we got home.

Now I stood in the checkout line with Bumble Bee tuna fish and Hellman's mayonnaise, Lay potato chips and Colby cheese, chicken, and fish. And yet, we rarely missed anything in Mexico. Simple eating made for less choice and fewer disappointments. How quickly we became picky about our favorite cereals or breads. Choices became wants, and desires mysteriously became needs.

As I unloaded the basket, the fluorescent lights made me dizzy. The conveyor belt rushed along, every item moving in a frantic race to get to the bagger who jammed the food into a paper bag. I understood how my psychiatric patient Margaret felt when I took her to buy groceries. I wanted to scream, "Stop! Take it all back. I don't want it."

I paid with food stamps, our only successful achievement since coming home a few weeks before. I felt guilty but we needed them. We had no work and we were still parked in our van in a friend's driveway.

I carried the heavy bag up Mass. Ave. to Porter Square. It was not as hard as toting all those buckets of sea water in Aticama, but I was flagging. I had been unusually tired, depressed I imagined from being home.

I headed directly for the bathroom when I got back and threw up.

"Robbie's irritated with us," Luke said as he stored our groceries. "We need more propane if we want to cook anything."

"They only see us when we use the bathroom," I said. "I don't feel well."

"I'm sorry Al, but I think we need to move on. Before we get kicked out."

***

"I'm pregnant."

"Jesus." Luke jolted back. "How did that happen?"

After days of nausea and fatigue I'd gone to the hospital for a test and saw the dreaded blue line.

"Bad timing. What are we going to do?"

I sat down next to him on our all-in-one bed, storage area, and sofa and put my head down in my hands. Luke put his arm around me and pulled me close.

His voice was soft. "I don't think we have any choice."

Like Pedro's desperate request for us to take Rafaela in Aticama, we were faced once more with how ill equipped we were, how unready to take care of anyone but ourselves.

***

I called my parents the next morning wishing I could go to them for comfort or advice. I hadn't even told them we were home. Mum said she was coming in town to go to Lord & Taylor and she would take me to lunch. I knew I would not feel like eating but a free lunch was always welcome on principle.

"Where are you and what's this number?" she sounded desperate.

"We're staying with friends until we get our own place."

I climbed out of the van when she came into the driveway and we shared a powdery kiss hello. I could not invite her into the house, so I showed her the inside of the van.

"This is our little home, Mum. It took us all over Mexico. Pretty soon we'll have an apartment."

I should have lied.

"You're living in a driveway? Really Alicia, what has happened to you? What are you thinking?"

I am thinking about the abortion I am having tomorrow. I am thinking about what Luke and I are going to do for money. I am thinking that I have not seen you for a year and you're already annoyed with me.

I said nothing.

"I'm not even going to mention this to your Father."

Either she was doing me a favor or was too horrified to tell him. Or both.

***

I woke up queasy and shaky. Luke held my hand as we walked across town to the clinic.

Was this the best we could do? A small nondescript building in a poor neighborhood with a sign reading East Cambridge Free Clinic did not advertise abortion, but in 1976 everyone knew where to go. We were quiet as we walked in. It was the most somber thing we had ever done together. I flashed back to the tiny white coffin in Aticama.

Right at the entrance to the clinic several pale bland women with long skirts waved Bibles in my face like weapons and chanted, "Baby killers." I held my head up as if I knew what I was doing. But there was a weeping in my belly. Yes, we were lucky to have the choice, but it felt more like necessity.

The waiting room was crowded with women white and black, a few younger than I was and others older. No one spoke to or looked at one another. All heads were face down, everyone thinking their own thoughts. Luke and I sat silent, tight against each other for a long time. The warmth of his body was a comfort.

I was called into an office to speak to a counselor. Are you sure you want this procedure, have you discussed it with your partner, is anyone coercing you to make this decision? Sign these papers affirming your free choice and absolving the clinic of any wrongdoing.

It was disconcerting.

I walked back into the waiting room. Luke looked like it was happening to him, too. He gave my hand a small squeeze. There were several women by themselves. I was lucky to have a man to hold the pain with me. I loved him for that.

Sometime later a woman came out of another room and called me, first name only. Luke was not allowed to come with me. I walked into a small, gray room, barely heated with a surgical table right in the center. She gestured for me to sit down. The doctor appeared through another door, said to lay down, feet in stirrups, open my knees that felt glued together. I would experience strong cramping from the suction. Like when a speculum was inserted. Then I heard the whirring sound of a machine and I realized he was vacuuming out my baby. I held that thought for a second, then shut it down.

He said I was about seven weeks.

It was all very fast for an ache so deep.

They both said to get up slowly. Sit for half an hour in the waiting room. Go to the emergency room in case of heavy bleeding.

Luke's fallen face and sorry eyes were waiting for me. There was no trace other than a little blood, like a heavy period. It was the second time the universe had offered us a child and we refused.

***

"How do you think we're doing?" I asked Luke a few days later.

"You seem to have recovered, Al."

"I meant together, the two of us."

We continued an ongoing discussion of our relationship, taking each other's psychic temperatures, as if we were ill. But we never discussed the abortion. There was nothing to say.

"Mexico was good," Luke said.

"You were sick for the first two months."

"Yeah, but we got through it together."

Luke was all about the *we*. It was not whether something was easy or hard, but whether we did it together. He would get frustrated if I made plans that we had not discussed. The way we became a couple he said, was to share, to do things together, to give up some of the 'I' in order to make a joint decision. It rankled me. Don't tell me what to do, don't fence me in. All I needed was another adult to try to control me. He tried to be patient, as if he held a big picture that I was not ready to see.

***

Life went on deceptively easily after our abortion. I do not think I ever fully processed it or realized how it affected me. I put it in the same compartment that I had for anonymous sex or personal freedom. Whether it was too difficult to think about or too easy to forget, I moved on. And Luke moved on as well. I went back to Barney's restaurant and he returned to work at Earth Guild Grateful Union. We found a cheap apartment outside of Cambridge. A priest's mother had died, and he wanted to get the apartment off his hands. Luke began massage school and I made plans for my graduate studies. We got into a rhythm of work, study, work, study.

Luke came home one afternoon after class, two months or so into his year-long program. We sat at the kitchen table drinking tea. It was exciting to have a table, to say nothing of having our own apartment. I felt the luxury of a home together, each of us moving forward on our own path.

"I have a small piece of bad news. You won't believe this, Al. They kicked me out of the program. I was brought before a triumvirate of three women. They held court and I was convicted."

"Huh? What does that mean?"

"It means I'm out. They expelled me."

"You've gotta be kidding. How can they do that? You paid so much money."

"Yeah, well, the head of the program has henchmen or henchwomen and he gave them the authority."

"What did you do?"

Luke was always on the edge of trouble. He had left a credit card maxed out in California, they had put a boot on his car for unpaid traffic tickets, and now?

"I questioned him. I pushed him. He expected the class to take everything he said and swallow it. I wasn't going to do that."

"Oh…now you know how I feel when you try to control me."

"I'm not trying to control you, for shit's sake. And that's a different situation. The director's a dick. And he doesn't like men because he can't twist them around his little finger."

I was angry with the school, but I could imagine Luke being provocative. He had a hostile edge when he was mad. He did not like going along with the program, whatever the program was.

"It's your bad news, not mine. I'm about to start school, and I won't be bringing in much money," I said.

"Don't worry, Al. I'll keep giving massages."

Luke had no license to practice, but we had to live.

"You better clean up your act. This is getting old."

I was humiliated and worried our friends would find out. Hippie days were over, at least for us, but Luke had not caught up.

30

THE HOT TUB - 1976

It was impossible to ignore the peacocks' proprietary, but aimless occupation of the property. The silly birds wandered screaming in all directions.

I had arrived at the Westerbeke Ranch in California for a week-long residential introduction to the Ph.D. program at San Francisco's Humanistic Psychology Institute. A university without walls, like Goddard, it offered degrees to students studying alternative, innovative subject matter.

The Ranch in Sonoma County, twenty miles or so from the city, was also a destination for all sorts of group meetings and was rented by the Institute.

Soon after I arrived, the school's faculty and one hundred new students gathered to meet one another, present our admissions proposals, and form our doctoral committees.

Luke and I had been back from Mexico for six months. The moment by moment present state of mind in Mexico gradually shifted. It had to shift because my life in the states was all geared to the future, organizing, planning, and managing. As I accepted being back, I grew excited about the doctoral program because it offered an opportunity to present what I considered to be interesting new ideas about the integration of Reichian theory with

Developmental Psychology. As far as I knew at the time, no one had put the two theories together. Reichian therapy neglected the therapeutic relationship, focusing only on the patient's experience of his own body. Object Relations (the developmental theory I was interested in) was centered on the therapeutic relationship but did not acknowledge the importance of the patient's physiological experience. My thinking found a way of combining the two so that Reich was grounded in more recent psychodynamic thought and, conversely, Developmental Psychology could be included in body-oriented therapy.

Every student was required to come to California for a week at least twice a year. Sounded like fun. An academic kind of camp like the Goddard conference I had attended during my master's program. This time I would not be distracted as I was at Goddard by anything sexual. I was in a committed relationship. Sex, other than with Luke, was the last thing on my mind.

I spent a night in the city and took a taxi early the next day to Sonoma. A cool morning fog lingered over the ranch carrying the moist green menthol of eucalyptus. I took some deep breaths. The Ranch, a stucco faced motel-type layout that could use some fresh paint, offered individual rooms, each with their own bath. The rooms opened onto a terraced area and outside pool.

I found my room, number ten, and met my roommate who had arrived earlier from Florida. She was unpacking, barely acknowledged my presence, and kept her back to me. I had questions, but I could see she was not going to be any help. I put my bag down at the foot of the other twin bed and left the room.

At a loss of what to do until lunch, I walked around the grounds dodging the peacock poop scattered on the grass and offering a brief hello to other wandering students. I kept to myself, pretending I was engaged in a comfortable exploration of the property. I sat under a tree and read. My stomach was grumbling with hunger, but no one seemed to be offering food. All that time waiting and wondering left me self-conscious about being alone.

The moment I saw people going into the dining room I followed along. I stayed quiet during an early supper. Fellow students of all ages, from different parts of the country, talked with one another while I grew increasingly isolated. I had waited too long to break in and now I was trapped inside myself. At the end of the meal a general announcement directed us to the location of each group and the schedule for the evening posted on the dining room door.

Before coming to California, I had received a letter from the Institute. I was lucky, they said, to have Jim Berenson—a colleague of Abraham Maslow, and co-founder of the Humanistic Psychology movement—as my committee chairperson. Even though Reich was not considered humanistic, Jim's reputation would lend my dissertation gravitas.

Ten of us settled in a large circle as Jim introduced himself. He was a tall, kind looking man with bright eyes behind thick tortoise shell glasses, casual and friendly, a bit reserved. Jim introduced an assistant professor, Richard who co-led our group and would be a second member of our committees. I pegged him immediately as a player, handsome in a Hollywood way with a perennial tan. Something in his eyes made him appear defensive.

We went around the circle introducing ourselves and our area of study. A young man from Virginia was studying holographs. I did not know what they were at that time, much less understand what he was doing with them. An older guy from Chicago was studying Wittgenstein's philosophy and the evolution of language. My roommate's area was the world of dreams, mostly dreams in her world.

The variety of alternative subjects explained why all of us had chosen a university without walls.

Back in Cambridge, Reuben and Harold had agreed that I needed an alternative program if I continued my Reichian studies. They hoped I would write a theoretical dissertation that would expand Reich's position within psychology

My heart thudded and I started to sweat as my time to speak approached. It made me angry with myself because I lost track of my own excitement and knowledge. I forgot that I possessed a body of understanding and interest that others may know little about. I felt a glare, the harsh light of attention, focus on me.

"And who do we have here? Where'd you come from?" Richard turned to me with his head cocked, curious, but more sardonic than kind.

"I'm from Boston." The words came from the back of my throat.

"Ohhhh.... she's a Boston beaver."

I shivered as he feigned an exaggerated expression of surprise and delight. He imitated me, using a Brahmin New England accent that I did not have.

Everyone laughed.

I had come to believe people in groups are cowards, no one stands up for anyone else. I laughed weakly too, trying to go along with the joke as I turned red and shrank further into myself. I had not heard the term *Boston beaver* before, but I got it.

Later when I was forced to speak again, he raised his eyebrows and said, "Ohhh, the lady from Boston can speak. One can only imagine what else she has to say."

He played with me and flattened me, all in two brief interactions. The name stuck for the week whenever Richard had the chance to address me.

***

My individual meeting with Jim was scheduled for ten the next morning. I slept badly and woke up early. I felt shaky and wished I could go home.

I tried to pull my thoughts together. My roommate was lying on her back with her eyes open. I said good morning. Her hand flew up like I was the vampire in *The Horror of Count Dracula,* and she was trying to resist my bite. She told me to refrain from speaking to her in the morning because she needed complete silence to recall her dreams. I apologized.

She was a weird bitch.

Any thought of my room as a safe place disappeared. I felt angry with myself again, this time for allowing her to take over our room.

Jim had suggested we meet in the inside pool area where it was warm. Good idea to bring my bathing suit. I would tell my friends back home that only in California would I meet my chairperson in a bathing suit. I put my suit on under my clothes and grabbed my notebook.

As I walked from my room across the terrace to the dining hall a male peacock strutted his stuff in front of two females. He backed right smack into them and flared his fancy plumage, giving them everything he had. The hens were blasé and turned their backs. It made no difference that his fan of feathers was magnificent.

I remained shy at breakfast, but San Francisco's sour dough bread made delicious toast and I had several pieces with plum preserves and coffee. I began to feel my excitement again. There was also a relief that my meeting was with Jim and not Richard. They were complete opposites and Jim's reserve was more familiar to me. I thought he seemed shocked by Richard's sexual innuendos in the group. I thought Jim might stand up for me. I did better one on one and I hoped he would listen and hear what I had to offer.

Jim was sitting in the hot tub which was adjacent to the large pool. He gave me an enthusiastic hello and told me to come on in. I took off my clothes and he said I did not need my bathing suit, that the water was so nice without it.

He was naked.

I froze.

When I was fourteen, Mr. M, Father of a boy I knew, was pulling me onto his lap, drunk, laughing, smiling widely, head back, "You beauty you, come warm me up." And I did. It happened repeatedly and I felt turned on and horrified all at one time. I fantasized about him, alone in my bed, a pillow pressed between my legs. I felt guilty that my body was out of my control and I was aroused. I looked for opportunities for it to happen again. I would have had sex with him if he had asked. It would have been my first time.

"Take it off," Jim said.

I took it off and climbed into the tub. Like a good girl. I was not aroused but did I even consider the possibility of saying no?

I sat as far away from Jim as was possible in a four-person tub with my arms crossed over my breasts. I cringed, unable to keep our legs from touching. I could see how excited he was, how turned on, and I could not believe I had ended up in this California school.

Is this what it takes to get a Ph.D.?

"Tell me how you came to Reich." he said.

On automatic pilot, I described my experiences with yoga, the way that led me to Eastern spiritual thought, to Harold, and then Reich, one thing following another, while in a silent background my mind darted from corner to corner, frantic to find an exit. The chemical odor of chlorine, there to kill off any dirty germs, was no help for this invasion.

I continued, "I experimented with my own eyes, focusing on the pin light of a flashlight, and I felt the way moving the eyes with the light stimulated the brain, which led me to thoughts about the infant looking at the mother."

"Fascinating," Jim replied. "The eyes as a pathway to the brain."

His eyes sparkled, his arms spread wide, enveloping the edge of the tub. He looked so comfortable, so completely in charge, entitled with his erect penis.

I began to shiver. My nipples shriveled into two tiny dots.

I continued, "And reading *Object Relations* theory out of England made me think about the importance of eye contact with the mother and its early role in the formation of the self."

"So, you believe the mother looking into the eyes of the infant and the baby returning that look is pivotal in development," Jim said. "Was that true for you?"

He had no trouble looking directly at me while I did everything I could to avoid his stare.

I did not give him a direct answer. "And working with Reichian eye movement in therapy can help with the healing of early trust issues," I said.

My mind raced to Mother. Where was she when I needed her? Why didn't she protect me from Father? Where had she ever been?

I imagined Jim thinking, *Where is my potent drink with the miniature parasol and red cherry on a colored toothpick?* He shifted in the tub, spreading his legs wide, hitting up against my thighs.

"An interesting rich proposal. But difficult to craft a theoretical dissertation," he said.

"I'm good with theory," I said. "Better than I would be with a statistical thesis."

At that moment I would not have been able to add two single numbers together.

I refused to look directly at him. What would it be like to vomit into the water?

What was he thinking? He became pathetic in my eyes. For Christ's sake, he was a smart man known for several books on Humanistic Psychology. He was one of the fathers of the movement. Jim was a shy man caught up in the Esalen model of free expression to do whatever. Yet, I felt I had to protect his ego, avoid shaming him as if his maleness was so fragile it would disintegrate if I said something like *What the fuck are you doing, you idiot?*

I said nothing.

"I look forward to talking with you further as the week goes on," Jim said.

I wrapped myself in my towel as I carefully maneuvered out of the tub to avoid exposing myself.

After our meeting, I went back into my room and hid until supper. My roommate was nowhere to be found. There was the typical bright light of a California day, and she was outside enjoying it. All my energy, even if anxious, was gone. I felt like I had been hit by a car and could not get up. I needed emergency treatment, but there was nothing. I was on my own.

I dozed on and off, opening my eyes briefly, but saw Jim's probing eyes and skinny thighs cradling his erection, and shut myself down again as if I could make it go away by remaining unconscious.

I went to supper, stayed silent, frozen. I picked at my food, but it was only for show. The chicken tasted spoiled, the fresh vegetables sour. I retreated to my room again, missing a meet and greet evening of fun and whatever else they were doing with each other.

In the hot tub I should've been more easy-going, no big deal, made a joke of put your penis back in your pocket and listen to me.

I wanted to go home. There were five days to go.

I hated Jim. But I needed him.

***

We reconvened the following morning out on the grass in the shade of the eucalyptus trees. It was a generic optimistic California morning, cool with the scent of the menthol trees wafting in a soft breeze. California always seemed too good to be true, unconcerned about humanity's deeper problems. I could hear Jim saying something like this was *an opportunity for each of us to talk up our ideas in more depth*.

My attention was in pieces. I did not know how to market my proposal anyway, but today my mind was underwater, unable to shake off the feel of Jim's legs in the hot tub.

We sat in a circle to discuss our Ph.D. projects, taking turns to present our ideas. The group began with a woman who had arrived a day late and lay on a lawn chair in the center. Judith was loud, complaining in a New Jersey accent that her back was in so much pain, we were lucky she made it. Yes, thank god she made it. Her doctoral thesis was more significant than anything the rest of us had to present; the transcription of a still anonymous person who was channeling *The Course in Miracles*, a mammoth three volume treatise offering a path to soul consciousness. That meant she was writing (translating) words that were being spiritually channeled by whomever. She was so obnoxious I wondered why anyone would want her to be transcribing their material. She rightly understood that the content would become famous in the esoteric world, but no one knew that at the time. She took up an inordinate amount of time and energy with her bodily complaints. I was too scared to talk, but I clenched my jaw and glowered at Jim for all the attention given to her.

When my turn came, I stumbled over my words. I struggled to move outside of myself and be present in the group. Richard referred to me as BB, which elicited small uncomfortable smiles from the group. It had always been a problem for me that my interior thoughts rang louder than anything I could manage to say to another person. It was my norm in the group meetings.

Jim tried to help, reflecting back what I said and translating what was inarticulate to the group. Some people asked questions like who Wilhelm Reich was and why was he important, etc., and that helped me talk more. I felt stupid and inadequate. I listened to my peers, unable to stand up for what I had been so excited about at home.

Each day Jim seemed anxious to jump into the conversation, fill in the blanks in my presentation. Ordinarily, I would have appreciated the support. What did he want from me?

***

As the residency wound down, Jim and I made plans to talk weekly on the phone, as if nothing unusual had occurred in the hot tub. Richard winked as he said goodbye. All in good fun. Several of the east coast students shared a van to the airport. I kept my head up until I boarded the plane and found my seat. Then I glued myself to the window and cried like a baby helpless to protect myself.

I tried to sneak into the apartment when I arrived home, but Luke was waiting.

"So, tell me everything. How was it?" he asked.

"Oh fine. It's a good beginning," I said.

My stomach flipped. I ran to the bathroom and threw up.

"What's going on, Al?"

"I don't know. I must have caught something on the plane."

Luke's brow furled. "Did something happen out there?"

"What do you mean? No. Nothing happened. I'm just tired."

I had already had a week of lies. What difference did one more make?

I did not want Luke to know how badly I had done. I felt ashamed that I had been made fun of, as if it was my fault. How had I lost so much ground? A year ago, I had been almost cocky, confident with all those guys I had picked up. I had felt strong and free. I had protected myself and held the reins. Even with Luke I had kept some cool. Why had I suddenly let all that strength get away from me?

Images of Jim in the hot tub continued replaying in my mind. His eyes bulging behind his glasses, leering, his long skinny octopus-like arms, his expectant penis. They made me feel sick and dirty. They took my breath away. Such a mild apparently kind man with such a well-recognized and respected reputation. There were few words at that time for trauma, (other than early studies of Vietnam vets), no stories of sexual abuse filling the airwaves, no treatments for the victims. In my therapeutic circles, it was not talked about, at least not in body-oriented programs which were mostly dominated by male psychologists. I was making too much of a small incident. I had to put it away and go on with the program. That would be me standing strong, not letting another man get to me.

Where was the line between being beaten down and my own deliberate habit of making myself smaller so that I wouldn't be a threat to anyone? I did not want to admit how disappointed I was in the program, and even more, how I had allowed myself to be disempowered. But worse, was that I did not say anything to anybody about the hot tub.

In 1976, shame and fear were the operative words describing sexual abuse. I was shamed and humiliated and afraid to speak out. A stronger woman would have stood up for herself

Instead, I tried to bury the experience and the rage that followed.

31
HYSTERICAL CONVERSION

Later that same year, Luke and I went to a talk, invited by friends who said, "You have to see this incredible man!"

The audience sat waiting until a door opened at the front of the conference hall. The man who emerged was pale, of medium height, dressed in an ill-fitting suit and tie. A cadre of young men, also in suits and ties, followed and surrounded him in a closed circle. I counted twelve, all similar in their appearance. Each one spankier than the next, all their edges rounded off, not open, not closed, not cold, not warm, but clean and white. I had never seen anyone in the real world that looked like them.

Californian, I thought.

Janet said they were John-Roger's disciples.

During our year in Mexico Luke and I received letters from friends back at home who gushed about an amazing spiritual teacher named John-Roger. We all knew of sham gurus who had fallen into disgrace, but JR, as he was affectionately called, was the real thing, at least all our friends (the spiritually oriented ones) said so. The fact that he was American might have made him more familiar.

He stood looking out at us, impassive, serious, and unremarkable. His most outstanding features were his tight blond permanent and thin blotched skin that looked like he might be allergic to sunlight. A disembodied voice over an intercom told the audience of one hundred or so to give JR his space and please not to approach him. The audience sat on the edge of our seats in anticipation.

When he finally spoke, he was dry and pragmatic. "Brothers and sisters, how do we live in this world? Tough, isn't it."

Like most of the gurus I had seen, JR chuckled when the conversation turned to suffering. The implication was, *if only we understood something important, we wouldn't have to suffer so much.*

JR continued, nodding, yes there was so much pain, so many messes all around us, so little we could control. "Follow universal laws," he admonished.

Luke whispered, "This must be the white version of a Tibetan Lama."

JR was direct and frank, did not smile much, and made his suggestions as if he did not care whether we agreed or not. It was our choice. He seemed to understand what it meant to be a frail human being in a chaotic and unmanageable universe. I heard him offering a way to transcend the mess. He went on to describe a level of manifestation, all of us at the mercy of our desires, mistaking material success for happiness

That was exactly what I felt, in pain and totally out of control. Someone heard me and all my desires. I wanted so many things: success and recognition, understanding, unconditional love, satisfying sex, a father who accepted me, and a dog like Old Yeller.

Why JR? Why not one of the many Indian gurus who have come through a long line of teachers? We had other friends who were with Muktananda or Maharishi. Was it timing? Here he was arriving on the scene when Luke and I were in a rocky transition from a peripatetic lifestyle to something more grown up.

His simple recommendation, "Surround yourselves with light and always, always, do it for the highest good of all."

All JR's thoughts and behaviors, he told us, were contained in that principle. He would never do anything that was not for our highest good. Those words became a motto, a talisman, a secret handshake, the first key of MSIA (Movement of Spiritual Inner Awareness). The invocation was a means of protecting ourselves and others from our own worst instincts, a purification of our own behavior and action. It helped me to feel less guilty for my imperfections.

He told us he'd been an English teacher named Roger from a Mormon family in Nebraska, and he'd had an epiphany in California when someone named John came to him in a vision and gifted him with sacred teachings and powers. Just a regular humble guy who happened to have been struck by enlightenment, human and godlike at one time. I did not pay too much attention to his background. Most spiritual leaders came from something unremarkable.

"Everybody I met in California had an epiphany," Luke whispered.

"Hush," the woman in front of us said.

Janet had told me that he and his disciples were celibate in order to retain purity in the body, the vessel of the higher self. From that first night it was made clear to us that our energy could hurt JR's energy. We carried with us the inherent danger of contamination. We had to keep our distance. The disciples were there to protect his aura. It felt a little insulting because it emphasized the poverty of my own spiritual progress.

"What? Are we all chopped liver?"

"Quiet, Luke."

He was not taking it seriously enough. I had noticed that gurus tended to be funny, as if they were in on some joke that the rest of us had not gotten. I resented that a bit, but they appeared to have the secret recipe. I wanted what they had. JR chuckled again at all of humanity's foolishness and foibles, but he added his own sense of compassion. We were all humorous in the eyes of spirit, he suggested. We could not help it, we were human.

"Of course, he made sense," Luke said later at home. "He didn't say anything that anybody doesn't already know."

"I know, but there's nothing new under the sun anyway, and there's something special about JR."

I assumed I was ahead of Luke on the spiritual journey, which was why I chose to suspend all judgment and leapt into the deep waters of devotion in the Movement of Spiritual Inner Awareness.

***

Luke and I sat on the rug with six others in the living room of a woman named Andrea who was decidedly further along the path than the rest of us. Small groups had formed all around town to meet weekly, meditate, and discuss JR's spiritual discourses, which were sent monthly by mail for a small fee. Each with a topic for study: spiritual longing, the trap of the ego, the mystery of the separate self, the danger of despair.

We had each received our own mantra from one of the disciples to use in our meditation. The mantra was whispered in our ears in an otherwise silent individual appointment and forbidden to be spoken aloud or shared. Luke and I never disclosed our mantras to each other.

Whenever I asked a question in my group the facilitator, Andrea, was patient with me. She was so full of light that she was radiant. I felt chastened by her big blue eyes. She was radiant with light which suggested my vibration was too low. My thoughts were negative. I was heavier and darker. Other members would say it was time to move on implying I was clogging up the flow of higher energy with my persistent negativity. I began to question my own doubt. Was I simply being cynical? Was I all too ready to disbelieve? I started to see my doubt as a flaw in my personality, a smug kind of intellectualism.

Looking back, I can remember sensing a shift in my mind. One pattern of thought gradually being replaced by another pattern of thought, the belief system I was learning in MSIA superseding what I had previously thought to be true. I saw myself being drawn in by a spiritual promise. I did nothing to stop it. I only hoped my tenacious negative suspicion and emotions would not block my ascension to higher levels.

***

I slept badly. I had gone to bed frustrated after the group. I could not seem to stop questioning. Yet not only were my questions unanswered, I got the distinct feeling I was not supposed to be asking them in the first place. "I just don't get the Mystical Traveler," I said. "Who is it? Is JR the Traveler? Is it Christ?" The idea of the Mystical Traveler was a central component of MSIA and yet no one could say what it was. "JR and Jesus seem one and the same?"

"Try to reflect on these questions in the silence of your own heart," Andrea said, sweetly.

Was she telling me to shut up?

"Okay," I said, chastened.

"Can we get back to tonight's Discourse?" someone asked.

The Discourse was *Surrendering to Spirit*.

I woke up in the middle of the night with my head burning, a headache that felt like a fire in my brain. It was as if I was under siege. I thought rage was attacking me, an invader from outside. I could not think it through because the headache was blinding. Pain supplanted rational thought. I got up and went into the living room. I did not want to wake Luke, nor did I want to talk. I put cold wet washcloths over my forehead. I sat on the sofa in the dark and sobbed, gulping not from emotion but from the throbbing burning sensation.

I yelled and growled into a pillow to release my jaw which was clamped tight, like the aura before a seizure. I wanted to throw it up, pour it out, get rid of it. Images streaked through my mind. Father in a blind rampage lashing out with his wild eyes and thundering growl. Jim in the hot tub, his lewd legs slithering underwater toward my thighs. Mr. M drunk with me on his lap, a grinning satyr, riotous laughter as he moved me around his lap. Images exploded like flashes of bright blinding lights that burned to ash. My body was doing everything it could to dispel my rage, my archenemy. There were no words. It seems obvious now, it was all the men who had transgressed, but back then I couldn't connect the frenzy in my mind with the men in my life.

And maybe JR was a painkiller. Maybe he was also a cause of my inner turmoil, but that did not occur to me. There were too many other men I was upset with.

Exhausted and drained, I meditated in the early morning hours to try to calm myself.

I went to our next meditation group hung over, bloodshot eyes, a dull thudding in my head. I attempted to stay as positive as possible because no one wanted to hear about my dark nights. Everyone except Luke was stubbornly and irritatingly positive, which made me burn inside. I had snarky retorts to various members who were striving to move up a spiritual ladder from the emotional to the etheric level of consciousness. Everyone was shining the light on every little thing. They were even calling on the light to find parking places.

"The thing is," I ventured, "if you cannot deal with some of the bad stuff in the world, what good is it to rise to the etheric level?"

"Perhaps that's the point, Alicia," someone said, cloning Andrea, "to rise above the chaos of this world."

All my doubts and questions were repeatedly shelved, like little children who are told if you cannot say something positive, do not say anything at all.

After a while I closed the door on all my bratty, childish retorts and aligned myself with the group. With that, I began to receive the rewards of membership in a closed, special, and favored group. I was a part of something, I was climbing the spiritual ladder, JR loved me (everyone said he did) and everyone associated with him loved me, too. I watched others who remained skeptical or negative and saw how they were automatically pushed to the sidelines, unable to receive the love.

***

Luke and I were thrilled with our new home except for the couple who lived above us. The man was the librarian in the German library of Harvard University. While his pale blond wife gave us a meek hello, her Aryan husband glared at us whenever we passed each other on the sidewalk.

One day, he spat on the sidewalk like a snake throwing its venom then hissed to Luke. "What are you anyway? I know you're something."

Luke looked Semitic and those words went right through me. Luke was speechless, looked frightened and explosive at the same time. We had been poisoned. I looked at their backs as they walked on, and I began to shake.

"We need to put him in the Light, Luke. For the highest good."

"Really, Al?" He looked at me like I was crazy." This is not voodoo. It's not magic."

"I know, but we need to fill ourselves with Light, right?"

It was as if our neighbor's hatred was seeping through the floor above us. MSIA was my talisman, protecting me from all the darkness in the world. Now, I see how desperate I was to protect myself from my own rage.

***

I finished breakfast and like a robot went immediately to the typewriter. I put carbon paper between two sheets and made a copy as I typed. My dissertation proposal was a hot potato in my hands. So blurry eyed from living most of every day in my mind I wrote down my thoughts as quickly as possible, overriding my own critical judgment. I wished I could go over my ideas with Jim on the phone, but the thought of hearing his voice gave me a pain in my gut.

I mailed something out and began waiting for a response every day. It would come when it came was Luke's advice. There was nothing I could do to hurry it up.

A thick envelope arrived in five days. For some reason I thought that was a good sign. My hands shook as I read his letter. *While we find your proposal original and thought provoking, the committee agrees that your writing and organization are 'hysterical.'* My stomach came up into my throat. *We see broad sweeps and generalizations without the specific focus and detail required to make your arguments. Please go back, rewrite and submit again.*

What did 'hysterical' mean? It was insulting. How about telling me how to correct it? I tried to flesh out my writing and add specific examples. My mind continued to freeze up. It felt like they were giving me a long rope and I was strangling myself. I sent off the next version even faster than the first, as if that would make difficult feelings disappear.

Jim sent my rewrite back, just as quickly. This time he said, *Go back to the drawing board.*

Start all over again?

I threw the letter down on the floor and yelled, "Fuck all of them!" as I stamped my feet and punched at the air.

"Al, calm down. Let it sit for a while before you respond."

"You don't understand how crazy making this is. What do they want from me? I have no idea what they are talking about. I cannot even talk face to face to ask questions. I'm banging my head against a wall."

"Well, don't do that. But you have got to get yourself under control. I thought that was what meditating and JR were for."

"They're going to tell me to surround myself with light."

I had already tried that. I was always surrounding my doctoral program, Jim, "Boston Beaver" Richard, myself with Light. (I can laugh now at my magical thinking, as if I was some golden haloed angel who could purify all thoughts and feelings of their negativity, but I was serious.) It did not work. The committee, my proposal, even my own thoughts remained dark shadows in my mind.

I was unable to move forward. It did not occur to me that my thought process had been crippled by the events with Jim and then buried by my spiritual practice.

***

I took my troubles to my next session with Reuben.

Why did they say my thinking was hysterical? What did that mean?

Reuben looked kindly at me and said my thinking was avoidant, that it was hard for me to look at some of my own feelings, and that I glossed over them so that I didn't have to face things head on.

But I was always having feelings, wasn't I? I was blinded in the way something that is too close becomes impossible to see. Reuben suggested I look up Hysterical Conversion Disorder. He said it might explain my seizures. And in the same way affect my thought process and my work on my proposal.

I left Reuben's house low that day. It was my first real psychological diagnosis and it sounded serious and bizarre. I found a book that explained Hysterical Conversion. It was an ancient mysterious syndrome as old as the age of Egyptian Pharaohs, but it was real. Seizures were one of its symptoms and the convulsions took the place of emotions that were cast off or hidden. No one knew exactly what to do about it.

I wondered if I would have been one of those women with St. Vitus' dance, the kind that men thought were crazy and dangerous in the Middle Ages. One curious thing is that modern-day research showed that soldiers with combat trauma displayed similar symptoms.

32

THE WHOLE WORLD IS ANGRY

It was1977. Body oriented therapy was on the forefront of psychology. Reuben was the face of Reich and Reich was a grandfather of all body treatment modalities. We were a motley group who followed Reich and Reuben. I thought many of them were pretty kooky and blatantly needy (we called them oral characters) but I did not consider myself like them. Eight of us, all fledgling therapists, sat cross legged in a small circle in our underwear on the third floor of a Green Street walkup in Cambridge. Reuben, our facilitator, also stripped down to his white jockeys, his European elegance diminished by his paunch and furry chest.

I could tell Reuben was a little nervous. He was used to one on one in his private office and was out of his element leading a workshop. But as we began working, one person at a time, analyzing bodies, yelling, and screaming at the top of our lungs he relaxed.

The room grew hot, the air damp with the sweat of emotional venting. One of the women got up and stood in front of us. A heavy-set woman with undefined features, she was already in tears, saying the person who had worked before her made her think about her own father. These workshops had the effect that one person's emotional release stirred up others, solidifying and heightening the group atmosphere.

I enrolled in training workshops almost every weekend, accustomed to sitting undressed in unventilated rooms, observing other members baring or resisting baring body and mind, and waiting for my turn to reach for some deeper emotional experience. I still assisted Harold when he was leading groups. He had a girlfriend now and the sexual energy I felt from him toward me had dissipated, which was a relief. He and Reuben were not getting along. I noticed Harold provoking Reuben into arguments over Reich. Harold had found Alexander Lowen, a student of Reich's who had developed an abridged and more popular version of Reichian theory and technique. Their conflict made me nervous and uncomfortable. I was afraid I would have to choose between them when I wanted the support of both men. Back then I overlooked the fact that I was permitting charismatic male facilitators with oversized egos to analyze my body, label me with a quick diagnosis, and coopt my expression of rage toward the men in my life to demonstrate their own techniques. In truth, the men I was so angry at were no different from them. I tried placing them all in JR's Light for the Highest Good. It did not help.

Reuben suggested that the woman in tears about her father scream into a pillow. Within seconds she took the pillow away from her mouth and let out a blood curdling screech.

"All right!" Reuben said, "that is a real scream! And your face has come alive. You look radiant, doesn't she?" He turned to the rest of us obviously pleased that he had helped the woman connect with her anger.

There was a pounding on the door. My heart skipped a beat. Reuben padded barefoot over to the door, his hairy naked chest, his belly hanging softly over his jockeys. A loud and serious knocking continued. He did not ask who it was and opened the door. Two cops stood on the threshold scanning Reuben from head to foot in slow motion. They peeked in with their eyes wide as they surveyed a near naked group sitting in a circle on the floor. They looked at each other.

"What the hell is going on here? We thought someone was being murdered," one of them said.

"Your neighbor complained," the other one said in a South Boston accent. "She says the stomping on the floor is making the plaster crumble on her ceiling. She says the yelling is frightening the bejeezus out of her. She's an old lady for god's sakes."

"What the heck?" the first cop said. He stared, looking twice at the bared breasts and bellies of the women.

"I apologize, officer. As you can see, everyone is fine. We're having an afternoon workshop," he said like it was a tea party.

He breathed heavily, but he always breathed with difficulty. He did not appear at all self-conscious.

"Workshop for what?"

We watched Reuben closely, knowing he was used to people who were threatened by our body work whether it was the traditional analysts at Harvard or the FDA's imprisonment of Wilhelm Reich.

Reuben took a deep breath, "It's emotional work that we're doing. We're learning about feelings."

The second cop repeated the word *murder* as he looked Reuben up and down. We sat frozen, waiting. Reuben laughed, always deflecting by joining in when others were critical of him.

"Well, not really killing people. We're trying to learn how to let feelings out so that we *don't* murder anyone."

That did not come out right. The cops looked at each other. A quick decision had to be made. Were they going to arrest Reuben for disturbing the peace or shut us down?

"We're all psychologists, Officer," Reuben said, "learning to assist individuals who need help navigating difficult feelings."

That sounded better. The room was stinky, like old tomato soup, not only from the two people who had worked, but the rest of us who were just plain anxious in the presence of what we could have called frightening fathers.

"Unh unh, glad you told us."

They looked at all of us. They did not cross the threshold.

"I'd be glad to show you what we do—"

"Forget it. We don't need to know," the South Boston cop said with his hands raised, fingers splayed. Any more information might require them to do something. "Just keep it down. We can't have you terrifying the neighbors."

"Absolutely not. Thank you, officers."

Reuben closed the door, raised his bushy eyebrows, and made a funny face at us. It was not the first time a body-oriented workshop had caused neighbors to complain, but it was new to have a visit from the police. Locating workshop spaces where it was safe to make a lot of noise was challenging. The possibility of angering neighbors was a constant concern.

Reuben lit a cigarette. "All right, we better scream into a pillow for the rest of the day. Let's take a fifteen-minute break." He breathed out a smoke-filled sigh.

***

When it was my time to stand in front of the group it did not take much on Reuben's part. He knew my body and my issues. My own anger sat vigilant on the surface of my being. All he had to do was have me breathe and let some sound out. A hot acidic fury rushed up from my belly into my mouth. I grabbed the canvas bat and began pounding the stool, my face contorted into a sneer, growling, strangely and upsettingly like Father. "I hate you Dad, you damned crazy bastard, I wish you were dead," I screamed. I lost track of where I was and what I was doing.

Reuben quickly gave me a pillow and I screamed. Again, and again, I slammed the pillow against the stool until I wore myself out and collapsed onto the ground. I didn't cry. There was no sadness, only pure rage. I went home with a headache, knowing I had done good work.

***

Perhaps because I was angry so much of the time, I noticed anger everywhere I went. People were yelling in our group, in our weekend workshops, in Luke's sessions with Velma. In our friendships there was always some kind of conflict brewing because they were yelling in their therapy too. Looking back, I think there were a lot of young people like myself who had discovered they were angry—about Vietnam, Nixon, Civil Rights, and with their own parents—and found channels for letting it out. The success of cathartic techniques in psychology was perfect timing.

Catharsis was its own goal. Sobbing or yelling; or yelling while sobbing. I had a well of undifferentiated rage and there was a relief in its release. But I sensed an unexpected consequence. The more I expressed my anger, which I did at every opportunity, the angrier I became. It could be the fact that releasing some rage allowed the rest of it to surface. But I considered that the anger was feeding on itself.

I often had a headache after a session of yelling, and I still felt angry. It took me time to admit it because a high value was placed on free expression, something I was good at.

Yet, I realized all the yelling and hitting in the world was not going to take the place of standing up to my father.

33

ME AND MY SHADOW

I told the other two women in the group to sit on our comfortable sofa. Despite its impractical soft blue flowered chintz, it was the first real piece of furniture Luke and I had bought together. It made me feel grown up.

I brought in three straight backed chairs from the kitchen for Reuben, Harold, and me that Luke and I had picked up off the sidewalk in front of one of Brattle Street's rich Cambridge homes. Meeting at our apartment gave me a feeling of pride. I had a home, a partner, and I was in a professional group. A supervision group had formed consisting of Reuben, Harold (my other mentor), Luke's therapist Velma, Ildrie (an older clinician who wanted to learn about bodywork), and me. I was the youngest, and I felt proud and important.

The meeting was to decide on what would go into the first edition of a new journal we were publishing together.

Tensions were high because competition had intensified over the past few months between Reuben and Harold about who was more important in the lexicon, Reuben's idol Reich, or Harold's idol Lowen. Furthermore, the last time I had assisted Harold (in the training group he ran) he had me stand in front of the group and said, "We have an example here of the hysteric, the woman who flirts but runs away, the woman who draws a man in and rises above and rejects him."

I had been too stunned to respond, but the words were fermenting inside me.

"Just because Lowen didn't invent the concepts doesn't mean he hasn't contributed to them. In my mind he makes the whole thing much clearer," Harold was saying to our supervision group.

I could hear the room sighing. We had barely begun, and Harold was off again.

"We've discussed this over and over again," Reuben said. "This edition is about Reich."

"Please, you two, let's try to work together," one of us said.

Luke came into the room briefly, delivered a pot of mint tea with a mix and match of five mugs and put it down on the table in front of the sofa. Everyone said hello to Luke, except Harold. In a strange and mutually agreeable hostility, they had not spoken to each other since my last breakup with Luke three years before.

Harold waited until Luke left the room. "It seems to me all of you are protecting Reuben, like he's the big daddy."

He looked directly at me. He was poking. He looked smug.

"No one's protecting anyone, Harold," I said.

I shook my head, rolling my eyes at Reuben, wondering if he was as disgusted as I was.

"Harold. This meeting is not about us, it's about publishing new ideas," Reuben said. He turned to me, "I'm hoping you'll write a case study on the eye movement you've been doing with your schizophrenic patient, Alicia."

"I see what you're doing. You are changing the subject. Admit it," Harold's voice was getting louder.

Reuben was provoking Harold, using me as the weapon. As a patient I looked up to Reuben as a perfect human being. As a peer I observed his flaws. I was not accustomed to seeing men as equals. In my mind they held all the power. The fact that so many male egos needed a constant massage presented me with a contradiction I had not resolved.

If I had to side with one of them it would be Reuben. But truthfully, I was fed up with both men. How had we ended up in this pathetic cockfight?

The tension in the room thickened. I gritted my teeth. I would not lose my temper, I would not, no matter what Harold said. Velma, a shy kind woman, was silent as usual. Whenever there was any sign of conflict, she disappeared, just like Mother. I knew she was doing good work with Luke, but it made me mad when she hid from any conflict in our group.

Harold turned to me. "I know how devoted you are to Reich, Alicia. Devotion can be blinding."

"I still have my own mind, Harold," I said. The muscles in my cheeks began to vibrate.

"And your so-called *spiritual path* is telling," he sniped.

That was a low blow. Harold and I had first come together sharing spiritual paths. He had been critical and disappointed that I took on MSIA full force. I was about to slug him if he refused to shut up.

"That you're a *mystical character*," he continued, "you see everything through your own beliefs."

I swallowed hard. Even if there was some truth in what he said all I heard was whining. The whine that grows in intensity right before the two-year-old explodes in a full-blown tantrum. He was a snide bastard looking for a fight. My heart was throbbing fist, about to burst out of my chest.

"If only you would recognize it, take a good look at yourself. Maybe you would not get lost in guru worship," he pointed his finger at my face.

"Alright, Harold, let's try to stay away from attacking others' characters," Reuben said.

Reuben's eyebrows had frozen into a straight line across his forehead, and he was breathing heavier than usual. Velma took a sip of her tea and put the mug down gently on the table, careful not to draw any attention to herself.

"You have your own guru Harold. His name just happens to be Lowen," I said.

I watched his sallow face turn red.

There were a few random attempts to calm everyone and a collective throat clearing.

I leaned back against the ropes of the boxing ring readying to go back in. The muscles in Harold's face were straining.

"Harmony at all costs," he sneered. "Especially with you, Alicia. I see what's underneath your *harmony*. I see you."

"Jesus, Harold, you can't stop stuffing everything down my throat. Back off."

"There you are. There's that rage. You are a character assassin. Right behind that high-minded ground you stand on. It's all magical thinking."

I could hear a rising roar in my head. My face was hot, and I smelled my own sweat. My hands wanted to wring his puny neck.

"There's the pot calling the kettle, Harold. Look at what you're doing." I heard my teeth grinding.

"You can't stop, can you?" Harold yelled, "You're a frigid bitch."

My head jerked back. There it was. He had been holding that one for a long time, ever since I rebuffed him. I stood up and blew hot air out like a dragon breathing fire.

"Only with you, Harold! Arrogant son of a bitch!"

My jaw began to seize up. I stopped breathing for a moment. Harold stood up and faced me.

Luke poked his head into the room. "Everything okay in here?" he said.

I went over to Luke. "Hi honey." Luke stepped back, put his hands on my arms, I was shaking. My clenched jaw let him know trouble was brewing. I nodded at him and went back to my chair, shooting arrows out of my eyes at Harold.

The room hushed. Velma's eyes opened wider and she shrank into herself. Reuben lit a cigarette.

"You can't smoke in here," I snapped.

Reuben said he forgot. The walls were a quivering glass surface about to shatter. I could not speak. Why wasn't anyone helping me? They were all cowards like Mother. I was left to fight the battle by myself. I glared at Harold's snarky, supercilious, beady eyed face. Suddenly everything went white.

I snarled like a cornered animal. "GET OUT!" I screamed at Harold. I pointed at the door. "Get out of my house!"

Harold looked righteous, victorious. A knowing smirk was plastered on his face. He had gotten to me. Why should he leave?

I said it again, screaming this time. "Get out!"

I heard myself and I was shocked, as if it was not coming from me, but from a shadow self. He lingered, expecting someone, anyone to tell him to stay. No one said a word. He backed out of the room slowly, afraid to turn his back on me.

Finally, he turned and slinked out, his shoulders squished into his neck. When the front door closed, everyone took a deep breath.

"Let's call it a night," Reuben said. He might have looked pleased.

I was dizzy, hot. What had I done? I was not sure, but it felt big. I had done something of consequence, and I did not know where it would lead. I had scared everyone, including myself, but there was no denying that a powerful white rage had exploded from inside me.

34

GRACE UNDER PRESSURE

Days after the supervision group, I continued seething, my body still hot.

I sat across from my parents in The English Tea Room on Newbury Street. There was not much about it that was English, but the food was home cooked and cheap. I looked at Dad and wondered why Harold had received the store of my rage and why I had never been able to get that angry with Dad. One answer was that it was too dangerous with Dad. If I blew up, Dad could blow harder. His explosion was a weapon and he threatened with the totality of his rage. Dad appeared smaller to me. Had he lost more weight? When Mother went to the bathroom he looked around and then leaned toward me, as if we were conspiring.

"I have a feeling time is getting short," he said in a near whisper.

I did not respond.

"I'm saying we all have our time on this earth. Ol' Man River, as the song goes..." his voice rumbling low under his breath, nearly breaking into song.

Dying was one of Father's favorite topics. It made me angry, especially on the verge of yet another serious operation for Dad. He was playing the King Lear card again, a tyrannical old guy trying to hold on to his power. He needed me to be frightened for him. He wanted me to hold his fear. It worked. My heart started drumming.

“Don’t mention anything to your Mother.”

“Really Dad?”

It had to be our secret, too much for Mother, but apparently, I could take it. In true alcoholic fashion, I knew never to betray a secret. I gritted my teeth. He was pulling me in, pitting me against my own Mother. I felt like I was older than the two of them and was supposed to be responsible for whatever they couldn’t handle. No wonder I couldn’t grow up.

Dad ordered Sole and rice pudding his expression grim. He rarely smiled anyway. No one is more sober than a dry alcoholic. I had the full three course meal that the Tea room offered for 99cents. I tried to make a few jokes when Mum sat down again, but the real conversation was over.

***

Mum and I sat on bright plastic chairs in Beth Israel’s surgical waiting room. I flipped through Life magazines. My breathing was shallow and constricted. Mum stared straight ahead; quiet and stolid, a *Ladies’Home Journal* unopened on her lap. I pictured Dad on the table, images of his open belly, his organs exposed to the world, blood spurting into his chest cavity, the surgeon unable to stanch the bleeding. I sprinted ahead in my mind: he would bleed out, I’d never see him again, I’d be sorry I’d been so hateful and stingy with my love. If Dad died it would be without forgiveness for trying to hold me back from my own life. He would be gone, leaving me with an acrid bitterness.

I paced, which only served to make my heart pound harder and my hands colder. I drank cup after cup of machine brewed burnt coffee. I scanned my spiritual discourses without seeing what I was reading. I ate a Sky Bar and a Baby Ruth. A rat gnawed at my brain. I could only imagine the worst.

"How do you think it's going Mum?"

She made that funny sound in the back of her throat. "I have no idea. Stop pacing and sit down."

I wanted comfort. I wanted her to say, *I understand you're afraid. Let's have faith your Father will come through.* Then she would hold me and let me cry. My emotions had always been a problem for her.

At the four-hour mark, a nurse came through the doors of the surgical wing. Had he died on the table? My heart leapt out of my body. She pulled her mask down to her neck and spoke to Mother.

"It's taking a lot longer than the doctor anticipated. Your husband has so much scar tissue from the cirrhosis and prior surgeries. It is difficult to get at the stomach. So far, his heart is holding up."

"I see. Thank you." Mum nodded; her stoic expression firmly entrenched in her set jaw.

It did not sound good. They were wearing him down. I continued to circle the room, sit, jump up and pace some more. The air conditioner blasted cold air. An intercom voice called for this doctor and that nurse. I perused the candy machine and bought another Baby Ruth. I meditated using my sacred word, but my fear was greater than my detachment. I couldn't settle.

I was a teenager sitting at the kitchen window in endless anticipation of Dad's return from the hospital.

"Stop waiting," Mother used to say to my teenage self. "You're only making things worse lurking by the window."

I tore open the candy bar wrapper. “Why didn’t you tell me that he was bleeding in his intestines?”

Mum was silent.

“Is he dying?”

“Stop, Alicia.”

It was only a few days before that I had beaten metaphorical Dad over and over with a bataka bat in the weekend workshop. I did not really want him to die, but I wanted our conflict to end. I needed to gain power over him. I worried my bad thoughts were polluting the universe—as MSIA cautioned—or worse, affecting the surgery. How was I supposed to control my thoughts? So many of my angry thoughts and violent images would be unacceptable to people.

I dozed in my chair, jerked my head back up then walked the halls of the hospital. Mum never flinched. She got up once to go to the bathroom. I brought her a ginger ale.

Luke would be concerned with so much time passing. I had told him not to come, but I missed having him there. I needed to hear his voice, so I called. I told him I was afraid he would not make it. He was reassuring, a steady voice in a crisis, reminding me Father was tough. I took a long breath. I felt stronger after speaking with Luke. Things would work out.

Then the surgeon came out through the swinging doors.

They had lost him. He was gone.

My body went cold. The surgeon shook Mother’s hand and sat down next to her. I held my breath.

"That's one stout hearted guy," he said. "Your husband came through, but there's not a lot of stomach left."

Mum held onto to the surgeon's hand and smiled for the first time. "Oh, that's very good news," she said. She exhaled, long and deep, the breath she had held onto all day long.

I shook my head in disbelief. He had made it. One more time, he had defeated the reaper (he often referred to death as if they were on a first name basis). Mum had been through a lot with my father. His passionate Marine Corps self, his toxic drinking, his crazed raving, and now when he was finally sober, several nip and tuck operations. How did she do it? I wondered if he appreciated how strong she was, the way she could endure, run a marathon with him, live on the edge of uncertainty. She withstood it all with a forbearance I did not have.

For a moment I admired her.

I wanted to go home to Luke, but Mum said we should wait until the nurse told us we could visit Dad in the recovery room. Another hour passed. My head nodded near sleep. Mother nudged me, and I followed her into the chilly ICU with its acrid antiseptic odor, lights dimmed, machines beeping at irregular intervals. I saw him lying there, one of many patients recently out of surgery.

Mum took his hand.

I looked down at him, "Hi Dad."

He opened his eyes, looked at Mum and then at me. "Is the Doc finished with me?"

"All done dear, everything went well, they told us."

He looked breakable, like a piece of pale porcelain. Where was our Marine Colonel? His bare skinny legs jutted out from his johnny. Tubes were everywhere, in his nose, in his arm, a catheter disappearing up his johnny. His cheekbones protruded and his cheeks caved in, like a skeleton. He didn't seem to care that I saw him that way. I looked down on him and smelled sickness, fluid, blood. Mum leaned over and kissed him tenderly.

Dad was good at going right to the brink of complete darkness and then pulling himself back from the precipice.

In my mind, I was an animal, sensing weakness in another animal. I felt the impulse to attack. Dad had no way of defending himself from me. I pulled out all the tubes, one by one. I put a pillow over his head and held it there. He was too weak to struggle. In a few short moments he was gone.

I heard Mother speaking to him, telling him to rest. She would be back the next morning. I looked down at him once more, at his fragile body, at his look of confusion. I had been leaning so far into him for so long, that I feared I'd fall over if he pulled back. In truth, I wanted us both to stand tall. The worst thing for me would be to end up stronger than Dad.

***

I sat across from Reuben in the Plough and Stars Pub with my arm circled around my plate. He smoked, talked, and ate all at once and I was afraid he would blow smoke or spit on my food. We had met for a weekly lunch at the Plough for the past year, ever since my therapy had terminated and I had returned from Mexico.

"I really lost it with Harold."

He nodded. "He had it coming. He doesn't seem to be able to share his toys."

He took a long drag and then a big mouthful of the lunch special for the day, chicken cacciatore. I pulled my plate closer to me.

"I don't know what we do about the supervision group," he said.

I said I was sorry to cause a problem. Reuben said it was not only me, he had the same problem with Harold. Changing the subject, he asked how my thesis was going along.

"I'm having trouble proving my theory. They keep saying my thinking is hysterical."

"Maybe there's a part of you that is still trying to keep a distance," Reuben said.

I heard him, but I had no idea how to change the way my mind worked. What was so obvious to others remained hidden from me. Reuben said I needed to struggle with it. I felt dense and stupid. The resolution was so obscure to me that I did not even know what questions to ask.

"I've been thinking about withdrawing from my doctoral program." I did not realize I was seriously considering that until the words came out.

Reuben stubbed his cigarette into the ash tray as he asked why? I explained as best I could what the program was doing to me (as opposed to thinking about it as me doing the program). Multiple pages of writing had gotten me nowhere with my committee. I had constant headaches from hours at the typewriter and every time I heard from California it was bad news. Reuben agreed a theoretical paper was difficult. But he said I could do it if I wanted to and I should leave the door open for a while.

It felt wrong to quit. I hated to disappoint Reuben, but the knots in my mind were tightening so that I was unable to think my way through the problem. I wanted his help in sorting out what I was unable to unravel alone. Yet I knew I had to figure it out myself. I had a clear vision in my head that I had been able to articulate with my colleagues, but I could not present it correctly in my thesis.

And I did not have Mother's grace. I was unable to tolerate long periods of uncertainty with unanswered questions. She was able to live in the moment under great pressure, while I tried to make up a future long before it appeared. I understood that was something I needed to learn, but I did not know how.

The option of a temporary leave, suggested by friends, was not palatable. I had to make a final decision. If I withdrew, I knew I would never go back.

LESSON SIX:

SEEING WITH THE HEART

35
LOVE IS COMPLICATED

Something dark and inexplicable occurred far away, and I did not know what I felt about it or what I should feel.

Twenty people gathered in Reuben's living room for his older son's funeral service. Church for Reuben was the honest expression of feelings. Close friends, family, and a few people like me who had graduated from patient to colleague sat in a circle, silent, our heads bowed holding hands as music filled the room. The mournful piano of a Chopin Concerto sounded like weeping.

Reuben's son Jacob from his first marriage had been struck by a train in the town where he lived in Norway. While no one would ever know for certain, it looked like he had taken his own life. Jacob died on an early spring afternoon—the high season for suicide I learned—a time of year when an energizing surge of hope crashes headlong into despair.

I had not spoken to Reuben since Jacob's death. I kept my eyes on him in the circle wanting to fathom what he must be feeling. I imagined the Light that JR spoke of filling the room. Unlike Harold, he had the kindness to let me have my own beliefs whatever they were, but I knew he thought it was a mystical evasion of reality.

Reuben spoke, his head down, shoulders collapsed, his voice buried deep in his heart. "Most of you here, my dear family, my friends, my colleagues, never had the opportunity to meet Jacob, much less to know him. A lovely young man, but troubled. I will always regret that I didn't take the time to know him better."

Reuben looked over at his ex-wife, Hannah, and nodded. "There are no excuses. I was not a father to Jacob. I will always regret that. And now"—Reuben began to cough and choke—"Now it's too late. There are no more chances. Oh Jacob. Oh, my son."

He sat hunched over the chair; his remorse too big for his body to contain it. His chest heaved, and he choked, wept, and choked again. Hannah walked over and stood by him her hand on his arm. At last they could share their love for their son.

A current of sorrow swept the room. All the loss and longing moving through us. My body thrummed. I could have wailed. My family was broken too. It was not anyone's fault. I held back my sobs. This was Reuben's time. I could not figure out what was sadder, the fact that Reuben had lost his son or the truth that he had never had him in the first place.

Reuben was not to blame, but I wondered. Jacob came to visit his Father only once that I knew of. For all his twenty some years, he'd lived with his Mother. Why did Reuben leave him behind? He'd told me he needed to get away from his wife, but why didn't he take any responsibility for fathering? Jacob must have been so hurt, so rejected, and it must have left him with no confidence, no belief in himself. I pictured Jacob alone, despair filling his head until he could not go on any longer.

Did Reuben hold onto the thought that he had more time to be a better Dad, to make up for abandoning his son? I guessed it was more comfortable to think Jacob was better off with his Mother. I wondered if Jacob had come to America hoping Reuben would say *Stay with me. I'll take care of you. I'll be your Dad* like Reuben had been a good father to me.

Someday it would be too late to make things right with my own Father.

Everyone loved Reuben, but who did he love? His other son Sam sat with forehead furled, his mouth tight. He looked sad and mad all at one time. I knew how he felt. Each feeling got the other one jammed up until it was hard to tell rage from sorrow.

Harold sat directly across from me. I could not avoid looking at him. He was somber but his jaw was fixed. Our eyes met once, and I saw he was frozen against me as I was frozen against him. Our relationship was not salvageable. I was still shocked by my blowup. I told Luke my vision went white seconds before I blew. He said it was scary watching me. I'd expected a punishing headache to follow. It never came. My outburst agreed with me. Look out world, there is a lot more where that came from. I had not realized that my rage was powerful. It made me feel strong, but I was more complicated than I thought. Was I becoming Father?

In the background I heard a few of Reuben's closest friends speaking, for Jacob, but primarily for Reuben. I was too young to know what to say and I was too horrified by how Jacob died.

His son Sam got up and put on a recording of Bach's Requiem while Reuben's oldest friend, a brilliant eccentric psychiatrist led us in a secular prayer that Jacob would now be at peace.

***

Jacob's death threw my own darkness and insecurity into a glaring light. When was I going to step out of my fear and allow who I was to be enough so I could move forward? Did I have to be perfect? Did I need a Ph.D.? Thanks to Reuben—and, I had to admit, Harold—I knew I had talents: a searching mind, clear vision to see deeply into people, and a capacity for empathy and compassion. I had no desire to restore anything with Harold. It would have been much better if I could have spoken to him calmly and said, *Thank you for supporting me and helping me to know my own strength. Now it's time to go my own way.* But Harold did not allow any thoughts that differed from his and I was too angry and scared to have any perspective.

After Jacob's funeral, I could not imagine sitting with Harold again in our supervision group. It was one of the first times in my life where I did not override my own feelings with the cloying burden of loyalty.

36

BLOWING IN THE WIND

On a Monday evening, like every other Monday for the past two years, I sat down, focused on my mantra during the group meditation then prepared to discuss JR's latest discourse. The topic of the week was *Sitting in Your Own Truth.*

"I like the idea that if we're in proper relation to the world our own paths unfold in a clear way," I said.

I was hoping that meant that my blowup with Harold was not so much about my being a raging woman as it was me sitting in my truth and moving along my own rightful path.

I looked forward to this small meditation group, a place of calm and harmony where I did not have to grapple with my anger. Even if that harmony was achieved by silencing dissent, it was helpful to put some of my conflicts aside.

"Someone said JR is having sex with his disciples," Frances blurted out.

"Could you repeat that?" I said.

Frances laughed, an annoying habit she had whenever she mentioned anything that was not completely positive.

"You know me," she said wagging her head back and forth, "I hate spreading malicious gossip. And honestly, I don't believe it for a minute. Someone has started a dark rumor."

Frances squished her nose and mouth and looked around the circle, as if she had given voice to a dirty thought.

I shook my head like someone had thrown cold water on my face.

"Wait a minute," someone popped up, opening his palms wide, "JR is celibate and so are his disciples. They took vows. So, how could they have sex?"

Exactly!

Who would break that vow?

I left the group with my mind on the spin cycle. I did not want to hear any more and decided not to talk to anyone about it. It could be a matter of waiting for it to blow over.

***

Tremors rolled through the Movement. Clandestine gatherings at private homes sprang up all over town. Everyone was agitated, leaping to conclusions with sparse information.

My instinct, along with many others, was to protect JR. His love was our love and his way our way. The rumor was a knife stabbing him in the back. But it did seem incestuous if it was true.

The disciples had appeared so clear and confident, as if they had no doubt about the sacredness of their paths. Now I felt a horrified fascination. I was watching a cohesive group spiraling into chaos and I was a witness as well as a participant.

***

JR's silence left a gaping hole in our thinking, which was his mistake. The space lent itself to being filled with all kinds of scary thoughts, the worst one being that it was all true.

Luke and I spent more time than usual at our kitchen table. One morning, as I picked at my scrambled eggs, I thought they looked the way my brain felt.

"I don't know Luke. Are we a bunch of lemmings ready to go over the edge with a stupid rumor?"

"Speak for yourself. It may be true. Pour me more of that coffee please."

"What do you mean? Do you know something I don't?" I glared at him, the distance from one side of the table to the other growing by the minute.

Luke lit a cigarette and blew out a long leisurely trail of smoke. "Well, what do you think?"

"I can't believe you're acting like you've known something all along, as if no one could fool you." I did not know what I thought or how to think about it. It annoyed me that Luke thought he was right most of the time. It was even more annoying that he often was.

"Would you have listened if I'd said anything?" He looked at me, his eyes fixed and stern.

No. I would have attributed his doubts to a cynical attitude that I thought Luke used as an excuse for his inability to surrender to something greater than himself.

I looked at Luke like he was a suspicious stranger. On the other hand, what had I given to MSIA in exchange for my spiritual progress? Another frightening question: had I been brainwashed? That did not seem likely. I was always questioning and searching for truth. Surely, I would have sensed something. I had made fun of people in cults. How could they be so stupid?

"That is not fair, Luke. Now you're saying you were keeping the truth to yourself?"

"No, I'm saying it doesn't surprise me. Gurus do this all the time. That doesn't mean the teachings aren't true."

I had been so certain JR was not just any guru and happy that we were sharing our spiritual path. Luke and I meditated together and supported each other. And all the time Luke was doubting the whole thing? Suddenly we were at odds about the degree to which we had been duped.

"Okay." He took his dishes over to the sink and looked at the clock on the wall. "Time for our morning meditation," Luke said. "Speak of the devil," he joked.

"That's not funny."

I went into the bedroom and slammed the door. I fumed. I sat down on my zafu, closed my eyes tight, set my jaw and focused on my secret words. I realized I had no idea what the mantra meant. It was Sanskrit, but we'd been discouraged from asking too much about the words. They were sacred and did not lend themselves to everyday conversation. As I repeated the mantra to quiet my mind it sounded stupid. Maybe it wasn't real. Maybe everyone had received the same mantra thinking theirs was somehow special to them.

My head was spinning.

***

One evening, a few weeks into the crisis new information arrived from California. "John-Roger has divulged the existence of a demonic force at play here, known by the name of the Red Monk."

"Are you kidding?" one man asked.

It was so bizarre I had to squelch a laugh. Really? It was the first we had heard from JR since the rumor appeared. Were they making things up in California to protect him? I saw some eyes rolling and others wide and waiting.

Our group facilitator was serious. He said it with a straight face, and he was no idiot. "I'm simply relaying the information given to me by the Center. JR says he'd hoped to shield us from the Red Monk."

So, JR was trying to protect *us* not himself. Huh. I tried to think it through. One implication was that someone in the group was either carrying the force of the Red Monk or actually was the Red Monk. Suddenly we were all suspect. I started to feel like I was in a horror movie. When everything becomes creepier and creepier and the naïve characters make the choice that leads them closer to their demise rather than away from it.

No one looked at anyone else, but I knew we all wanted to check each other out. *Could it be you? I've never liked your toady devotion. Or you? You've always been so obsequious.*

I wondered if anyone suspected my questioning and sometimes negative presence in the group. Could I be the Red Monk and not know it?

JR had spoken about evil as a force that was real, that it could enter one's consciousness if one's thoughts were seduced by its power. I wracked my brain. Had he always said this or was it a recent admonishment to prepare our minds for believing in the Red Monk? In the beginning his constant refrain had been, "In all things, surround yourself with light, and always for the highest good." That was the way we welcomed all gatherings, both a blessing of our time together and a safeguard for our spiritual selves, like the Serenity Prayer in AA. I felt its protection as a balm for all my negativity. Was JR warding off something dark all along? Where was it coming from?

If I was any example of a human being, I had plenty of my own darkness. I did not need to hear about the existence of a Red Monk. I needed the light. I saw the way JR had positioned himself as our shield against the force of evil. Now we were to understand that the Red Monk was here and was among us.

Another woman said we should not mistrust one another, that it would destroy us. But she was too late. I wondered if JR had miscalculated.

There were murmurs of agreement, but the damage was already done. The group was splitting apart. There were many others present who did not speak. What were they thinking? I looked over at Luke who wore a small unfriendly smile, like he was done, and we had all gone crazy. There he was cynical Luke at it again.

An outspoken guy reeled off a series of still unasked questions. "What exactly are we supposed to do about the Red Monk? Why isn't JR here in person to talk with us? It's not only who is the Red Monk. Who is JR?"

The group flattened under a leaden load of doubt and broken trust. The room began to reek. I had a good nose for the scent of ammonia, a constituent of fear. We all stank.

In some previously neglected area of my mind a small light flashed. Truth has a way of building strength, eventually overcoming the lie. It seemed sudden, bit it was a gradual coming into reality. I realized that JR was not thinking about us at all. No, he was in a panic. My therapist mind reeled with the thought that he was paranoid, frantic, scrambling to get out from under his own deceit. I saw the Red Monk was a shill to distract us from any independent thinking. He must have thought we would buy it.

Then I knew with clarity that it was all true. If only he could have come forward and said, *I'm sorry,* and humbled himself. Breaking the vow of celibacy was not the end of the world in my mind. Maybe his sexual appetite was out of his control, like Dad's drinking, and he could not help himself. If he had asked for forgiveness, many of us would have cried and welcomed him back.

Maybe.

It was not that I'd ever fully believed what suddenly seemed to be ridiculous claims, but I'd allowed them to occupy an uncontested and protected corner of my belief.

In the daylight, JR was as false as his kinky blond permanent.

Andrea, gentle Andrea, had stayed silent through all the meetings. She knew better than to oppose anyone's thinking. She said simply that we each needed to find the truth in our own hearts. I looked at her pretty open face, her golden wavy hair, her clear blue eyes. She saw something beyond the quicksand the rest of us were unable to climb out of. She simply refused to go there. Her truth lay with John-Roger.

There were others who stuck with him, Frances among them. I felt the poverty of my own twisted devotion and inevitable disillusionment. Belief was pure. Doubt was muddy. Andrea had always said to me that I had the strength of a personal love. What she meant was that my love could not transcend the person.

Andrea remained pure and steady, able to love in a truly spiritual way where it made no difference what JR did or didn't do. I wished I could be like her. Instead, I fell back to earth, full of crushed hope and disappointment. As JR taught us, I was sitting in my own truth, but it did not feel good, and there was no victory.

It would be our last meeting with MSIA. The end for Luke and me came like a California mudslide, sudden and utterly complete in its destruction. Yes, we had friends in MSIA who felt deceived as we did, who agreed that whatever JR once was, it had all come crumbling down. But the mutual group love had depended upon a shared belief and devotion. I love you because you think like me. It fed on itself. There was nothing to be gained by talking about the unwelcome truth. Sharing disillusionment was no basis for maintaining friendship. I did not lose the friends I'd had before MSIA but any relationships that had been formed within the movement were dissolved.

***

Coming out of a brainwashed state was like waking up after a grand mal seizure. I was hung over, barely able to remember where I had been, as if I had been in a black out. I was astonished at the ease with which I had entertained so many magical thoughts and beliefs. I had had such pride in my independent self and yet I'd so readily given it away. I remembered the annoying reading I'd received from Gregg Tiffen who said I had no separate sense of self and needed to move beyond devotion. Leaving MSIA was a waking up that was so different from being asleep that one had no relationship to the other. I had been ejected from an alternate universe.

What amazed me even more than John-Roger's betrayal was the way MSIA went on as if nothing had happened. It occurred to me it was like the way my family went on as if Dad was not ill.

Psychopaths always rise to the top, Luke said. We shared what we learned in MSIA, the spiritual perception that came out of a practice, a community of belief, the real-life lessons for creating a positive life. We reminded ourselves about the pearls that could be found in a pile of shit. But when I woke up, I could not sort through the piles and find what I wanted to keep. I could only feel shaken that I'd given over so much of myself. Luke wondered why it was so difficult for me to separate out the teachings from the man. It would take time before I could look back and see any value in MSIA.

My question then became: Where could I go for my spiritual search?

37

BLUEBERRIES FOR LUKE AND ALI

I practiced my bioenergetic breathing in the car on our way out to Groton: into the belly, expand the diaphragm, fill the chest, and then back down through the belly.

Here we were, once again, needy supplicants looking for approval. The forecast of rain late in the day was off, but the sky was a steely gray. The familiar drive felt longer than usual. It wasn't that I wanted to arrive. I wanted the drive to end.

"I'm scared," I said.

"It can't be any worse than the last time," Luke said, as much to himself as to me.

"If Mum pulls another Queen Elizabeth, I'm leaving."

Luke laughed, but I saw his shoulders rise toward his neck.

"I mean it. It's not funny."

The only thing different was that we were better prepared for rejection. I had seen my parents regularly over the past two years, but without Luke. I couldn't handle the feeling of being torn between them. This time Luke didn't have to remind me that he and I were a team. I wasn't having disparaging thoughts about him. I wasn't looking at him as I imagined Dad saw him, which would be that he was inadequate. I did not start a fight in the car, and I did not pull away from him. How many times had I thrown Luke under a bus when I thought I had to choose him or Dad? At least I understood that the problem was between me and my father.

Strangely enough JR had encouraged and supported couples when we were in MSIA, treating Luke and me as something special in group gatherings. He used to say, "Here we have an example, the sacred love of two in union greater than any one of us alone. This love is what we strive for."

In fact, that was not true. We had a long way to go in loving each other, but neither of us bothered to disavow that perception because it served us. Luke and I never spoke of it together, but the respect we received required and then inspired us to behave better. Before we knew it, our good behavior became a habit.

Dad was the wildcard. I wasn't confident I could tolerate his disapproval. I had to face again how weak I was in relation to Dad. Was I still so unformed as a person that my survival required me to stay connected to him?

"Want me to speak to him?" Luke asked.

That was tempting. I could sink back into my young self and let Luke take the rejection. I hesitated. After a deep breath I said, "I'll ask him."

"Al, we agreed this time we're telling him, not asking him."

I had to fight to keep from collapsing inside and remember that this was not about Mum and Dad dictating to us. I repeated to myself the words, I have something to tell you.

Dad seemed oddly nervous when we arrived, stripped of his usual formality and distance. It threw me. I suspected it was the calm before the storm, that they'd decided to stand together in opposition to Luke and me. I gave each of them a cautious peck on the cheek and Luke shook their hands. The four of us carried dishes and serving platters out to the porch. I could hardly speak. I was on high alert. They were so quiet. What were they thinking? Had Dad picked up something new in us? He was creepily intuitive in relation to me. I could never anticipate what he might do. It was a mistake to come. My heart fell in defeat. I'd already lost the battle.

It was a warm summer night when we sat down to supper with the birds singing their evening songs in the giant copper beech tree on the back lawn. I remembered how much time I'd spent in that tree as a child. Other than the corn on the cob, Mum had grown all the vegetables, the summer squash, succotash, and cucumbers in vinaigrette. It was odd that my parents were chatty. Mum was unusually cheerful. They'd recently taken a trip to France and Switzerland. Travel satisfied one of her life goals, although she had to forego Italy. Dad held Fascism against the Italians.

"We want to let you know that we're getting married," I said, swallowing twice as a lima bean went down the wrong way. Was that me speaking?

"And we hope you'll give us your blessing," Luke added.

He patted me on the back. My fork jangled against the plate.

Dad cleared his throat twice, a harbinger of bad news. "Well. I was wondering when you'd get around to it. Better than living in sin, as they say."

Not exactly a blessing, but it had to do.

I forged ahead. "We'd like to get married here, down in the garden."

Had I offended them, sticking a marriage they didn't want in their face?

Mother nodded. Why did she nod? Was she following Dad's lead? And where exactly was he going?

"My only requirement is that you have a good health insurance plan," Dad said to Luke.

Was this what we had been fighting about for five years? Of all the things he could have said, that was not what I expected. Thinking back, it fit perfectly with Dad. The man was supposed to take care of the woman. If Luke had good health insurance, he could take care of me!

By that summer, Luke was working the night shift at Bridge Over Still Waters, a non-profit organization in Boston offering medical, dental, crisis outreach, and counseling to teenagers on the edge. He was a natural with kids. He discovered he wanted to be a therapist and more importantly, he'd developed some confidence. Maybe Dad smelled the change in him and backed off, the way an animal will not attack another animal if it senses it might lose a battle.

"I have a good policy through my work," Luke said. "That won't be a problem."

He could say he was a counselor which would go over better with Dad than his previous job at the crafts store. But Dad never asked him what his work was.

With that issue taken care of Dad said they'd pay for an afternoon wedding outside with champagne and hors d'oeuvres in the house. We had tried to talk about it before, after returning from the Farm, but Dad cut us off and we gave up. Now it was like they were planning it. I glanced at Luke with my head back and my eyes popping. He smiled; his face handsome when he relaxed.

"That's very generous of you," he said.

We had Maine blueberries with vanilla custard sauce for dessert. Lightening bugs flashed in the early evening darkness. I could smell the honeyed sweet night fragrance of nicotiana blooming near the porch. We sat together like two couples, almost a double date.

"Talk to your Mother about plans," Dad said as he hugged me goodbye. "And congratulations young man." He shook Luke's hand.

"We should have told them five years ago instead of asking permission," I said as we drove back into the city.

"If you think about it, Al, we weren't ready. It wasn't your parents who stopped us. It was us."

For the first time I considered not blaming my parents. It was true, they didn't make it easy, but I saw that behaving like a kid instead of an adult allowed them to treat me like a child. One amazing thing about my life was the way that as I got myself on my right path, other parts of my life tended fall into place. Another good lesson that came from MSIA. My parents' blessing opened a door in my relationship with Luke. My heart was beginning to sing. I'd been given permission to love.

"You did a great job, Al. You told them, just like we planned. You stood up."

"I'm excited. It's happening. We're getting married!"

I felt like Dad's yoyo. One minute he was cruel, the next he was kind, he treated Luke like something inferior, then he gave him respect. I was happy. But I never knew when he might turn again.

38

A ROOM OF MY OWN

I stood in the middle of another therapist's office that I'd rented by the hour.

My mouth was dry, my throat constricted as I waited to meet my first private client, Elaine, whom I'd spoken with over the phone. She'd been referred to me by Reuben because she couldn't afford his fee. I surveyed the room worrying how it would appear to her. Macramé hangings on the wall and prints that were bought and framed as part of a brown and blue color scheme seemed generic and cold. I felt more like a dentist than a therapist. It wasn't me.

I heard her footsteps coming up the stairs and took a deep breath. Attempting to appear calm I shook Elaine's hand and motioned with my hand for her to come into the office. As any practitioner of Reichian or Bioenergetic bodywork would do, I asked her to take off all her clothes except her underwear. My words startled me, even though I had never questioned it in my own therapy. I knew immediately I should've had her sit in a chair first and tell me why she'd come. *I'm sorry Elaine, I have no idea what I am doing. Thank you for paying me to learn on the job.* I couldn't say this out loud. It was important for her to believe I could help.

Reuben had reminded me that we all had our first patient, and that I'd be surprised how much I could do simply by being myself. I told him it was like jumping into cold water with no life preserver, hoping I could stay afloat until I learned how to swim. I was shy about meeting new people under any circumstances. Now I had to pretend a level of comfort I didn't feel and still be authentic. Some inexperienced therapists who I met in training workshops put on affected airs of caring or spoke in psychobabble. I was determined to be real and use my natural abilities. I was smart and honest, I had a sense of humor, and I really did want to help. Is that enough?

I'd had plenty of angst over what to wear. I was supposed to look professional. Women therapists in Cambridge tended toward frumpy and matronly with Birkenstocks, African prints in shapeless styles, and long strands of beads. There was a boutique on Huron Avenue that advertised a unique look for women. It appeared to me that a lot of them had shopped there in search of an individual style, and now they all looked alike.

Could I wear pants? Not jeans, but casual pants? My Navajo skirt? I knew who I was in that skirt. I liked me in that skirt.

"Yes, okay," I'd said to Luke when he said, "Pants, fine. Purple skirt, no way."

I wanted something that would make me feel comfortable, not too stiff. This was not a performance. Luke said I would be fine whatever I wore, but first impressions were crucial. I finally decided on the gray slacks and white blouse I wore when going out with Mother. It wasn't me.

Elaine looked more professional than I did. She wore a skirt with a matching fitted jacket and a blouse that buttoned up to her neck. I took a deep breath and sat next to her as she lay on the couch. My repertoire consisted of a few lines (what brings you here, what are you feeling, breathe) and then I wasn't sure what to do.

But I didn't even get the chance to ask her why she'd come. As soon as she lay down, she started breathlessly pouring out her problems.

"I've tried so hard, but he won't talk to me and I know something is going on…I'm afraid he's thinking of leaving me…"

I couldn't get a word in.

"I can't sleep. I'm so upset…it's interfering with my job. I can't concentrate."

"I can see how upsetting that must be," I said, using a basic empathic technique.

It didn't slow her down. Her tsunami of words overwhelmed my capacity to think. On and on she went. I remembered Reich's use of the concept of the red thread. His idea was that an individual has a basic character trait that they fall back on in times of stress. Finding that trait and following it would lead to the deeper truth of a person's character. Quick, think fast, what was her most obvious characteristic. Her non-stop talking became background noise to my internal chatter. Of course, the non-stop talking was the thread. It was so obvious! As soon as I grasped the red thread, I calmed down. I had permission to start at the beginning. I didn't have to figure out what was going on, I could let my thoughts go and follow the thread.

I wondered out loud with her, what was she trying to communicate to me? There was no space for me to respond. What did she think that was about? I wasn't sure I'd put that very well. But I didn't have to worry about that because it was as if I wasn't in the room. Elaine kept on talking. I sat back in my chair. What should I do now? I had to interrupt her. I inserted myself. Right here, right now, I suggested to her, what would happen if she let some space be here between us?

She looked blank.

I decided to tell Elaine that we were detectives working side by side, searching for clues. I suggested her becoming curious about her own behavior. I realized I had received bad modelling from all the charismatic male trainers whose pattern had been to attack head on and break down peoples' defenses with no empathy for the client's natural tendency to protect themselves.

As she talked, I remembered the warmth of Reuben's hand on my chest and the way it gradually made me feel safe. I asked if I could place my hand on her chest, keeping a good distance from her large breasts. It gave me something to do as a distraction from her barrage of words. I hoped it might be calming. I felt like a medical doctor with a stethoscope pressing down gently with my cold hand on her outbreath as I listened for her breathing. I could feel the tightness and contraction, easy to detect because her chest didn't move at all.

"Let's focus on your sensations for a moment. Can you tell me what they are right now, right here in this room?"

"Cold, my stomach is grumbling," she said reluctantly. "What does that have to do with my husband?"

"Well, it's a place to begin, a way to orient yourself at a moment in time. When you become present in the sensations of your body, your awareness deepens and then you may find you know a lot more than you think you do about the issues in your marriage."

That was good. Elaine seemed pleased as well. I'd read that in Suzuki's *Zen Mind, Beginners Mind* and I was using what I'd studied as I moved through my first session. I persisted in focusing on her sensations and did not answer her questions about her marriage. I couldn't come up with a quick response anyway. I had to trust in the process.

By the time the session was over I felt like we had a path to follow, or at least I had a plan. We hadn't solved the problem that brought her to therapy. Reuben had told me that a patient's reason for coming was often not the central issue. I knew the next session would be better because we had broken the ice. I didn't know her deeper issues, but as Elaine's awareness of her own chatter increased, it would allow us to gently remove a layer of defense. I began to be excited about sharing the journey with her, and I had a glimmer of how to guide her.

***

Reuben encouraged me to get my own office. I agreed it would make me feel more confident and professional. I looked around Cambridge for something I could afford on my small income and found a tiny room that shared a suite with a woman I knew from previous training workshops. Since I last saw her Leslie had changed her name from Goodman to Goodwoman, which seemed awkward to me, but she claimed it made her feel more like herself. For $50.00 a month I could do anything I wanted with the space.

I'd walked by the Central Square building for years on my way to and from Harvard Square. An extended Roma family occupied the downstairs apartment. A neon sign in the window for Psychic Readings flashed red day and night above the silhouette of a Gypsy woman looking into a crystal ball. More shady looking adults and scruffy looking little kids passed in and out of that apartment than I could count. I wondered if the Roma woman was truly psychic or if it was a con.

A homeless man and woman sat smoking on the stoop. The man held a brown bag covering a pint size liquor bottle. He'd take a slug and then pass it to his companion. I kept my eyes down as I walked up the steps for fear that they were Westborough State Hospital clients from my job three years earlier at the Ambulatory Unit. I was afraid and ashamed that most of them had landed on the streets.

I pinched my nose as I entered the hallway and sorted through various smells: the sicky sweet stench of cockroaches, the reek of urine emanating from dirty beige walls, and a heavy tomato soup odor of sweat, all of which made me ask why I was paying money for this place. I walked up the unlit stairs, passing a down and out woman with dyed black hair coming down. A disheveled young man with greasy hair floated by me as I walked to the office at the end of the hall.

The carpeting in what was to be my little room was lime green shag, slightly nauseating in sight and smell. If the place repelled me, what would it do to my patients? I considered running out, but I told myself this was what I could afford and in a short amount of time I would have a real office in a clean decent space. Over the next few days, I repainted the walls bright white, washed the one dirty window, and vacuumed the rug several times. There was nothing more I could do.

***

My first client in the new office, also referred by Reuben, was a young man named John. I remembered to have him sit in a chair first and asked him why he'd come. He cleared his throat and said he had a problem with erections. I responded, okay, as if he'd said it's a bit cloudy today. Why did Reuben ever think I could work with this guy? I asked him to take off his pants and lie down on the bed.

"Are you in an intimate relationship?" I asked.

He flinched visibly and said, "I was, or rather I am, but," with a pained look, "it's not going to last if I can't have sex."

I felt like I was invading his privacy, that we really shouldn't be talking about this together. Most clients were apprehensive in their first session, but this was worse. His eyes looked frightened and pleading.

A roach crawled up the wall next to John's head as he lay on the bed. I reached across him with a Kleenex and squished the insect, trying not to look disgusted. John didn't notice, preoccupied as he was with his own discomfort. I asked some questions, when did this begin, had he ever been able to have an erection?

Were these the right questions? My mind was scrambling. What did I know about sexual dysfunction?

While he was answering, I had a disturbing train of thought. He appeared passive, even helpless. That was his red thread. I flashed to one of my casual pick-ups a few years back who had been impotent and kept trying to have sex with me, and how I became increasingly uncomfortable and unable to respond each time he failed.

I never wanted a man to be vulnerable. I thought their egos were too fragile. And here I was sitting with John looking down at him on the bed. I felt what it was like to have an inordinate amount of power in a relationship and how easy it would be to humiliate John in the name of breaking through his defenses. I had always accepted the dominance of male trainers in their workshops. I rationalized that they used it as a training tool to demonstrate and teach. Being a helpless woman had been familiar, even comfortable.

When I placed my hand on John's chest to focus him on his breathing, he pulled back instantly. It felt sexual he said, and yet he had no erection. He was already failing with me. I should not be doing this. I should not be making him feel worse about himself. I became acutely aware of my power and I didn't like it. In that moment I realized I knew something of what John was feeling, humiliated by his helplessness. That was what I experienced in training workshops, although I'd never admitted it. What would I have done if I did? Confront the trainers? Quit? It was the price of admission, the cost of learning from the masters.

Why or how John had become so helpless I didn't know, but I felt it and underneath his self-abasement other layers clearly remained to be discovered. I thought about how angry I felt when

Luke had applied to his psychotherapy program and told me he had to stand naked before the trainer, Jon Pierrakos in his interview. We concluded it was a test to see if he'd be accepted into the Core Energetics training program. It was also a disturbing way to let Luke know who was boss.

"Please keep your clothes on as we go forward," I heard myself telling John as we finished our first meeting.

"Why?" he asked. He seemed disappointed. "I thought that was part of body work."

"It can be, but it's not necessary. I want you to be comfortable with me," I said, as I carefully gathered up another roach crawling on the wall beside him.

Staying dressed did not alter the fact that I had no idea how to help his sexual dysfunction, but at least it gave the message that a woman in a powerful position was showing him respect. As Reich had taught me, my best technique was my own body. John didn't say he felt humiliated. I knew John's feeling because I felt it in my body.

In fact, I concluded it was wrong for me to work with any patients undressed. I was only doing it because that was what I'd been taught. But all the trainers I had worked with had overlooked the context of Freud and Reich's work as medical doctors using a medical model. It was a relief to make my own decision and find my way forward as a woman. I wanted to empower my clients to be whoever they were meant to be. That required meeting them on equal ground. And I had empowered myself. I would do the work in my room in my way.

***

I met Reuben for our regular lunch at the Plough and Stars. Reuben hadn't been the same since the death of his son. He was still consumed with writing his biography of Reich, but his air of anxious exhilaration had been replaced by flat withdrawal. He'd always had a melancholy spirit, but had his eyes always been so turned down and his eyelids so heavy? If I'd tried to lift him, his body would have been dead weight. His burly physique was almost gaunt I felt an ache for him. I didn't know what to say about his son.

I told him how excited and absorbed I was with my new patients. "I was made for this job," I joked. "I've been counseling all my life, starting with fixing Dad. He always thanked me for my concern. I could tell he liked talking to me."

Reuben did not respond. He coughed up phlegm and took a long draw on his cigarette.

"The problem was that he was drinking while we talked and either forgot or only felt worse because he couldn't stop."

I laughed, but it felt hollow. Reuben pushed the food around his plate, chain smoking instead of eating. I waved a cloud of smoke away from the table and continued.

"So, I expanded my rescue efforts to other grownups around town. All my friends had at least one alcoholic parent. I had so much material to work with," I said.

I thought about sitting with Dad on the sofa at the age of ten discussing Anne Frank and her family hiding terrified in the attic. I felt honored to be discussing something so profound with Dad. I also understood he was drunk. Mother had already given up on him. I thought my companionship might comfort him.

It was taking a lot of effort to lift Reuben's mood.

Reuben finally spoke, "Drinking was particularly bad after the War. Did you have any success?"

I thought for a moment. "Not really. But failure was not an obstacle for me. I kept trying."

"That will serve you well as a therapist, help with the plodding pace of change," Reuben sighed.

At any other time, I might have asked him to look over my dissertation, but Reuben's grief had taken him away. I mentioned quitting again. He was non-committal. I saw that whether I got a Ph.D. or not was not important to Reuben. I was left to make my own decision. I wasn't sure if I cared enough to complete it. I might have been doing it to please Reuben.

And something else. I said that Reich was brilliant in his thinking, understanding that the same energy in the universe was also in the human body. But Reich was a medical doctor—like Freud—and he paid no attention to the relationship between therapist and client.

Reuben nodded and said with a sad smile, "Hannah and I would never have married if he'd looked at our relationship while we were in treatment with him."

I imagined that both our thoughts went to Jacob, who would never have lived or died without Reuben's failed marriage. I could see the red thread of Reuben's brilliant cerebral self leading downward through his grief into a place of regret.

"In my therapy with you, Reuben, it was the power of our relationship that healed me. It was your love."

He smiled for the first time. "Yes, and Reich's techniques saw us through your darker feelings. One doesn't negate the other."

"Yes, but I didn't need to take my clothes off to get better."

"You may be right. We do it because that's the way Reich worked. Maybe we should rethink it."

I knew he wouldn't change his style. But he sounded open to me working in my own way. Or he might have given up caring.

When we hugged goodbye, I felt what was missing, the bear-like flesh that had made his body appear strong. His chest was sunken, his gray flannels hung low on his hips, his belly was gone.

He was diminished as I was becoming more of myself. I stood straight, my shoulders went back, and my eyes grew clear. Newfound confidence took me by surprise because I'd been so long accustomed to making myself smaller. Through my profession I was beginning to see who I was, to solidify as a person. I was continuing to grow.

And on top of everything, I was getting married.

39

NOTHING TO BE PROUD OF

The Amtrak train rumbled south alongside the Rhode Island shoreline on its way to Grand Central Station in Manhattan. I sat across from Luke and gazed out the window looking for a familiar pair of swans that were always together close to shore. It was 1977 and I had a fledgling private practice with Reuben's referrals and word of mouth. Luke and I were to be married in the fall.

He was two years into his psychotherapy training program. Core Energetics was popular and successful with alternative body workers who wanted a curriculum that incorporated the spiritual into its Reichian derived mind-body practice. Luke loved the program, its intensity, its hands-on learning, and the support and camaraderie of other students. He was to have an oral exam later that day.

For four years, Luke left home on Thursdays of every fourth weekend and didn't return to Massachusetts until Sunday night. I had come with him one time only, because a requirement of his training was to meet as a couple with Luke's advisor. Our session with Norman wasn't until 2:00pm giving us time for a quick lunch and a leisurely walk to the Core offices on the Upper East Side.

Luke took me to his favorite diner. He said he often saw Dustin Hoffman at breakfast. I'd like Norman, he continued, as we slid into a booth. He'd been a real ally for Luke. I took his hand across the table and told him how excited I was for him. A good group of people he told me. Mostly women, I gathered.

I was accustomed to having Luke come into my territory. Now he was meeting and working with people I'd never met. I wondered how close he was getting to other students in the program. I couldn't admit that I was jealous when he listed them: did he mention Heidi first for a reason or was there someone in the middle of the list who he especially liked? Amanda, Jennifer, Adrian… is that a woman? "No, a guy," he said. And Mel. Oh, was that a man? "No, short for Melissa," he said. And a few others, clearly women. Luke thought Adrian might drop out and that would mean Luke was the only guy. Women would surround him, but he said he didn't mind. Of course, he didn't mind. I thought how intimate the work was and how they would all know Luke's personal history.

Still, I wanted to support him. I was proud of him, for getting into the program, for being respected by its founder, Jon Pierrakos, and working fulltime at the Runaway house in Boston while managing all his classes and course work. One session with his teacher, Norman was the least I could do.

I'd also done several weekend trainings with Jon Pierrakos myself, and I liked Jon's Mediterranean warmth and the approach of Core Energetics. I imagined the session would be a positive affirmation of Luke.

***

When Luke's therapist opened his office door to greet us, I was surprised he was no older than I was, yet he was one of the primary teachers. Cocky, was the word that came to mind.

His handshake was hard, asserting his male dominance. And suddenly, I felt pressured to stand up to him.

He gestured to a small tight circle of three chairs, and asked, "So, what do you see as your primary issues with each other?"

He jumped right in, no small talk, no making me comfortable, nothing therapeutic He looked at me narrowing his eyes with a piercing gaze, not the way one animal initially looks at another animal, I thought, unless he's challenging you. It was like he was saying, *I see you, whether you want me to or not.*

I felt like saying, *No, you don't see me, you have no idea who I am so back off buddy.*

I crossed my legs and held onto the seat of the chair with both hands. I drew a blank at his question.

Luke didn't look bothered at all and said, "We could communicate better. We tend to let things build up."

"How 'bout you, Ali?"

"Alicia," I countered.

But he didn't back off. He kept coming.

"And then when you get around to the hard feelings, they're worse than they might have been if you'd confronted them earlier." Norman chuckled as he looked straight at me.

Very funny. That was the first time I had heard Luke complain about our communication. My snarky self was sure Norman had perfect communication with his partner.

"I think we both have a lot of fear and insecurity," Luke said.

He didn't have to hang out my dirty linen. I knew he was doing exactly what they expected at the training. I refused to join him.

"You haven't said much, Ali. I'm wondering if this is difficult for you to face. Maybe you have a trust issue with Luke."

I smiled without my eyes, like a monkey grinning when it's cornered. "It's Alicia. I don't think so, but I haven't thought about it." This wasn't true. I was always worrying and wondering about how we were communicating.

Luke looked at me as if to say, *Have I said something wrong?* What was wrong was I was being blindsided.

"We all agree to be as transparent as possible if we're to do this work," Norman said.

"I'm perfectly aware of that. I'm transparent when I need to be," I said as I shot a few darts his way.

What an idiot. He hadn't picked up on anything. My stomach was upset. By the end of the hour, I didn't like him, and I worried he'd turn Luke against me.

***

After the session, Luke took my hand as we walked along Madison Avenue, two young paupers in Manhattan's heart of gold and glitz. I glanced at one rich woman after another, their poufy hair, Prada handbags and skinny ankles with bulging calf muscles made me feel inferior. It was a warm May afternoon, one of New York City's best times of the year.

"What happened in there? You sounded so angry," Luke said.

"It's hard opening myself to someone I don't know or trust. You could have warned me, Luke. He's a bulldozer."

"But you do all those workshops where you don't know anyone, and you're used to all those trainers."

"He's so cocky," I said.

"You sound like your Mother."

We walked by one fancy boutique after another with the price for one dress more than the tuition for Luke's four-year program.

"That was a low blow and you know it. How could you talk about us behind my back?"

Luke opened his palms to the sky. "Jeez, Al, he's my therapist while I'm in the program. He's been a big support for me."

"Well, good for Norman." I dropped Luke's hand. We passed by a fancy patisserie. "I want a Napoleon," I grumbled.

Luke looked at me with his eyebrows raised.

"What?" I snapped.

"No, that's fine. Sure, by all means, let's get you a Napoleon."

I'm sure his eyes were twinkling, but it wasn't funny to me.

We found a table by the window where I could watch more jewel encrusted women pass by while I ate through five layers of pastry and crème filling. It tasted like mush in my mouth.

***

Luke stayed behind for the weekend while I rode the train home in a sulk. I brooded as I looked critically at the same pair of swans on Long Island Sound, still gliding together, still faithful, probably because there were no other swans in the area to compete with. I felt hopeless for a moment. Maybe it was impossible to have a grownup relationship where both of us were free and happy. Luke had trouble when I was moving ahead, but he tried to be generous and praised my successes. Now when he was finally moving and growing, I had turned sour. I had to admit my red thread didn't always lead to something I was proud of.

I took out *Seth Speaks,* one of my stable of spiritual books. I was down on gurus, but I was still searching.

I couldn't focus on the book. I wanted to kick myself for losing my temper with Luke and Norman. Luke was expanding out into the world and gaining confidence. He was finally excited and happy. I should be glad for him. But who knew how much he'd grow and where it might take him? Who knew if he'd grow beyond me? At least when he was stuck and depressed, I didn't have to be concerned about anyone finding him. That was a bad thought. But I argued to myself, *Now, everyone can see what is charming and loveable about him.* It was very worrisome.

I wondered if Norman picked up on that dynamic. He probably felt sorry for Luke having to contend with my smallness. And it wasn't only Norman. I was jealous of all the women in Luke's program.

I put *Seth Speaks* away.

Why didn't Amtrak ever clean the grime on its windows? I could barely see out. Periodically the train came into a station, ground to a stop, and sat for a few minutes with the doors open. A woman walked down the aisle with her Louis Vuitton bag, the cloying sweet fragrance of Worth's Je Reviens trailing behind her. Too much perfume. I checked myself out in my small pocket mirror. I thought of the bad Queen in *Snow White*, someone I secretly admired. She was powerful and beautiful with a possessive kind of power and a frightening beauty.

The thing was, it is one thing to think with generosity, it is another to act on it. I didn't like sharing Luke. I felt acid rising into my throat. Luke was a woman's man. I could tell women were drawn to him, the unspoken question being how he responded to them. I was dark inside.

As soon as I got back to our apartment, I dumped my suitcase on the bed, sat down at the kitchen table, and wrote to Marcia, the chair of my Ph.D. committee. I'd never met her in person. Just thinking about having to deal with her made me mad. My letter shouted, *"I quit!"*

I had hundreds of typewritten pages in a cardboard box by my side. I felt like sending them all to her. *Here, you take them. They're not doing anything for me*. I was finished with the ever-changing school requirements, with its stupid coup d'état of one set of chauvinistic professors over another, and with my inability to give them what they wanted.

I never told the school what had occurred with Jim in the hot tub. I felt like I'd be whining. Now he was gone. I wonder now if something more had happened with some other woman and that was the reason Jim had left. It never occurred to me at the time that I might not have been the only one. But I never inquired, and nothing was ever said. Jim died in the 80's.

There was a five-year window for reenrollment without losing credits. But I knew I would never go back. I was about to join yet another group, the ABD's (All but Dissertation), those students who never completed their dissertations, but thought they should at least receive some recognition for all the work they'd put in. My decision felt right, although part of me worried I would regret not having Ph.D. after my name.

I put my school withdrawal letter into an envelope, sealed it, and stamped it hard with my fist. Then, riding on the same energy, I wrote to Harold:

> *I've wondered why we were close. What did you really want? Was it mostly about sex? Is that why you were so angry with me? Is that why you tried to tear me down and humiliate me? I thought you respected me, but that was only if I thought the way you think and believed the way you believe. Now it looks like you didn't really care about me. None of it was for me. It was all for you, what you wanted, how I reflected you back to you.*

You know, I'm not the only one who has gotten so angry with you that I saw white. You poke and provoke until someone has to say BACK OFF. And even then, you don't let up. You keep at it until the other person explodes. You are the king of passive aggression, the little emperor who has lost his throne, whose Mummy only gave him sour milk.

Furthermore, Harold, you are a beady eyed, woman hating, small minded egomaniac. You could be so intelligent if you didn't close yourself off with circular arguments, if you weren't a tight assed rigid fanatical thinker who found a belief system and is now blinded to all other thinking.

You couldn't tolerate me as a separate person who may not have totally agreed with you. You couldn't let me be myself. Maybe it's because you're so near sighted that you can't see past the tip of your nose. People grow Harold, and they change, and we need to grow with them. We need to expand ourselves. You are unable to do that. It's all about you and only you.

I stopped to take a deep breath. It was a nasty letter.

I put it into an envelope and sealed it, grinding the stamp into the paper. I took both letters and stomped up the street to the Post Office. I shoved my letter to California through the mail slot, allowing a big hallelujah to move through my body. It was over.

I held onto the letter to Harold. It felt hot in my hands. It would burn him when he touched it before he even opened it. I wouldn't regret it for a minute. I let it rest on the edge of the slot. But, on second thought, I didn't need to say more to Harold. We had already fought and broken apart, yelled all kinds of mean stuff at each other. I'd cast him out of my life. I could move on. I grabbed it back, ripped it in half and tore it in shreds. Then I picked up all the little pieces dropped on the ground and deposited them in my bag. In case I changed my mind.

Our supervision group dissolved. We only managed to publish one edition. Women like me needed help to move in male circles. We wanted to be admired, recognized by smart men who had a following in their professions. There was always a price. There had to be a better way. I thought of Dad, another man who didn't want me to move beyond him.

My thoughts circled back to me. Luke going off on his own and having his own experiences was threatening to me. Just as Harold was threatened by me growing close to Reuben.

None of us knew how to be separate and connected at one time. We all got tangled up together until it took an explosion to pull us apart. Harold was like Dad. He loved me but as an extension of himself. And I was like Harold and Dad. I loved Luke, but as an extension of myself.

What a mess.

I was ashamed, and at the bottom of it all I was afraid. I was finally understanding how special Luke was, and I didn't want to drive him away.

40

THE ENEMY OF MY ENEMY IS MY FRIEND

Mum stood at the stove stirring a cream sauce for chicken a la king. "Are they here already?" she fretted. "It's not even noon."

"Don't worry, Mum. Luke and I'll keep them company."

And here we go. I walked out to greet them in the driveway. It was inevitable. The parents had to meet. We had delayed it for as long as we could, but it was late June and there was going to be a wedding in the fall. I could count my worries: Mother, Eleanor would be chilly; my Dad, George would be affected; Luke's Mum, Anne would most likely behave while judging my parents in her mind; and his Father, Lou would tell Jewish jokes that no one would get if they weren't Jewish. And he was mawkishly sentimental.

Mum and Dad had invited Luke's parents to come up for lunch, since the wedding was to be at their house. It was the first time for each of them to meet someone Jewish, someone Christian. I imagined Luke's and my presence was incidental. We were the eye of the storm, dead quiet while the four of them swirled around us.

I could hardly enjoy my breakfast the morning of the luncheon.

"Let's get there early," I said. "I need to check things out."

"What are you checking out Al? What's the point?"

"I want to see what my parents are wearing. How intimidating they plan to be. I wish I had a Quaalude or some of my old seizure meds."

"It's out of our hands, Al. Try not to worry."

We arrived at the house at 11:30am to survey the scene. Mum looked composed, no need for her to worry since she was on her own ground. I looked at her A-line skirt and round collared blouse with the gold circle pin at the top, all very Waspy. Dad in his tweed sports jacket over a button-down blue shirt. And a Harvard tie. His closely cropped hair gave him away as a Marine. I could only hope they'd be welcoming to Luke's parents, but it didn't look good. I was still recovering from our first meeting when they treated Luke like a dangerous foreign intruder.

And now, here they were, Anne and Lou were fifteen minutes early. We went out to greet them in the driveway. They stood under the maple looking up, admiring the house. One of the favorite family outings when Luke was young had been to take Sunday drives through wealthy neighborhoods to admire the stately New England homes. We took his parents in through the north door (less intimidating than the front door) and went into the library. I told them Mum was in the kitchen and Dad would be down very soon. My parents seemed to be taking their time. Lou was looking at all the family antiques nodding with his hands clasped behind his back.

Dad appeared, wiping his hands on a dish towel. "Excuse my hands," he said, "I was washing dishes."

Dad was a good cook and he always cleaned up if Mother was cooking. He said it came from KP duty, hours of peeling potatoes. He was at his most gracious, but stiff. He stood ram rod straight, his shoulders back, like a Marine at attention. My heart was buzzing.

"What a lovely home you have, Mr. Thorne," Anne said.

"Please, call me George."

That was good, Dad. He could be charming with attractive women. He offered them a drink, alcoholic of course, even though he couldn't drink anymore. It was the only polite thing to do and WASPS were notoriously thirsty as soon as they arrived.

Dad told them, "the liver's gone." I cringed.

There was no non-alcoholic alternative. Anne said she would wait, and Lou welcomed a scotch on the rocks. Luke looked at me with his mouth stretched tight and eyes wide. Lou so rarely took a drink.

Conversation started off bumpy, mostly concerning the portraits on the walls which led Dad to expound on the family history.

"Eleanor's Father designed and built an addition to the original 1800's house," Dad said, emphasizing that 'new' was still 'old' in WASP terms. Or maybe it was that old is still new, I always confused the two.

"Here's my Mother," I said, as Mum entered the library and brought history into the present. How cool would she be? But Eleanor was surprisingly personable and even a tiny bit warm. She and Anne both demurred when Dad again offered cocktails.

We went into the dining room two by two, like entering a grand ballroom in the previous century. Luke's Mother with Dad, and his Father with Eleanor. Luke and I followed. He squeezed my hand, and I tried to catch my breath. I felt large sweat stains on the underarms of my white blouse.

It took some time for us to get seated. George stood at the head of the table waiting. He pulled out Anne's chair. Lou started to sit, then stood up. Eleanor had already sat down at the other end of the table. I felt dizzy, wondering who was supposed to do what. And when.

Luke and I sat down last.

Anne and Lou sat facing the large windows with the deep wine-colored velvet curtains. Between the windows, portraits of Mr. and Mrs. Benjamin Bussey stared at them from the wall. I saw Lou looking at them, and my eye traveled to Mrs. Bussey's burgeoning breasts. My cousin Rozzie and I always made fun of the Busseys at holiday dinners. They looked so pleased with themselves as they looked down upon us, the motley remains of the family fortune. It occurred to me as Lou was studying the portrait that her breasts bursting up and out as they did from her Empire-waist dress were the material proof of their ample wealth. No wonder Mr. Bussey looked so pleased. Dad took off on the Bussey story, all their property and money bequeathed to Harvard, the big family disappointment. Lou was duly impressed.

Anne spoke with Mum on the side, "Delicious chicken a la king," asking if she made the pastries. Mother told her, "Pepperidge Farm." Anne would have made them from scratch.

I began noticing stereotypes everywhere. Mum's soft Yankee r's, her silver cigarette case engraved with her Mother's initials. She opened the case and took out a Kent cigarette, offering one to Anne who thanked her, but no. Eleanor only smoked in social situations and never inhaled. George said he had given that up as well, smoking had gone the way of the whiskey.

Lou felt called upon to expound on his family history. Luke and I turned to each other and exchanged glances. Couldn't Luke step in and cut his Father off before he went any further? Luke shrugged. My mouth stretched wide as I clenched my teeth. I had to put my fork down. Lou proudly detailed his Father's defiance of a Russian officer in 1905 and his subsequent flight from the Ukraine, coming to this country as a young man, settling initially in Texas because he loved Zane Gray cowboy stories. Dad looked very serious as he listened and nodded.

"He married a woman from Odessa when Odessa was the Paris of Russia." Lou said. "She married down. Her intended fiancée had gone and married someone else before she arrived."

Dad nodded again. "Very interesting."

Uh oh. Marrying down was not good. Was Lou's story proof to Dad that I was marrying down? But a thought followed that Mum had married down and that was why the family history was so important to Dad. It wasn't his story. It was Mother's. I felt so dizzy I couldn't finish my chicken, a dish I loved because of the sauce in the buttery pastry shells.

Maybe Lou would stop. But no, he continued as he looked at Dad. "My Father owned a successful grocery store and worked long hours. Unlike the children of today who don't appreciate true sacrifice."

"I agree," said Dad. "Our children have had it too easy."

"He was a wonderful man," Lou said, as his voice cracked, "sacrificing himself for my brothers and me, working into the night every night, all through the weekend, generous to customers who couldn't pay." Lou grew teary. "There won't be another like him." He took out his handkerchief and blew hard into it, wiping his tears.

Mum took a puff of her Kent and blew out the smoke, her way to cover over whatever was embarrassing.

Anne gave Lou a look that would have stopped a herd of horses in the dust. "Lou," she barked. She turned to Dad and said, "My husband is too sentimental." She glared at Lou.

"I tried to teach Luke to take care of his younger brother. The way my brother took care of me." Lou's voice was shaking.

I elbowed Luke hard. Do something. Stop him. He was about to sob. This was an unresolved bitter dispute that Luke had with his Father because Luke had refused to take care of his younger brother. Luke's Father saw him as disloyal, irresponsible, forever a disappointment. We had entered dangerous territory.

Luke cleared his throat several times. His Mother looked across at him. He had her attention, but Lou didn't notice. Dad cleared his throat and looked away. My crying was bad enough, but any sign of a man in tears was anathema to Father. Lou was climbing to a crescendo of melodrama. Somebody had to do something. My face was hot and sweaty. Luke's connection to Father was only beginning to be cordial. Lou was about to ruin it.

"Dad," Luke had to say it twice to grab Lou's attention, "Ali's Father was in the South Pacific during the War. Just like your friend Arthur. They might have been there at the same time."

War, soldiers, battle. Thank you, Luke, I thought. *Thank you.*

Dad moved on to the Solomon Islands and the Marine landing on Guadalcanal. He asked Lou where he served during the War. Lou said he'd been needed at home, had cleaned all the uniforms for the soldiers. Yes, that was an important job, Dad allowed. He looked relieved to get things on neutral ground again.

As Luke and I cleared the dishes and took them out to the pantry. I whispered to Luke that I was exhausted, and we still had to get through dessert. Mum had asked me to take a tray out the front door where Dad had set up two chairs for her and Anne on the lawn. Dad ushered Lou into the library. I warned Luke that Dad might offer another scotch to Lou. Holding one's liquor was a valued WASP trait. For Lou, more scotch would mean more maudlin. Luke said he'd try to help the men converse and keep a lid on his Father. I said I would supervise Eleanor and Anne, pull out some interesting family story to fill the silence until it was time for them to leave.

I poured two glasses of iced tea with tall silver spoons, added sprigs of fresh spearmint to each, and arranged homemade brownies on a lovely Chinese plate. I put everything on a tray and headed out the front door. As I balanced the tray, I stopped behind them overhearing their conversation.

"I never thought we'd see this day, Eleanor," Anne said.

What day was that? Was this day a good day or a bad day? Their first born marrying a shiksa was not part of the plan.

"Luke has been our most difficult child," she continued, "a problem from the day he started walking. I had to ride the bus from one end of the line to the other, just to get him to sleep."

I froze in place as I listened. Mother had never ridden a bus. That could not have helped her feelings toward Luke. But I was stunned by her response.

"I know exactly how you feel, Anne. Alicia has been, well, she's been impossible. Ever since the Beatles came in 1962. We haven't known what to do with her, wandering all over the country, working in restaurants, riding motorcycles, wearing those awful clothes."

Anne laughed. "Luke was banished from Elizabeth Park when he was three. I couldn't even socialize with the mothers."

"Oh dear," Mum said. "Alicia was a good little girl, but something went terribly wrong."

Anne sighed. "Luke's hair and beard, I hardly recognized him when he came home. Giving up such a good job, moving onto a boat, ach. We even sent Lou's brother and wife to check on him in California, to bring him home. Lou was distraught. And then he disappeared into Mexico."

"Oh Mexico. Don't get me started. That was the final blow. We couldn't imagine what she would be doing in that country." Mother's tsk-tsk was echoed by Anne.

And we all knew what happened in Mexico. I watched them commiserating and competing for who had the hardest time with their child. They didn't grasp, or maybe they did, but couldn't say it, that Luke and I would never have met if we hadn't felt we had to leave our homes, that it was the wanderings of two lost rebellious souls that brought us together.

They agreed that both of their children had gone against everything they believed in, indirectly acknowledging that our coming together was the obvious illustration of their mutual defeat.

"All is well that ends well," Anne said.

"Yes," said Mother, less enthusiastically.

I took the tray and sat it down in front of them. They sipped their tea and nibbled on brownies as they sat together companionably looking out over a front lawn that led gracefully down a long hill to Main Street.

41

THE LAST STRAW

The wedding Luke and I never thought would happen took place. Although anticlimactic the two families came together with a non-denominational minister and shared champagne and laughter at a simple reception. By 1979, two years of marriage grounded our relationship.

Although I didn't think it would make any difference, I felt more secure and trusting of Luke after we married.

Reuben encouraged me as a professional woman to keep my own name, but when I thought about it, taking Luke's name was no different from keeping Father's name. Now I understood why my office mate had changed her name to Goodwoman. I didn't want to make up a whole new name. I dropped Thorne and became Alicia Fine. I got used to referring to *my husband.* Speaking of myself as Luke's wife took longer.

After seven years we were a bonified couple in our parents' eyes. Luke's parents warmed to me gradually and steadily. Mother needed another twenty years to fully take in Luke, but that was to be expected.

Not surprisingly, Dad and Luke had a lot in common. A talent for working with their hands, an appreciation of history and beauty, and a love of the sea. Sometimes Dad called him son.

Luke's hard-won confidence grew with the recent completion of his training program and the beginning of a private therapy practice. My jealousy of other women was an unwelcome visitor who refused to leave. I was possessive, a recent discovery that I hated about myself. Luke appealed to women. He was gentle and understanding with a female sensibility. It scared me. I realized he could have a lot of women if he chose. So why did he want me?

I kept an eye on him in social situations. He often went off on his own at parties where I wanted to keep him close. I was suspicious of what he was saying to other women, how sexual he was being. The more I saw Luke for who he was, the more worried I got that other women saw the same Luke and wanted him. The more I thought I loved him, the more jealous I became.

Somewhere I understood this was not the meaning of love. Possessing someone was not loving them. I hoped time was on my side. I was proud of Luke, and Dad's respect for Luke increased my own. Everything I read said that true love wanted the best for the other person. I knew it, but I didn't feel it. This was my secret.

One Saturday in mid-August, crisp and clear under a cheerful blue sky, my parents, Luke and I, and our visiting friend and colleague Steph, took Dad's 21-foot inboard boat out for a day trip. The three of us were enjoying a week's vacation at Mum and Dad's summer house on Cape Cod. With Father at the helm, we motored out of Crow's Pond where the boat was moored and into the placid waters of Pleasant Bay. We cruised between the outer beach on one side and the graceful Shore Road summer homes on the other where rows of Blue Hydrangea bordered by blooming Privet Hedge filled the ocean air with a privileged peppery scent. We approached the cut-through, a narrow channel connecting the Bay to Stage Harbor. We slowed the engine to a soft putt-putt.

"Watch the bottom, Alicia, and tell me if it's getting too shallow."

"We're going through at low tide, Dad. That's risky."

"We can make it. Here." He handed me the boat hook. "Measure the depth."

Luke sat in the stern between Mother and Steph. "Isn't it great to be out on the water," he said, raising his face up to the sun. "Especially when it's calm."

Steph agreed, although she was not used to boats. Luke was finally comfortable again on the water. It had taken him years to get past his fear after the stormy seas on Destiny.

We meandered through the flat shoals between Monomoy and Morris Island with a clear view of a sandy bottom and entered Stage Harbor, all of us remarking again what a perfect day it was for boating. Mum passed out ham and cheese sandwiches that she'd made on fresh oatmeal bread from the Chatham bakery. We ate the sandwiches with Cape Cod chips and drank minty iced tea. The soft ocean air made the simplest of foods taste delicious.

We came upon the Stage Harbor Yacht Club's teenagers racing Avalons, the lean blue hulls and white sails all pointing in the same direction, tacking tight up into a light wind. Dad wove slowly between the boats, careful not to create a wake. He was a stickler for the rules of the sea. Sailboats always had the right of way.

I yawned and sighed, my face softened by the balmy breeze, my body swaying gently with our boat's gentle rhythm. We admired one magnificent yacht after another moored peacefully in the Harbor—so many wealthy owners who rarely used their boats—as we continued heading toward the entrance, between two sandy peninsulas into Nantucket Sound.

"It doesn't get better than this," I said.

As we entered the Sound, I saw white caps coming toward us. The boat bounced in a rough chop causing a jiggling of our full stomachs. Mother's iced tea splashed on the deck and she held onto her straw hat as a gust blew up the front brim.

"Oh dear. Why don't we turn back, George?" Mother asked.

"We're fine, Eleanor." So quick to dismiss her.

As we got further out into the Sound the white caps came faster, the boat slapped up and down, and warm saltwater sprayed into our faces. The waves grew bigger. A prevailing southwest wind that created our calm Pleasant Bay could cause dramatic weather in the Sound. Unlike the Atlantic where the swells tended to be round and the sensation was of a whole ocean lifting a boat up and down, in Nantucket Sound the waves crested in shallower waters, broke at their peaks, and whacked you. Dad's response was to push the throttle forward and pick up speed as if we could escape the waves. The bow rose sharply and all of us on deck chairs in the stern were suddenly closer to the water behind us.

I gathered everyone's cups and put them in the sink below. I stood beside him at the helm. "Slow down, Dad," I said. "Why do we have to go so fast?"

Steph was white, and her eyes were big as she pulled up her hood and grabbed onto the boat's side rail. Luke gave the calm down signal with his hands, but looked at me, as if to say, *can't you do something?*

Waves broke over the bow and began hitting us harder as the boat slammed up and down on the water. Dad revved the engine, increasing the speed, and spun the wheel turning the boat sharply this way and that way.

"George," Luke said. "This doesn't make sense."

"Shut up," Dad said. "I know what I'm doing."

He began to go in a circle causing waves to break over us in every direction. As he pushed the throttle further forward, the bow rose steeply again causing water to rush over the transom in the stern.

"Dad," I screamed as our chairs slid back. "You're going to swamp us."

"Shut the fuck up," Dad yelled.

The wind was loud, but our screams were louder. The boat listed badly to one side and then the other as water began to pour over the gunnels.

"Please. Mr. Thorne. Slow down. You're scaring me." Even soft-spoken Steph was yelling.

"All of you shut up and sit down. Fucking wimps."

Dad jerked the wheel back and forth, until the boat began sliding as if on ice. I threw up my lunch over the side and began to cry.

"Please Dad, please," I screamed at him.

"Stop behaving like a baby. Shut up."

You're a cartoon of a crazy person. You're a crazy bastard. You're going to kill us, I thought. I thought back to a summer when we lived in Pennsylvania and had the latest model of a cabin cruiser on loan from the Trojan Boat company where Father worked. Dad was desperate to hold down an executive position as his sickness became more visible. I was 12. It was Dad, Mum, and me onboard for the weekend. My lucky older brother, almost unknown to me because he was always away at boarding school or with friends, wasn't there.

On a tranquil Chesapeake Bay Dad drove the boat at full throttle in smaller and smaller circles until the boat was spinning, listing so badly that water poured over the gunnels. Mum and I were thrown from one side to the other as the boat crashed over top of an increasingly big wake, a wake that Dad himself had created. We screamed and begged, "Please, stop, please!" Waves rushed at us from all sides, and the boat fishtailed. I threw up over the gunnel, which only fueled his fury. He kept going and we kept crying until he wore himself out. That evening as we sat below in a peaceful harbor and ate hot ham and butter sandwiches, he said he'd only wanted to test the boat, to see how far over we could go, take her to the point just before she capsized.

I put my hand on Luke's thigh and held on tight. He reached down into the warm water and washed the vomit off my face.

As we fell into each other, he said, "Enough, this is crazy."

Luke stood up his feet wide apart to stay balanced on the deck. He lurched forward, holding the starboard side rail as he moved toward Dad. He stood beside him at the helm. I heard him yell, "I'll take the wheel, George."

"Hell, you will," Dad yelled. "Watch out."

Dad elbowed him sharply in his side. "Move back," he said.

Mum and Steph clenched our canvas chairs. Mum's straw hat was long gone. Their faces were dripping salt water. Luke looked back at me, questioning. My head moved frantically up and down. He reached his right hand to the wheel so that he and Dad held it together. "I've got it George, I've got it," he said.

Dad swore at him, but Luke had already pulled back on the throttle so that we stopped fishtailing.

"I'll take us in George. It's okay," Luke said as he put his other hand on the wheel and moved in front of Father.

Dad swore, "Jesus Luke," but this time he cursed the wind, "The goddamn wind's coming from all sides. I hope you know what the hell you're doing."

"The wind's southwest, George. Let's get it behind us," Luke said.

It wasn't the wind blowing from all directions. It was Dad spinning the boat. Luke seemed to know how to allow Dad to be the Captain even as Luke took over at the helm. The wind came at us broadside temporarily and we lobbed precariously in the waves. The loud slapping noise as the boat hit the water up and down sounded like its seams might split apart. Luke began to turn the boat away from the wind.

"Can't you slow us down Luke?" I yelled.

"I will," he turned his head slightly toward me. "We still need some thrust to keep us on top of the water."

I realized Luke knew what he was doing. I could let him be the skipper, let him drive.

I blew a jagged breath out through sealed lips and sat back into my seat. He gradually turned the boat so that we were facing the harbor without getting swamped broadside. Luke varied the speed, but carefully, not too much, not too little so that we rode along the tops of the waves. Dad grew calmer. I had never seen that happen before. For the first time it occurred to me that Dad was afraid. A red thread that led from my father's rage to his tormented terrified self.

As the boat stabilized, so did my father, my mother, and to a certain extent, me. The waters remained roiling, the white caps continued to slap us, but we were no longer overwhelmed by the sea.

Luke succeeded in turning us away from the wind. He had calmed the storm.

My jaw could barely move. Even with fifteen years' sobriety, I saw Dad was still crazy. He didn't need alcohol to fuel his furies. There had been too much pretending over the years that nothing ever happened. Too frightened too many times. Too much shaking like a mewling baby.

"That's it. I've had it. I'm finished," I mumbled to no one in particular.

With the wind at our backs, the boat leveled out. Each wave lifted us to its peak from behind so that we surged forward. Essentially the boat body-surfed back to the entrance. Luke slowed us down deliberately, so that we could all calm down and allow the seas to push us. We entered Stage Harbor's sheltered waters.

The boat magically stilled, and it might have been easier to pretend it had never happened, that we were about to capsize.

"I'd appreciate your letting me off at the nearest dock," Steph was indignant as she wiped the water from her face. She was shaking, from anger, she said later, not fear. But I knew the two feelings always went together where Father was concerned.

I almost laughed. I was sorry for Steph. I had never seen her so afraid.

"We're okay now, Steph," I said. "From here on in we're in calm waters."

She agreed—reluctantly—to stay aboard. She refused to look at Father. Luke asked Dad if he wanted to take back the wheel. Dad didn't speak. It would have meant admitting he'd done something wrong. He stared straight ahead but stood by Luke's side so that if Luke stayed at the helm it was Dad's choice to have him skipper the boat.

We passed through the Harbor and the cut through, up into the head of the Bay and tied up at our mooring in Crow's Pond. Fortunately, we didn't run aground in the shoals.

It gave me some satisfaction to see what it was like for Steph to be with Dad. Luke already had the real picture. Steph's reaction reminded me I was not exaggerating.

***

I kissed the top of Luke's head as he sat at our kitchen table. "Good morning, honey," I said. "A good sleep?"

"Yeah. How 'bout you?" He reached up for my hand as I stood behind him.

"Bad night. Going over our day on the boat."

"Still brooding Al?"

We were back home a couple weeks after what was an idyllic time on the Cape, except for those terrifying moments with Dad. But if it hadn't happened, I wouldn't have seen Luke in action. My voice shook as I clenched my mug and asked Luke to pour me coffee.

"I'm going to do it today. I'm not going to cower," I said with my jaw sticking out and one fist raised.

"You've said that before," Luke said.

"I know. He could have drowned all of us. If it hadn't been for you, Luke, I don't know if we would have made it."

"I never saw your Dad that bad. He knows the sea so well, but he really lost it. I had to do something."

"You stood up to Dad, something I've never done."

My head hurt. I couldn't stop thinking about it and I couldn't find any relief. I'd made the same decision many times before and then backed off when I got in his presence. I wasn't sure this time would be any different. I noticed my hands were shaking.

"What are you afraid of Al? If you think about it, what can he do now?"

I couldn't answer. All I knew was my clammy hands, a nauseous stomach, and my sick head. I was worn out from being afraid and always angry. I was old enough to realize he wasn't going to kill me. Some formless fear deeply embedded in my body held me captive. I could say I'd be okay, but my body hadn't received the message.

I'd been awake all night, angry with myself, calling myself names, angry at Dad, sorry for him, scared of the look in his eyes that burrowed right into me.

The boat ride kept replaying in my mind, the image of his wildness becoming one with the roiling ocean so that the sea became the face of his terror and his rage. I'd known that look in his eyes before I even knew myself, so that as I grew, I confused myself with him. His sickness became my sickness, his suffering, my suffering. It wasn't something I wanted. As he struggled to keep from drowning my survival came to depend on his.

As I lay in bed my jaw began to clench. My dark friend was nearby. I tried to hold him back, opening my mouth wide, stretching my tongue, pulling my lips toward my cheeks until my entire face ached. I grew frightened as my jaw continued to tighten and then began its lockdown, which meant a seizure was imminent. I'd thought they were gone, but I was experiencing the familiar aura, the visceral sensation of a heavy black steel gate coming down slowly on top of me.

When I'd had seizures as a young girl, the first thing I always did was try to stop the psychic gate, push it back up in my mind. But it was heavy and leaden, unrelenting in its downward push. Too strong for me. I would try to scream for help, my jaw locked, and I couldn't make any sound. The gate came down upon me until I no longer knew that I was feeling anything or what the feeling might have been if I'd stayed conscious. It was all lost in the spittle, foam, and quaking of the convulsion. When I returned to consciousness, I knew nothing except a dull dimly conscious throbbing of my head and the dumb feeling of my brain's nauseous disturbance. I knew nothing about my father, nothing about what brought on my seizure, nothing about what I really felt. All that knowledge remained hidden in my body.

For some reason early that morning all these years later, I was graced by an intelligence that was previously inaccessible. I felt my jaw going down the well-worn path to its inevitable dark dwelling. This time, for the first time, I remained conscious. The black gate, my sick loyal friend was only waiting for its signal to shut down on top of me. I thought, *No, not this time*.

I was angry. I was afraid. But still, I was going to speak to Dad. And the gate stopped and retreated to the back of my mind.

I felt nauseous and my head pulsed, but I remained conscious. My jaw stayed clenched but not locked. I had not seized. I had no choice this time. To back out again would have meant falling back into the dark.

***

Luke wanted to go to support me, but I said no. He had done his part. This was mine to do.

I sat with Mum and Dad in the little dining room. Her tuna fish sandwiches with onion, celery, and dill were comfort food. No one mentioned our visit to the Cape. Nothing was said about the fiasco on the boat. Did we even have a boat? That was the problem. No one ever mentioned anything and that made you wonder what if anything had happened.

I was home again, their little girl again, their good little girl who had always been so sunny in the face of a family in trouble. I lived inside of her skin and my identity was based on shining my light on Dad's suffering. It would have been so much easier to stay in the womb of their reality. I reminded myself that the price was too high.

And was I their good little girl? Not really. In their eyes I'd fallen long ago. As Mum had said to Luke's Mother, I was a problem and a disappointment. In fact, what Luke loved most about me was exactly what they found wanting.

"Dad, I was upset about the way you put us all in danger on the boat."

There. I said it. I wanted to slide down in my chair. I forced myself to sit up and wait.

He cleared his throat, his lips went into his chin, which went into his neck and he refused to look at me. "Oh, come on now. Not this again."

"You could have killed us. There was no reason for you to behave that way."

"You know nothing about being in that kind of sea. I did what I had to do. And that husband of yours had no right to take the wheel."

His voice rumbled, like a pending storm. He had that familiar wild look in his eyes, his pupils lost in dark pools. Don't go any further. Stop immediately or else. I was like a jellyfish, thrown into a rough sea. But I'd dissolved into tears too many times or stuffed down what I really thought or felt.

"You had us all terrified. You had Steph scared to death. One more big wave and we could have capsized. Luke was right. Thank god he saved us."

"I have no idea what you're referring to."

It wasn't Dad's worst behavior, but he was a dry drunk, his rage always below the surface, pushing, angling to escape. Either I was going to stand my ground or continue to be helpless and afraid. I couldn't cater to him anymore. It was the last straw. I threw open my palms and thrust my chin forward.

"Really George?" I spoke like a stern parent. "You have no idea? You explode for no reason. You intimidate, you bully until everyone cowers before you. You're like some angry two-year-old god. You know exactly what I'm referring to. You can't treat people like that."

I grew taller as I spoke with the weird sensation of being more grown up than Father.

He grumbled. “You’re all psychologists. I thought you could take it.”

It was the first time he had spoken the word psychologist and recognized Luke and me as professionals. While I had no idea what he meant, I heard him backing down. He was looking for an excuse. Why hadn’t I done this before?

“I don’t want you to speak to me like that again. Or Luke. Or my friends. Ever. Or we’re done.”

I did everything but shake my finger at him. What was most shocking was that it wasn’t Dad who was threatening to withdraw his love. It was me. He stayed silent, staring at the floor.

42

A PARTICULARLY COMPLICATED PATIENT

He was seated in a small upholstered chair in the breezeway.

Light streamed in through walls of glass, but Dad's vision was limited. He was going blind with macular degeneration, a condition the doctor told him went hand in hand with a weak heart. The breezeway connected the main part of the house to the wing where Dad slept on a hospital bed. He had his usual attire of a tweed jacket, oxford shirt, and khakis. No matter how badly he felt, he maintained his appearance and was clean shaven.

Mum and Dad had sold the big house and now lived in a traditional cape house on Old Ayer Road, the same road Dad used to drive us at breathtaking speed when he was drinking. Mother had asked me to come out and stay with Dad while she caught up on errands that she had no time for because she'd been attending to him.

She said he wasn't well, an unusual admission.

My one and only truthful confrontation with Dad had been three years ago. We quickly returned to habit. I'd resigned myself to a limited connection between a father with his pride and a daughter still confused about her own identity. I couldn't express anything loving and he was mute about any feeling toward me.

Love sat between us like an elephant in the room.

I went to their house prepared. I could study my therapy notes of a particularly complicated case, a woman whose father was mentally ill and violent. It was challenging working with her because she made me think so much of myself with Dad. I wasn't sure how to help her with her Father since I'd already given up on my own.

I smelled the familiar scents of Old Spice and Vitalis hair tonic as I leaned down to kiss his cheek.

"The old ticker's giving me trouble," he said instead of hello.

"Okay, you can rest, and I'll do some work," I said. I took my jacket off and put my notebook down as Mum got up and prepared to leave.

"I took him in for a checkup yesterday and what do you think they found?" Mum looked at Dad like a school librarian scolding her student for stealing a book.

"My pelvis is broken," Dad said. He flinched from the pain.

"And he's been sitting with it for days. He was out where he wasn't supposed to be fixing the front door, and he fell off the step." Mum shook her head and sighed.

I'd been following the family tradition of denial allowing me to ignore Dad's shrinking self. In recent months when I'd seen him in the car with Mum, he looked tiny, his head barely rising to the passenger window. It shocked me every time to see him so diminished.

"I'll be back around five," she told us. She put on her fall car coat and took her bag off the hook by the door.

"Okay Mum," I said as Dad flinched again. I turned back to face him. "Ouch Dad."

"I've had a lot worse. I was blown up to the sky by a Jap bomb remember."

I yawned. This could be a long afternoon. I looked at Dad, at his gaunt face and protruding cheekbones, his hollowed-out eyes. His head appeared to have fallen into his tweed jacket where there once were broad shoulders. I felt a horrified fascination at his frailty, as if witnessing the demolition of an old building. My stomach fell. I may have been terrified and enraged when he was operating in full form, but I hated to see him defeated.

"I'm having some tea," I said, "would you like some?"

I brought in a cup for Dad with a few pecan cookies and sat down in the identical upholstered chair opposite him. I took my folder out and perused the clinical notes of a therapy session.

"This reminds me of when I had Diphtheria," Dad said. "I was in bed for months and every day my Mother and I had tea."

I put my papers down. "Was that kind of cozy?"

"I was my Mother's favorite."

That wasn't news to me. The news was that he was talking. I could see in his eyes and hear in his voice that he was back in another world. While he was not exactly speaking to me, he was at least talking in front of me, which made me think he might want me to be the listener.

"I was the only one of the three boys who could manage the black stallion. I'd ride Joe bare back, I'd wear a black cape, we'd gallop through the fields and jump the crick…I never fell off."

"You were a wild one, Dad."

I thought of the story of a teenaged Dad in his black cape singing on top of a telephone pole. That might have alerted the family to his disturbance, but no one admitted he was ill. And we knew so little about psychological illness. We thought of it as one more example of Dad's adventurous and romantic nature, like flying with his Marine buddy in a one engine plane underneath the Golden Gate bridge or walking the twenty some miles from Cambridge out to see Mother before they were married. It wasn't until years later that I understood Dad had a mental illness.

He asked for some saltines. When I came back from the kitchen, he was trying to change his position, grimacing, grasping the arms of the chair in pain. His bony hands were covered in black and blue bruises.

"I was trying to fix that damn back door. Hit myself with the hammer instead of the nail."

"I'm sorry, Dad, that you are in pain."

In the pit of my belly, I felt the hurt for all his suffering. Luke and I were wounded in our own ways, but we'd received help and understanding within a culture that was beginning to look at mental illness and PTSD. We had the luxury of time focused on ourselves and our own healing. Life had been hard for Dad, with no name for his illness and no help available for his wounded psyche. But at that moment I saw the way I had made his pain my own. My father didn't have a chance and we'd all paid the price. I thought about what a man he might have been if he'd been able to develop his strength, his intelligent mind, and compassion for others.

He drifted again. "Summers we rode the train from North Wales to Cape May and stayed at Aunt Peggy and Uncle George's. The horses and carriage had their own separate rail car."

He was getting the generations mixed up. Had he consciously chosen me to be the one to hold his memories? Or had I happened to arrive at the right time? I wanted to believe that Father was trying to connect with me. He was trying to convey something to me, but unable to say it directly. I could have been reading between the lines like I always did, looking in the silence for the love. He drifted.

"And of course, Mammy Lou always came along. Cooking scrapple and buttermilk biscuits. Swing low, sweet chariot," Dad sang in an exaggerated baritone.

I tried not to laugh. Mammy Lou had been another mother to him. I didn't ask where Mammy Lou's family was while she took such good care of Dad and his brothers. I wasn't going to go there.

"And then the Depression hit in '29, and Skipper lost all his money and took to drink."

"Yes, your Father was a mean drunk," I said.

"In the winter, the crick froze, and we could skate a mile up and back… In the spring the water ran fast… and the willows hung low over the banks… and the watercress was fresh, bitter. Mother made us watercress sandwiches…"

My heart dissolved for that boy who adored his Mother and feared his Father, who could ride bareback fast as the wind, who loved the natural world around him. I had a photograph of Dad at eight standing on the kitchen steps of their farmhouse staring at the camera with a mischievous smile, skinny and scruffy, band aids on both knees, legs and feet pointing in opposite directions. A boy who was broken early and then splintered by the War. I squeezed my eyes tight. I didn't want to cry.

I seared every image and story into my own memory. I knew I wouldn't hear them again. My shoulders grew tense with the effort of listening and holding on to every word. It was the longest talk we'd ever had. "I know, it wasn't a real conversation," I'd say to Luke later. Dad didn't know the back and forth of real conversation. But it was words out of a lifetime of silence. I leaned in as though I couldn't get close enough. He talked, and I listened.

"Dad, do you remember when we were on your boss's boat in Delaware Bay and he was pulling me on a line off the stern? Remember? That was so much fun."

"No, I don't remember that boat at all." He pulled back and his face looked blank.

I bowed my head. He had been drunk, all memories of me lost in blackouts. I sat quiet, resigned.

"I remember you on the Jersey seashore," he said suddenly. "You were wild about the surf. We couldn't get you out of the water."

My heart flew up. "We rode the waves together, Dad. They broke way far out and rolled in perfectly. We got the longest rides. Remember?"

"I do. That water was warm. You were quite the bodysurfer."

There. He remembered me as a little girl. And he complimented me. That was something. So much less than I hungered for and yet more than I ever expected.

I looked at my watch. "It's almost time for Mum to get home," I said.

"That reminds me, Eleanor." His voice grew deep and ominous, moving from past to future. "I want you to promise me you'll take care of my Mother after I'm gone."

"You mean you want me to take of my Mother. Of Eleanor."

He looked at me, startled, "Of course. That's what I mean."

"Of course, I will Dad," I said without thinking. "I can do that."

"Good girl. I know you can."

My shoulders collapsed. Whoever I was to him, I wanted to please him. I wanted his love in whatever way he offered it. But as I was letting one burden go, I sank beneath the weight of another. I knew that without Dad, Mother's needs would become my own.

The conversation ended abruptly when Mum came in the door. She looked a little less weary. I told her I'd be glad to come out any time to sit with Dad.

"Do you have to go?" he said. "Hmph. Leaving me again?"

"I don't mean to leave you Dad. But I need to go home and make supper for Luke and me. I loved talking with you, hearing your stories. I'll come back."

“You’re always running off somewhere. I can’t keep track of you.” He was plaintive.

I leaned down and kissed him. Our intimacy was like his skin, cool and dry, thin and fragile, like rice paper.

“Goodbye Dad.”

“Swing low, sweet chariot,” he rumbled off again in that deep bass with a far off look in his eyes, “comin’ for to carry … me home….”

43

I AM MY FATHER'S DAUGHTER

The phone rang at 6 a.m. on Sunday the first of May.

The bedroom was chilly with early morning air coming through the open window. I pulled up the sheet and blanket. Sleep was precious and I was determined to sleep in. I pretended I didn't hear it. The ringing persisted. Luke said he'd get it and I dropped off.

"Al. Wake up."

His hand was gently shaking my back.

"Who was that?"

"It was your Mother…"

I jolted awake, lifted my head, and looked at Luke. I knew.

"He's gone, Ali. She found him this morning, sitting in his chair out in the wing."

I sat on the edge of the bed. I shook my head to rattle my brain.

"How could that have happened?"

It must have been his heart my mother told Luke. It looked like Dad got out of bed and stumbled over to the chair. He was slumped over like he'd fallen suddenly asleep.

I kept shaking my head. I'd just seen him the other day. Yes, he was hurting, but he was very much alive. He'd talked about dying for so long that I began to dismiss the possibility. I wasn't finished. I needed more time to sort things out. I needed to say more things to Dad. That I understood why he was so out of balance. That I loved him anyway. I needed to have him say something to me like he loved me. And he hadn't meant to frighten me all these years. In a second, he was gone. The world was turning backwards.

I pushed myself up, sat on the edge of the bed, and put my feet on the cold floor. My hands clenched the mattress. Luke sat down next to me and put his arm around my shoulder.

"I'm so sorry, Al."

I didn't want comfort. I thought my Father was invincible. Nothing could touch him. He had always defeated death before, in the War, in multiple emergency surgeries. If he could die, Luke could drop dead. I could end up completely alone. The sun could burn up. I thought I'd always have a father, I'd always struggle with him, our conflict would never truly end. I depended on that struggle. It was the way I'd shaped myself. I needed him to push against to feel myself.

"I'll go with you," Luke said.

"No. Thanks, honey. I have to go alone."

I washed quickly and smoothed cream on my face. I put on jeans and an old faded black sweatshirt. I pulled my hair back into its long braid. I wanted to sit with Dad, even if only with his body. I wanted to be close to death, it was such a mystery to me. I told Luke I'd call him and let him know what was happening.

***

As I pulled into the driveway, I noticed the old unruly lilac bushes needed trimming, many of the branches bare, those with heirloom dark purple blossoms at the end of their bloom. I heard the mourning doves' insistent cooing when I opened the car door. The air had the bite of early spring. My mother stood at the door of the breezeway waiting for me. I wrapped my arms around my chest as I walked toward her on the path.

"Oh Mum, I can't believe it."

She did not respond.

I held onto her as we hugged, but she pulled back, her body tight. She was already dressed and composed, a trim gray flannel skirt and Fair Isle sweater suggesting she was ready to manage one more crisis with Dad. I sat on the edge of a chair in the breezeway. She wouldn't sit down. I looked up at her and asked how had it happened?

"I always come downstairs at 6 a.m.," she told me, "and go out to the wing first thing to say good morning to Dad. We had our routine: I helped him up from the hospital bed and to the bathroom. I held him while he washed and shaved, helped him dress in his khakis and that old blue shirt with the frayed collar." She shook her head. "He wouldn't wear anything else. And the same blue crewneck sweater with holes in the elbows. He was always cold he was so bony." Her voice wavered. "I got him seated in his chair, and then I went back to the kitchen to make him his breakfast." She went on as if her words might keep reality at bay. "I made his oatmeal the way he liked it, slow cooking those steel oats the night before, leaving it overnight in a double boiler, heating it back up in the morning. Dad said it had more flavor and texture that way.

I added cream and a big spoonful of brown sugar. You know Dad, the sweeter it was, the more likely he'd eat it." She paused for a moment with her hands open wide. She had done everything right. "When I went out to the wing close to 6 a.m., he was in the chair and I couldn't figure out how he'd gotten himself there on his own. His eyes were closed, and I thought he was sleeping. I shook him, so gently, and he didn't move. I rushed back to the breezeway to call you and your brother."

Her eyes were wide with wonder. I wanted to take her hand and bring her to a sofa so that we could sit down together. I wanted us to sit in our shock, side by side and take in that the impossible had come to pass. I wanted to lay my head on her shoulder and cry. But when I looked in her eyes, I saw we were not going to share this moment.

She stood stolid in the breezeway. Her face and body were frozen as if the door opening to the kitchen was to her future life alone and the door to the wing the terrible proof of her loss, and she did not know which direction to take. I could hear the persistent cooing of the mourning doves. Mum had always said it was a sad call.

"I'm going to go sit with Dad for a while," I said, as I stood up and glanced quickly at Mum.

She looked at me for the longest time with eyes as uncomprehending as a child. "I'll make breakfast," she said.

We left the breezeway through opposite doors. I wondered briefly whether I should have stayed with her. I was so dazed myself by Dad's disappearance that I couldn't attend to Mum, her unspoken burden of sadness weighing down on top of my own.

The first sun of the day was streaming into the wing. The air was cool and thin. My body vibrated. The room was ordered and warm with color. The salmon sofa with soft green pillows and a straw-colored throw (purchased by Mum and Dad in Ireland) neatly folded over its back. The Turkish rug in shades of blue, rose and peach. I looked out the large window upon the greening back yard with an aging gnarled apple tree in its center. A two-rail split fence bordered their property. The land extended out beyond as far as the eye could see to fallow meadow and a field of wheat blowing gently in the breeze.

There was his body seated in the wingchair, his eyes closed, his head over to one side, resting against the high back. I might have been frightened—his was the first dead body I had seen—but it was a matter of fact. I knew right away he wasn't there. I didn't touch him. Dad was somewhere gone away from that empty shell. I felt his absence and yet I was there, alive, quiet, and still in the shimmering yellow light.

Sitting on the edge of his hospital bed I imagined Dad waking up, a sharp knife's sudden piercing of his chest, struggling to get up off the bed, reaching for the chair's arm. Or was he already in the chair when he felt the stabbing in his heart. Was there a moment when he said this is it? Did he say no, please, no. One more chance? One more day?

A framed photo sat on the table behind his chair, as if only yesterday Dad was a soldier in the jungle of Guadalcanal. I thought of him landing with his men in 1942. Not even thirty, wiry and sinewy, bearded, filthy from mosquito filled pools of brown water infected with malaria. How brave he was. They slept in foxholes drenched by tropical rains with rats crawling over them. I saw him blown up into the air above the palm trees, sixty feet the medics guessed, landing on his back, his helmet crushed into his head. All his men gone in the blast. He had dreamed of a military life. The Marine Corps told him no. He was a wounded vet and he had done his part.

I closed my eyes and breathed in May's green air. The sun poured into my body. Everything that had happened with Dad, good, bad, terrifying, enraging, wanted to disappear in my mind into a room of the past. I could leave that room and walk through a door to another room where there was only the present. I could sense an open space. The edges of my body softened. Thought and feeling, images and sensations scrambled to rearrange themselves. Sometimes I had wished him dead. I had been terrified of him alive and terrified of losing him. I wasn't ready.

There was a twisting in my belly when I wondered if he was achingly lonely. He claimed he died in some of his surgeries and then came back, but he never told me what he saw. I wished he could have shared with me so that I could be helped by it and not be so afraid. All my questions unanswered and now there would be no more chances. I rested my forehead in my hand. Where have you gone, Dad? What did you understand about the rhythms of life and death?

I thought back to my time on the beach in Zihuatanejo, to the way silence and unfettered light revealed the natural world to me, the rhythms of dawn and dusk, the inevitable death of the small dog, the rebirth and renewal of the great sea turtle. I had lived alone in the heart of nature, my presence slowly becoming part of my surroundings and a witness to it all. I remembered how living on the beach brought all that was around me inside of myself. I understood what it was to feel whole, at least for a time.

I looked at Dad's body. There was no one there. I sank inside myself as I felt his long, painful, and tumultuous life, no help available for his fragmented wounded self, and now his deliverance. And some deliverance for me. Pieces of myself might be returned. No blame. Luke was waiting for me at home. I loved him.

The scent of new air, like crisply laundered white sheets pulled tight across a resting bed welcoming sleep. Every living thing spoke in its own voice. The tree frogs whirred, the liquid breeze of baby leaves, the sweet movement of the loving light within the room. Everything new and fresh, clean, and pure. One thing distinct from every other thing, and all of it in harmony and order. Was this what accompanied death?

***

Over the next days I walked through the world as if I had only recently arrived in a foreign country. I wondered why I didn't cry. Each day a series of moments, one distinctly separated from the next. Three nights passed while Mum, my brother, and I sat together in the breezeway, calling family, making burial arrangements, and planning a graveside military funeral honoring a war hero.

At 4 a.m. of the fourth day I was startled awake. Dad's image appeared in a blaze of light and presence in the space between my eyes. In Hindu esoteric thought there are energy centers in the body known as chakras. The third eye chakra sits between our two eyes, the center of clarity, inner seeing, and clairvoyance. I saw Dad's face in my third eye. A surreal bright light had switched on so that I saw him more clearly than I had ever seen him before. I realized that center had opened. Dad was a younger man in the spirit, fully healthy, someone I had never seen when he was alive. He was joyful. I checked to make sure I was awake and not dreaming. I looked over at Luke still asleep next to me. I closed my eyes. Dad was still there. I was privy to seeing him, but he did not appear to see me.

I waited until dawn to wake Luke up. He asked some questions and nodded. He didn't doubt it; we'd both had enough mysterious experiences over the years. I didn't ask how or why he appeared. It was a gift I received.

As I got up and went about my day, Father stayed with me. I was able to see what my eyes needed to see and still have sight of him in my third eye.

I said nothing to anyone except Luke, but when the funeral arrangements were complete, I told him I needed some time alone. I thought of a beach, one that I knew well on the North Shore. As a child I had been there with my family on summer Sundays, and I continued to go there with Luke. He didn't want me to drive. In the past few days, I'd had the hood fly up and shatter the windshield and I'd gotten a fat ticket for speeding. I gathered a few things in a backpack: a towel, some apples and water, my Walkman, and some music tapes. Luke put me on a bus that went north.

I looked out through the cloudy window at Luke waving and blew him a kiss. He was with me, but I was alone. Dad must have been alone in his experience, for most of his life. mother was alone in herself. My brother was only loosely connected to the family. Whether that was something true about this life, or was the distinct loneliness of our family, was not clear to me. I looked around at other solitary passengers and wondered if all red threads led inevitably to loneliness.

After a half mile walk from the bus station to the beach, I stepped onto the sand, took off my sneakers, and felt the cold coarse winter between my toes. In May's ocean chill the beach was an empty expanse except for a man running with his yellow lab and a small child playing in a vernal pool with her father. I walked a distance from them and spread my towel on the damp sand. I sat looking out, welcoming the saltiness of the air, the ocean's navy-blue depths with the sun sparkling on its tranquil surface. The warm enveloping Mexican waters were nowhere to be seen.

I stared for a moment and my mind emptied all thought.

I put my favorite Sikh's tape in the Walkman, a chant of, *Oh, my soul, it sanctifies the Lord.* Their sweet harmonies and soothing rhythms. I knew nothing about Sikhs other than their delicious vegetarian food in the Golden Temple restaurant, but instinctively, I trusted them. I chanted with them over and over. I closed my eyes and Dad was still there. As I focused on him, I saw how thin the membrane was between life and death. Vague apparitions appeared of people I had loved in life and ancestors known only by name and story. It was almost possible to see across to everyone in my world who had died.

A veil was opened.

I continued to look out at the endless sea. It had been there forever and would go on beyond me, beyond all of us. We wouldn't know until we arrived that this world was not all there was. This world was real, but then we were on our way to some other place, some other level of being. And so, the thread, if followed deeper, led beyond loneliness to a fullness that was unimaginable.

I breathed in a clean spicy scent, Dad's aftershave, wafting crisp and clear in the cold air.

I spoke to him, "You are so beautiful and awful in my mind. I hope you know how much I loved you, how much I hurt for you, how deeply you wounded me and scared me, how much I longed for you to accept me, how much I wished you could be a father to me, someone who would stand behind me and support me in the world. You were always ready for battle. The War ended, but yours went on. You taught me to be brave. You taught me to be a warrior, but I'm a warrior of the spirit."

An ocean of tears had been patiently waiting and now fell for the first time since his death. The tide had risen like a moon and grown full to overflowing until I sobbed. Dad remained in my vision. I wondered if he saw me. If he knew I wept for him. I cried for Dad. I cried for my family, each of us separated one from the other, alone in our own private pain. And I cried for myself, for my struggle, for my solitary pain. My heart emptied out.

Thank you, Dad for teaching me about life, about how hard it can be in its hurts and failures, in all the suffering accidental and unintended. And how wondrous in all its unearned beauty, all of us creatures on this earth trying so hard, wanting badly to know love.

Dad's presence began to fade. With every muscle in my body, I strained to hold onto his image. A helplessness came over me as an inner darkness began to fall. I was being returned to my normal limited vision. Did he leave because he knew I was okay, or was it inevitable that he would travel somewhere beyond what I could see?

"Where are you going Dad?" I tried to bring him back, my breath long and deep.

My sight shifted outside of myself. I looked at the horizon, the sun's glare bright on a hard surface. Something was floating way out at sea. Then my vision was drawn to the water's edge. The little girl was playing there, picking up pebbles. A sudden wave came out of the calm sea and broke, toppling her over. I heard her cry out. I watched her Father run down to the water and swoop her up into his arms. He carried her crying back to their blanket. He sat down and held her in his arms so tenderly that my heart filled for her. I looked back out into the distance. Anything was possible out there, a rogue wave could always come ashore, but for now the waters were still. It might all have been a mirage. I was prone to visions.

In the late afternoon I left the beach. I took one more look over my shoulder at the opaque navy waters and walked back to the bus station. I called Luke from a pay phone.

"Hi honey, I'm at the bus station. Is there any chance of you driving up? We could get some supper up here."

"Sure. I'll leave right away."

"Luke?"

"Yes?"

"I love you so much."

"I love you right back," he said softly.

I hung up the phone and sat waiting for Luke on a bench at the station. I thought love could be as small as a seed or as big as the ocean, or many things in between. In my small self it was so hard for me to trust another human being that it stunted my love. But there was a seed growing in Luke's presence. Some better part of me understood that if I could not fully love now, my love would grow with time. The larger self in both Luke and me had held us with patience and faith when we did not have access to our own hearts.

I had to laugh. This time, unlike the bus stop in Mexico, we'd be going in the same direction.

We drove to the Clam Shack together and shared Fried Clams with tartar sauce and a large dish of coconut almond chip ice cream for dessert.

About the Author: I am a New Englander through and through, although I left twice in the 70's and again in the early 2000's for years in Mexico. I have been a psychotherapist for forty-five years. Waitressing, wandering, constant reading and meditating all contributed to finding my way.

I live in Massachusetts on a fifteen-acre compound with my husband, two sons and one fiancé, three grandchildren, Raven, a black Lab, fifteen chickens, and a tractor named Reggie.

Although I have labeled this book autobiographical fiction, the only straying off the path of truth is necessary name changes and some rearranging of time.

Acknowledgments:

First, I am grateful to Mexico, a home in my heart, for its mystery, color and warmth, the land that inspired and challenged me to find my own voice.

Thanks to Boston's Grub Street for years of writing classes and a wonderful array of teachers. Thank you, Rich Marcello for your steady encouragement and excellence in teaching the craft. Thank you, Wendy, Jackie, and Molly for reading the manuscript in its half-baked form. Thanks to Joyce, a model of perseverance. A special appreciation of my writing buddy, Martha for your insightful critique and support.

Many thanks to James Buchanan for expert editing, and generous help in completing the manuscript.

Many dear friends read my writing, supported and encouraged me along the way: Steffi, Betsy, Sam, Ted, Cate and more.

Thank you to my sons, Matt and Lawrence and his fiancé Paige, who trust me as a writer as well as a mother, and never make me feel old.

And most of all, thank you Ken for always loving me, and believing in me even when I didn't.

Made in the USA
Middletown, DE
16 July 2021